LIFE SERIES

EXPLORE GOD'S WORLD

Science/Health, Series A

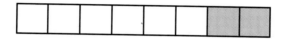

Ronald W. Ritterskamp, Editor
Daniel J. Wyrick, Editor

Produced under the auspices of the
Office of Education
North American Division
of the
General Conference of Seventh-day Adventists

Pacific Press® Publishing Association
Nampa, Idaho

CONTENTS

Page

UNIT I

CELLS, GENES, AND INVERTE-BRATES

INTRODUCTION

Have you ever looked closely at a cup of clear pond water? If you have, you may have seen some very small specks moving around in the water. Most likely these little specks were *Daphnia* (daf′ nē ə), a tiny relative of crabs and crayfish. *Daphnia*, also called "water flea," is found in almost any standing water. These animals move by using their antennae as paddles, and they keep a lookout for food and predators with their one eye.

While larger animals make interesting subjects of study, the smaller living things are just as interesting. In this unit you will have a chance to discover some of these. You will also take a closer look at cells and learn about heredity.

CHAPTER TITLES

CHAPTER 1

THE WORK OF SCIENCE

INTRODUCTION

The mechanic in the picture may not be what you think of when you hear the word *scientist*. Like most people, you may think of a scientist as someone in a white lab coat, working with test tubes, beakers, elaborate setups of tubing, and flasks filled with bubbling liquids. However, the mechanic is a scientist. While he may not work with glassware or microscopes, he does use precision instruments and devices to diagnose mechanical problems and to perform the necessary repairs or maintenance. Like other scientists, he tests, experiments, analyzes data, and forms conclusions.

In this chapter you will explore the work of scientists. You will examine how they perform and analyze experiments, and you will become acquainted with the tools they use in their work.

SECTION TITLES

When working on automobile engines, auto mechanics use the same methods that scientists use.

1-1 THE SI SYSTEM

density
mass
SI system
volume

OBJECTIVES

- Identify advantages of the SI system.
- Identify the basic units of the SI system.
- Explain how prefixes are used in the SI system.

One of the most important activities of science is being able to measure (fig. 1-1). If you live in the United States and use the English system of measuring, you must remember that 1 pound has 16 ounces, 1 ton equals 2000 pounds, 1 yard is 36 inches, 1 mile is 5280 feet (fig. 1-2). Of course, you will also want to remember that 4 pecks make 1 bushel and 60 grains equal 1 dram.

Fig. 1-1 Measuring is an important skill of science.

DID YOU KNOW?
Both Thomas Jefferson and John Quincy Adams proposed that the United States use the metric system.

U.S. UNITS OF MEASUREMENT AND THEIR EQUIVALENTS	
Unit	**Equivalents**
1 mile in length	63,360 inches or
	5280 feet or
	1760 yards or
	320 rods
1 cubic yard in volume	46,656 cubic inches or
	27 cubic feet
1 ton in weight	32,000 ounces or
	2000 pounds
1 gallon in liquid measure	128 fluid ounces or
	8 pints or
	4 quarts
1 bushel in dry measure	4 pecks or
	32 quarts or
	64 pints

Fig. 1-2

DID YOU KNOW?
Both in 1875 and 100 years later, in 1975, the United States formally adopted the metric system. In fact, since 1893 our national measurements have been metric.

The rest of the world uses a much simpler system called the SI system. The **SI** (Standard International) **system** began in France during the late 1790s. This system was developed in an effort to try to standardize the many systems of measurement used in the world. It was first called the "metric" system. The word *metric* was derived from the French word *metre*, which means "to measure." This early metric system was refined and adjusted through the years and gave rise to the current SI system of measurement.

TRY THIS 1-1: Body Measurements

Materials:
> graduated cylinder (100 mL)
> styrofoam cup
> water

Procedure:
1. In ancient times the cubit was a common unit of measuring length. A cubit is the distance from your elbow to the tip of your finger. Use your own "cubit" to measure the length of each item listed below.
   a. the height of your best friend
   b. the height of the door
   c. the length of your classroom
2. Determine the amount of space available in your mouth. To do this, fill your mouth with water. Empty your mouthful of water into the graduated cylinder and measure the volume.
   - What is the volume of your mouth?

This system has many advantages over the cumbersome English system of measurement with which you are most familiar. These advantages include fewer base units to remember, all units expressed as multiples of 10, a standardized system throughout the world, and the same in every language.

The SI system uses a basic unit for each type of measure. Each of these basic units is listed in figure 1-3.

THE SI SYSTEM	
Measurement	**Unit**
energy	joule
frequency	hertz
length	meter
mass	gram
power	watt
temperature	degree
time	second
volume	liter

Fig. 1–3 The SI system uses several kinds of units.

DID YOU KNOW?
It is incorrect to say that the weight of an object is 5 kilograms, grams, centigrams, or milligrams. Each of these is a unit of mass rather than weight.

RESEARCH IT
Who was Gabriel Mouton?

RESEARCH IT
Find out what the following
units are used for:
    load
    fortnight
    angstrom
    nail
    rood
    firkin
    chaldon
    tierce
    line
    pipe

From these basic units, other SI units can be derived. Some of these can be created by adding prefixes to the basic units. These prefixes can be used to make larger or smaller units. Common prefixes used in the SI system are *milli*, *centi*, *deci*, *kilo*, and *mega* (fig 1-4).

COMMONLY USED PREFIXES IN THE SI SYSTEM		
Prefix	**Value**	**Example**
milli (m)	0.001 (1/1000)	millimeter 1/1000th of a meter (0.001 m)
centi (c)	0.01 (1/100)	centimeter 1/100th of a meter (0.01 m)
deci (d)	0.1 (1/10)	decimeter one tenth of a meter (0.1 m)
kilo (k)	1000 times (1000 X)	kilometer 1000 meters
mega (M)	1 000 000 times (1 000 000 X)	megameter 1 000 000 meters

Fig. 1–4

When prefixes are added to a basic unit, they result in very large or very small units. For example, g represents grams. If k (representing "kilo") is placed in front of the symbol g, the unit becomes a kilogram (kg). A kilogram (kg) is 1000 times larger than a gram (g). In a similar way, if m (representing "milli") is placed in front of g, the unit becomes a milligram (mg), a unit 1000 times smaller than gram (g) (fig. 1-5). By using various prefixes with the base units, units 10,

RESEARCH IT
What is a micrometer?
How many millimeters
are in a gigameter?

DID YOU KNOW?
The English system of measurement used in the United States is also called "the inch-pound system." It was developed in England from older units beginning in the 1200s.

Fig. 1–5 If the 1 cube (right) equals 1 gram (g), then the 1000 cubes (left) equal 1 kilogram (kg).

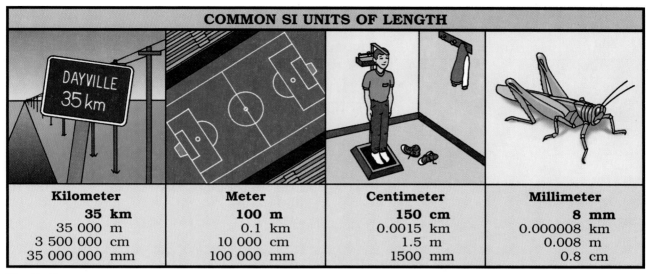

COMMON SI UNITS OF LENGTH			
Kilometer	**Meter**	**Centimeter**	**Millimeter**
35 km	**100 m**	**150 cm**	**8 mm**
35 000 m	0.1 km	0.0015 km	0.000008 km
3 500 000 cm	10 000 cm	1.5 m	0.008 m
35 000 000 mm	100 000 mm	1500 mm	0.8 cm

Fig. 1–6

100, or 1000 times larger or smaller than the base units can be identified (fig. 1-6).

Measuring is one of the most important jobs of scientists. They must be able to measure carefully and record measurements accurately (fig. 1-7). Some of the most common measurements scientists make involve distance, volume, and mass (fig. 1-8).

RESEARCH IT
What is a nanosecond?

DID YOU KNOW?
Originally a meter was equal to 1/10 000 000 the distance from the North Pole to the equator.

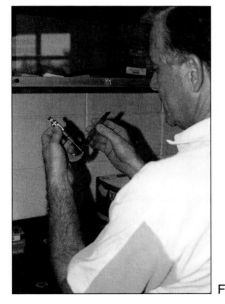

Fig. 1–7 A micrometer is used to measure thickness.

Fig. 1–8

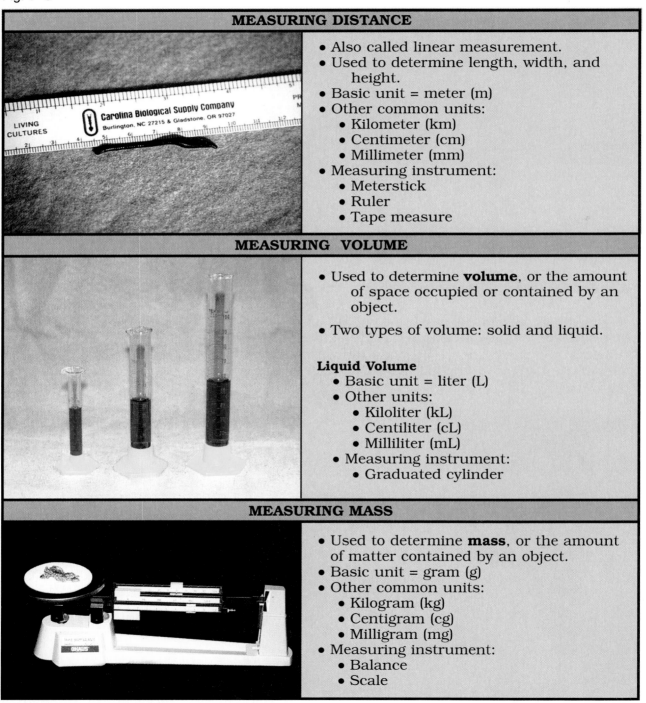

MEASURING DISTANCE

- Also called linear measurement.
- Used to determine length, width, and height.
- Basic unit = meter (m)
- Other common units:
  - Kilometer (km)
  - Centimeter (cm)
  - Millimeter (mm)
- Measuring instrument:
  - Meterstick
  - Ruler
  - Tape measure

MEASURING VOLUME

- Used to determine **volume**, or the amount of space occupied or contained by an object.
- Two types of volume: solid and liquid.

Liquid Volume
  - Basic unit = liter (L)
  - Other units:
    - Kiloliter (kL)
    - Centiliter (cL)
    - Milliliter (mL)
  - Measuring instrument:
    - Graduated cylinder

MEASURING MASS

- Used to determine **mass**, or the amount of matter contained by an object.
- Basic unit = gram (g)
- Other common units:
  - Kilogram (kg)
  - Centigram (cg)
  - Milligram (mg)
- Measuring instrument:
  - Balance
  - Scale

CLASS ACTIVITY 1-1: How Much Room?

Question: How can you use the displacement of water to determine the volume of an irregular solid?

Materials:
    graduated cylinder (100 mL)
    lead weight 7 g (1/4 oz)
    nylon fishing line
    rock (small)
    styrofoam chunk (small)
    water

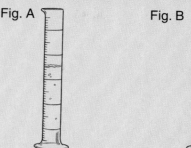

Fig. A   Fig. B

Procedure:
1. Tie one end of a 30-cm piece of fishing line around the rock.
2. Fill the graduated cylinder with 50 mL of water. Remember to read the bottom of the meniscus (fig. A).
3. Carefully lower the rock into the graduated cylinder until the rock is completely submerged (fig. B). Measure the volume again. This final volume is the volume of the water in the cylinder plus the volume of the rock. Record.
4. Calculate the volume of the rock by subtracting the initial volume (100 mL) in the graduated cylinder from the final volume (the volume with the rock submerged). Record.
5. Repeat steps 1 to 5, this time with the lead weight. Calculate the volume of the weight and record.
6. Repeat steps 1 to 5, this time with the piece of styrofoam. Since the styrofoam will not sink naturally, it will be necessary to somehow get the styrofoam fully submerged. Once the styrofoam is submerged, calculate and record the volume.

Data:

Item	Initial Volume	Final Volume	Actual Volume
Rock			
Weight			
Styrofoam			

Questions:
1. Which of the samples had the greatest volume? Which had the least?
2. Why does the volume of water increase when an object is submerged in it?
3. Would the displacement method work for determining the volume of most solids? Explain.
4. How could the volume of a sponge be determined?

Conclusion: Write 3–5 sentences about what you learned from this activity.

Fig. 1–9 Other measuring devices include thermometers, stopwatches, Geiger counters, and spring scales.

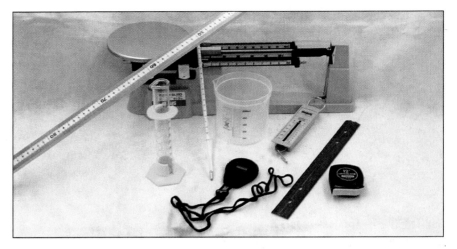

CALCULATION OF DENSITY
To calculate density (D) you divide the mass (M) of the object by the volume (V) it takes up.

$$D = \frac{M}{V}$$

Fig. 1–10

In addition to the common measurements just described, scientists also make other measurements, including temperature, time, and density (fig. 1-9). Measurements of time and temperature are simply done by reading a clock or thermometer. Measuring density, on the other hand, is a little more difficult. When measuring **density**, or the amount of matter per unit volume of an object or substance, scientists have to use the mass and the volume it occupies. To calculate density, you simply divide the mass of the object by the volume it takes up (fig 1-10). Figure 1-11 shows three cubes of exactly the same size. One is styrofoam, one is lead, and the other is sugar. Which has the greatest density? Which has the smallest density? By dividing the mass of each by the volume of each, you will discover that the styrofoam has the least density, and lead has the greatest.

Fig. 1–11 The size of these cubes is the same, but their densities differ.

REVIEW IT

1. What are the advantages of the SI system?
2. What is the SI unit for each of the following: length, mass, volume, and time?
3. What does each prefix mean: *milli, centi, deci, kilo, mega*?

1-2 GRAPHING

OBJECTIVES

- Explain the advantage of a graph compared to a table.
- Identify different types of graphs.

VOCABULARY
horizontal axis
pictograph
pie graph
vertical axis

The stamp in figure 1-12 was first printed in June 1898. At that time it cost one cent to send a regular letter anywhere east of the Mississippi, two cents if the letter was going somewhere west of the Mississippi, and ten cents if the letter was destined for Europe. The stamp you see here cost ten cents in 1898, but because it has never been used, it is now worth more than two hundred dollars.

Fig. 1–12 This stamp was printed in 1898 and cost ten cents.

The chart below shows the price of mailing a letter with the United States Postal Service from 1920 to 1995 (fig. 1-13). You can see by reading the second column that the price has changed many times during 75 years.

Scientists often use tables and charts to record the observations or data coming from their research and experimentation. While tables help to organize information, it is still necessary to carefully study the information in order to make accurate conclusions. Scientists often use graphs to illustrate the information. Graphs put this information into picture form and make it easier to understand and analyze.

YEAR	FIRST-CLASS STAMP
1920	1 cent
1925	2 cents
1930	2 cents
1935	3 cents
1940	3 cents
1945	3 cents
1950	3 cents
1955	3 cents
1960	4 cents
1965	5 cents
1970	6 cents
1975	13 cents
1980	15 cents
1985	22 cents
1990	29 cents
1995	32 cents

Fig. 1–13 This chart shows the changes in the cost of mailing a letter in the United States.

Four types of graphs are commonly used: bar graph, line graph, pictograph, and pie graph. Each type of graph displays data in a slightly different way.

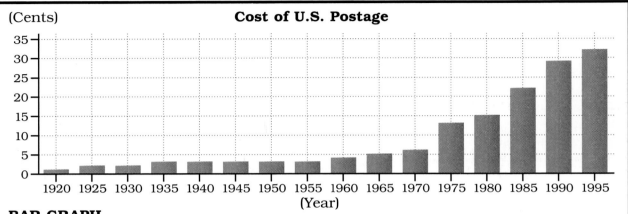

BAR GRAPH

The data about postage stamps is shown in the bar graph. The price of the stamp determines the height of each bar, and the bars show how the prices for stamps have increased over time. Notice that the graph has a name or title at the top. The **vertical axis**, on the left side of the graph, is a labeled scale that measures the cost of a stamp in cents. Across the bottom of the graph is the **horizontal axis**, which is labeled to show the time in years included in the data chart.

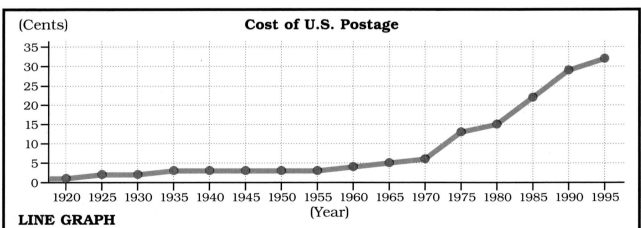

LINE GRAPH

The postage-stamp-cost data could also be shown in a line graph. In this graph the dots are placed at the same location as the top of each bar in the bar graph. But the bar is not drawn in. To complete the graph, the dots are connected by a solid line. The higher the dot is located, the greater the cost of a stamp.

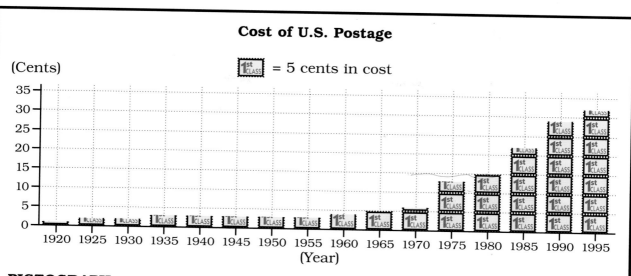

Cost of U.S. Postage

1st CLASS = 5 cents in cost

(Cents)

PICTOGRAPH

Another type of graph, called a pictograph, is shown here. Because a **pictograph** uses symbols to display data, it is often used for young children. This type of graph must have a legend, or explanation, that tells what each symbol represents.

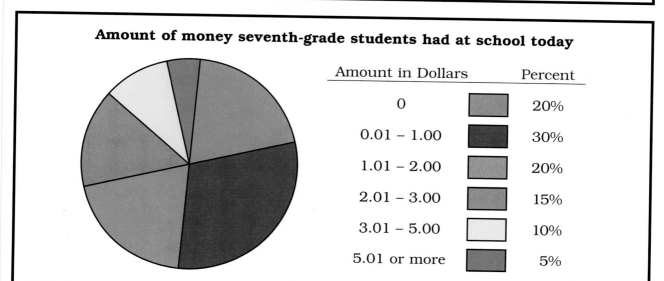

Amount of money seventh-grade students had at school today

Amount in Dollars		Percent
0		20%
0.01 – 1.00		30%
1.01 – 2.00		20%
2.01 – 3.00		15%
3.01 – 5.00		10%
5.01 or more		5%

PIE GRAPH

The fourth type of graph is the pie graph. A **pie graph** is a round graph that has pie-shaped pieces. Quite often this type of graph is used to display data that are percentages.

To create a pie graph, you must first draw a circle and connect a line from the center to the edge of the circle (fig. 1-14). Next, estimate where to draw your second line so that the piece between the two straight lines forms the fraction of the circle equal to the percentage to be shown—in this case, 20 percent. Continue to draw lines so that there is one piece of the pie for each percentage in the table. Label each piece of the circle with a dollar amount. The percentage amounts are not always labeled because the size of the slices already shows those amounts.

Fig. 1–14

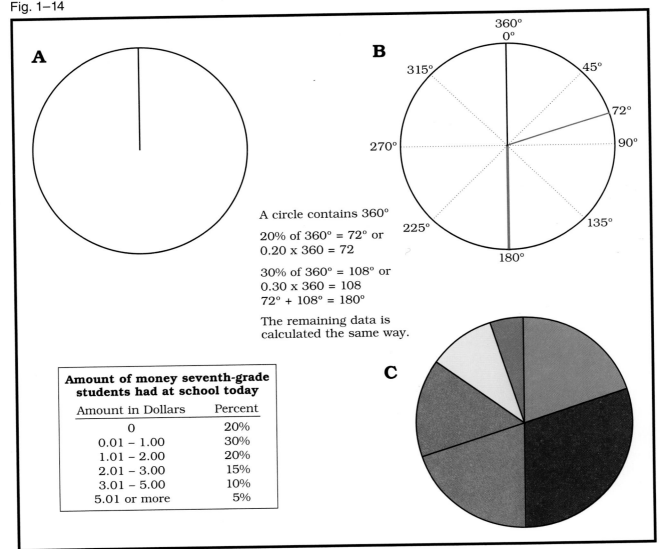

A circle contains 360°

20% of 360° = 72° or
0.20 x 360 = 72

30% of 360° = 108° or
0.30 x 360 = 108
72° + 108° = 180°

The remaining data is calculated the same way.

Amount of money seventh-grade students had at school today	
Amount in Dollars	Percent
0	20%
0.01 – 1.00	30%
1.01 – 2.00	20%
2.01 – 3.00	15%
3.01 – 5.00	10%
5.01 or more	5%

TRY THIS 1-2: Making a Graph

Materials:
> drawing compass
> metric ruler
> paper

Procedure:
1. Use the data supplied in the chart to create bar, line, pictograph, and circle graphs. Then answer the questions below.
   - Which graph do you feel best showed the data?
   - Show your graphs to two adults (other than your teacher) and ask them which graph best showed the data. Record their answers.

Favorite Fruits of Junior-High Students							
Apples	26%	Cantaloupes	4%	Grapes	19%	Strawberries	10%
Bananas	19%	Cherries	8%	Oranges	11%	Watermelon	3%

Graphs show the data in a form that can often be understood at a glance, without having to read all the numbers in a chart or table. Being able to accurately construct and interpret graphs is an important work of scientists.

REVIEW IT

1. What are the four most commonly used kinds of graphs?
2. What advantage does a graph have over a table or chart?

1-3 DEVELOPING AN EXPERIMENT

conclusion
data
experiment
hypothesis
material
procedure
question

OBJECTIVE

• List and describe the components of an experiment.

During the winter of 1839, Charles Goodyear, his brother, and several friends were in his kitchen discussing his experiments. Charles had worked with sticky rubber latex from rubber trees for five years, trying to make it more usable (fig. 1-15). In the middle of an argument, Charles made a sweeping gesture with his hand and accidentally knocked a large piece of rubber gum and a piece of sulfur onto a hot stove. The rubber gum and sulfur charred into a leatherlike substance that didn't dissolve. The rubber gum was no longer sticky; it had changed into rubber. Following this discovery, Goodyear nailed some of the rubber outside in the cold, and, much to his surprise, it remained flexible.

Fig. 1–15 Charles Goodyear worked hundreds of experiments over many years before discovering how to make rubber.

After five years and hundreds of experiments, Charles Goodyear had accidentally created commercial rubber. Soon many companies were using this new material to make hundreds of rubber products.

While some scientific discoveries are made by accident, most come from years of research and formal experimentation. Conducting experiments is the major work of scientists.

An **experiment** is a test or trial, composed of a series of steps, used to discover new information. Experiments are designed to help answer questions. Scientists use experiments to help them better understand the world (fig. 1-16).

There are many ways of developing experiments, but most useful ones have several basic components in common (fig. 1-17).

Fig. 1–16 Experimentation is one way scientists discover answers to questions.

COMPONENTS OF AN EXPERIMENT

Question, or Problem

The starting point of the experiment. A question or problem that may be solved by performing the experiment.

Materials

A list of the materials and apparatus needed for the experiment. This list helps other people check the accuracy of the experiment.

Procedure

A series of steps that can be followed to perform the experiment and gather data.

Data

Information collected by following the procedure, often recorded in a chart or table and later developed into a graph.

Conclusion

Analysis of the data—an explanation of what was learned from the experiment. It answers the questions, tells whether the hypothesis is true or false, and sometimes suggests changes and new ideas to try.

Fig. 1–17

In Goodyear's experiments, his question had always been, "How can I cause rubber gum to be more useful?" His list of materials would include the apparatus and raw ingredients used. The procedure would explain the steps to be followed when mixing, heating, and cooling each mixture, followed by an explanation of how to test elasticity. The data would include the elasticity measurements. His conclusions would discuss the outcome of the experiment and what he had learned.

How would you design an experiment? Where would you start? For example, how would you determine which brand of paper towel absorbed the most water? To help you answer these questions, look at figure 1-18.

QUESTION:
Start every experiment by asking the question you wish to investigate. Then form a **hypothesis** (hī päth′ ə sis), or guess, as to what you believe the answer will be. The experiment is designed to test the hypothesis.

EXAMPLE:
What brand of paper towels absorbs the most water? The hypothesis could be, "The more expensive the towel, the more water it will absorb."

MATERIALS:
The materials list identifies the apparatus, samples, and amounts necessary for the experiment.

EXAMPLE:
balance   paper towels (5 samples)
beaker (250 mL)   water

PROCEDURE:
The procedure clearly describes the steps that must be followed in performing the experiment. The steps of the procedure should be clear enough so someone else can follow them.

EXAMPLE:
1. Select five brands of paper towels for testing.
2. Cut a 20-cm square from each roll of paper towels. Label each square with its brand name.
3. Weigh each towel square while it is dry. Record the weight in the chart.
4. Soak each square in a bowl of water until it is completely wet. Remove from the bowl and allow the sample to drip for one minute.
5. Weigh each wet paper towel. Record each wet weight.
6. Determine the mass of water each brand of paper towel absorbed.
7. Compare the mass of water absorbed by each paper towel, and list them in order from most to least absorbent.

Fig. 1–18

Fig. 1–18 continued

DATA:

The data of the experiment includes the names of samples, measurements, tallys, and totals. This information can be organized into a table, chart, or list.

EXAMPLE:

Paper towel	Dry weight (g)	Wet weight (g)	Water absorbed (g)
Brut	11	13	2
Catalina	14	15	1
Generic	12	14	2
Tough One	17	20	3
Wonder	16	21	5

CONCLUSION:

The conclusion answers the question and tells whether the hypothesis is true or false. If the hypothesis is incorrect, it can suggest changes in methods or samples and offer other ideas on how to set up another experiment.

EXAMPLE:

This experiment was designed to test the absorbency of paper towels. The hypothesis was that the most expensive paper towel is the most absorbent. According to the data collected, Wonder brand towels, the most expensive brand, are the most absorbent.

As you can see, there are many decisions to make as you design an experiment. It is important to design an experiment in a way that other people can repeat it. Directions need to be simple and clear.

Imagine how you would set up an experiment to test several types of cloth to see which is most absorbent. Think about how you would design the procedure to test the hypothesis.

REVIEW IT

1. Name the components of an experiment.
2. What is the purpose of the procedure in an experiment?
3. How is data recorded in an experiment?
4. What is included in a conclusion?

1-4 THE TOOLS OF SCIENCE

OBJECTIVES

- Explain how to use and care for a microscope.
- Explain how to use and care for a balance.
- Identify basic apparatus used by scientists.

Scientists use many different tools for their work. Some tools are used to observe and measure; others are used to monitor and record. Two of the most common tools used by scientists are the microscope and the balance (fig. 1-19).

Fig. 1–19 Microscopes and balances are two useful tools of science.

RESEARCH IT
What is microtomy?

The compound microscope is the one most commonly used by students. Like most microscopes, the compound microscope is used to make very small objects visible by enlarging their appearance. This is accomplished by two lenses, or sets of lenses—one near the object and one near the user's eye. The curvature of the lenses and their distance apart determine the magnification of the microscope.

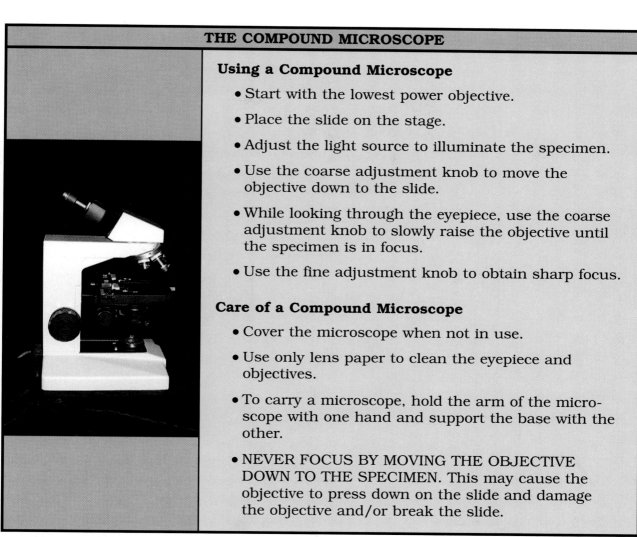

THE COMPOUND MICROSCOPE

Using a Compound Microscope

- Start with the lowest power objective.
- Place the slide on the stage.
- Adjust the light source to illuminate the specimen.
- Use the coarse adjustment knob to move the objective down to the slide.
- While looking through the eyepiece, use the coarse adjustment knob to slowly raise the objective until the specimen is in focus.
- Use the fine adjustment knob to obtain sharp focus.

Care of a Compound Microscope

- Cover the microscope when not in use.
- Use only lens paper to clean the eyepiece and objectives.
- To carry a microscope, hold the arm of the microscope with one hand and support the base with the other.
- NEVER FOCUS BY MOVING THE OBJECTIVE DOWN TO THE SPECIMEN. This may cause the objective to press down on the slide and damage the objective and/or break the slide.

Fig. 1–20

Figure 1-20 summarizes how to use and care for a compound microscope.

Balances are used to determine the mass of things. The triple-beam balance is commonly used in schools. It consists of a pan, three beams with sliding weights, or riders, and a pointer. An object placed on the pan causes the beam to rise. The sliding weights, called riders, are moved to the right until the beams become perfectly level again. When balanced, each rider points to a number on its scale. Figure 1-21 explains how to use and care for a triple-beam balance.

RESEARCH IT
What is the difference between phase contrast and dark-field microscopes?

DID YOU KNOW?
As early as 100 B.C., engravers were using water-filled glass globes as magnifying glasses.

Fig. 1–21

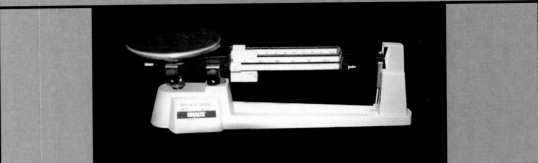

THE TRIPLE-BEAM BALANCE

Using a Triple-Beam Balance
- Adjust the balance to 0.
- Place the filter paper in a container on the pan.
- Record the **tare weight**, or the weight of the empty container.
- Place the item to be weighed on the paper or in the container.
- Move the riders in combination to identify the correct mass.
- Remove the item and clean the pan.
- Move all riders back to the 0 position.

Care of a Triple-Beam Balance
- The balance is a delicate instrument; handle it carefully.
- Cover the balance when not in use.
- Always clean the pan after use.
- Always make sure balance is adjusted to 0 before weighing an item.
- NEVER PLACE AN OBJECT TO BE WEIGHED DIRECTLY ON THE PAN. This can cause residue from the object to remain on the pan and make other calculations inaccurate.

Fig. 1–22 Electronic balances are accurate and easy to use.

Another type of balance, called the electronic balance, has no riders. Instead, it has a digital display that gives the weight very quickly (fig. 1-22). Electronic balances are popular because they are quicker to use and read, are more accurate, and can make more delicate measurements than the triple-beam balance.

In addition to microscopes and balances, scientists also use other tools in their work. You are familiar with some of these tools, but others may be new to you. Study figure 1-23 to learn the names of equipment commonly used by scientists.

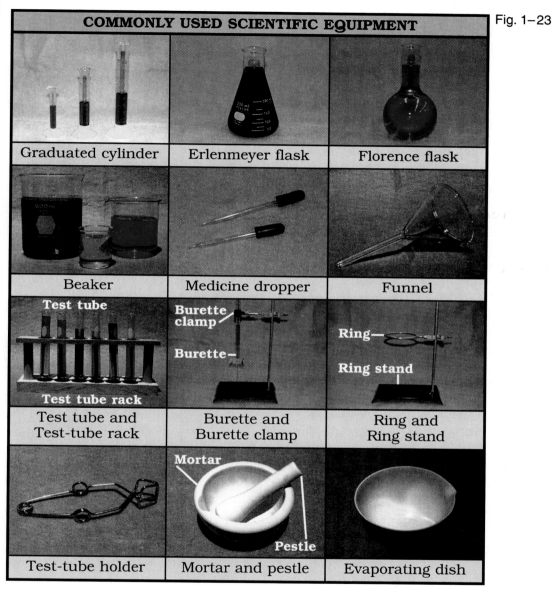

COMMONLY USED SCIENTIFIC EQUIPMENT

Fig. 1–23

Graduated cylinder	Erlenmeyer flask	Florence flask
Beaker	Medicine dropper	Funnel
Test tube and Test-tube rack	Burette and Burette clamp	Ring and Ring stand
Test-tube holder	Mortar and pestle	Evaporating dish

REVIEW IT

1. Where is the slide placed when viewing it on a microscope?
2. How do you focus a microscope?
3. How is a balance used?
4. Draw a simple sketch of each of the following:
   - a. volumetric flask
   - b. beaker
   - c. evaporating dish
   - d. burette clamp

CHAPTER 1 WRAP-UP

THINKING SKILLS: Comparing and Contrasting

For thousands of years people have measured things. At first, they used commonly available objects as units of measure. Stones, hand spans, and stride lengths were all used as units. As time went by, better systems were developed. Today, the two most common systems of measurement used are the SI system and the English system.

Look over the information below and answer the questions.

ENGLISH SYSTEM

The English system evolved over hundreds of years and is a blend of many different measurement systems. It consists of many unrelated units, many of which vary from place to place. Converting from one unit to another often results in complex fractions and is confusing and time consuming.

Common Units

Length—inch, foot, yard, mile   Volume (liquid)—fluid ounce, cup, pint, quart, gallon
Weight—dram, ounce, pound, ton   Volume (dry)—cubic inch, cubic foot, cubic yard

Equivalent Units

1 mile = 1760 yards = 5280 ft = 63,360 inches
1 ton = 2000 pounds = 32,000 ounces = 256,000 drams
1 gallon = 4 quarts = 8 pints = 16 cups = 128 ounces
1 cubic yard = 27 cubic feet = 46,656 cubic inches

SI SYSTEM

The SI system was designed to provide easy-to-use units that can quickly be converted from one to the other. The units are based on standardized amounts accepted throughout most of the world. Converting from one unit to another is based on values of 10 and is consistent throughout the system.

Common Units

Length—meter   Mass—gram   Volume—liter

Equivalent Units

1 meter = 100 centimeters = 1000 millimeters = .001 kilometers
1 gram = 100 centigrams = 1000 milligrams = .001 kilograms
1 liter = 100 centiliters = 1000 milliliters = .001 kiloliters

---

1. How many ounces in a gallon of milk?
2. How many milliliters of soda are in a 1-liter bottle?
3. What is the area of your classroom in inches? In centimeters?
4. Hubert wants to pour a concrete patio in his backyard. The dimensions of the patio are 12 ft x 15 ft x 4 in. How many cubic yards of concrete does he need?
5. Marge wants to pour a concrete patio in her backyard. The dimensions of her patio are 3.7 m x 4.6 m x 10 cm. How many cubic meters of concrete does she need?
6. Which system of measurement do you prefer to use? Why?

QUESTIONS AND PROBLEMS

1. Why was the metric system developed?
2. What are disadvantages of the English system of measurement?
3. Why is styrofoam less dense than sugar?
4. How are mass, volume, and density different from each other?
5. How could you determine the volume occupied by a small rock?
6. Why does an experiment need organized steps?
7. Why do scientists write conclusions to experiments?
8. Find the world population for every decade during the previous 100 years and use a line graph to display your data.
9. Why do you think it is important for laboratory equipment to be thoroughly cleaned after each use?

RESEARCH

1. Use library resources to research the history of measurement. Develop a bulletin-board display that summarizes your findings.
2. Read about the series of experiments the Wright brothers did before they were successful. Write a one- to two-page report and present it to the class.
3. Look through magazines and newspapers and collect examples of graphs. Organize your collection according to general types of graphs. Present your findings to the class.
4. Develop a series of posters designed to convince people to use the SI system of measurement.
5. Interview a doctor or dentist and make a list of the apparatus he or she uses at work. Draw a sketch of each item and explain how it is used. Make an oral presentation of your findings.

REVIEW

HIGHLIGHTS

1. The SI system of measurement has a few basic units (all other units are multiples of 10) and is standardized throughout most of the world.
2. The basic SI units are the meter (m)—length; liter (L)—liquid volume; and gram (g)—mass.
3. SI prefixes are added to units to increase or decrease values by multiples of ten (kilo = 1000, centi = 1/100, milli = 1/1000).
4. The advantage of graphs over tables or charts is that while tables and charts organize information, they are often difficult to read and must be examined closely to be understood. Graphs, on the other hand, organize the information into picture form, making it easier to understand and analyze.
5. Four types of graphs are the bar graph, line graph, pictograph, and pie graph.
6. The components of an experiment include the question, the materials, the procedure, the data, and the conclusion. These components are described in figure 1-17.

7. The use and care of the microscope is summarized in figure 1-19.

8. The use and care of the balance is summarized in figure 1-20.

9. Scientists use several types of laboratory apparatus. Several common examples are identified and illustrated on page 27.

VOCABULARY LIST

balance	hypothesis	question
conclusion	mass	SI system
data	material	tare weight
density	pictograph	vertical axis
experiment	pie graph	volume
horizontal axis	procedure	

PRACTICE

Multiple Choice. Choose the best answer.

1. The SI system is
   a. the metric system
   b. used worldwide
   c. designed with four basic units
   d. all of these

2. Which is not a prefix in the SI system?
   a. milli
   b. cilli
   c. kilo
   d. centi

3. Which type of graph uses small drawings to show an amount?
   a. pictograph
   b. bar graph
   c. line graph
   d. pie graph

4. Which graph is often used to show percentage?
   a. pictograph
   b. bar graph
   c. line graph
   d. pie graph

5. An experiment is
   a. a hypothesis
   b. a question or problem
   c. a test or trial
   d. all of these

6. Which list of three is in proper order for an experiment?
   a. data, procedure, question
   b. question, materials, procedure
   c. materials, conclusion, data
   d. conclusion, question, data

7. What is the main purpose of a microscope?
   a. to make objects closer
   b. to make small objects smaller
   c. to measure volume
   d. to make small objects larger

8. What is the main purpose of a balance?
   a. to determine mass
   b. to measure size
   c. to measure volume
   d. none of these

9. Where are samples placed on a microscope?
    a. on the base
    b. on the objective lens
    c. on the stage
    d. none of these
10. What is moved on a balance to cause it to balance?
    a. the base
    b. the riders
    c. the arms
    d. the fulcrum

Matching. Match each word with its definition or description.
1. a test or trial
2. what was learned from an experiment
3. amount of matter in an object
4. information collected by experimenting
5. starting point of an experiment
6. space occupied by an object
7. metric measuring system
8. graph that uses pictures
9. amount of matter per unit volume
10. steps of an experiment

a. conclusion
b. data
c. density
d. experiment
e. mass
f. pictograph
g. procedure
h. question
i. SI
j. volume

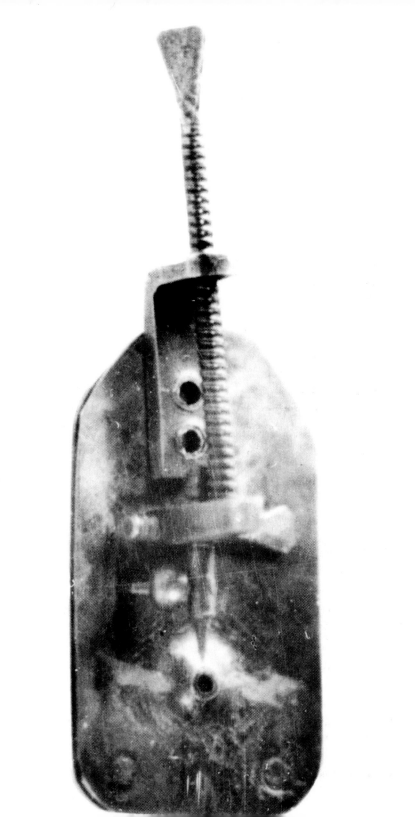

CHAPTER 2

LIVING CELLS

INTRODUCTION

The instrument pictured on the left doesn't look like a microscope, but it is. In the mid-1660s, a wealthy cloth merchant named Anton van Leeuwenhoek (lā′ vən hōōk) built this microscope. While his was not the first microscope, it offered many improvements that allowed better observation of the microscopic world. Improved microscopes that followed Leeuwenhoek's opened a new world to scientists, giving them their first view of the building blocks of life—living cells. Since the first observations of cells in the seventeenth century, scientists have learned a great deal about the structure of living things. But the more they learn about cells, the more they find they do not know.

In this chapter you will learn about the structure and processes of cells.

SECTION TITLES

Leeuwenhoek used his microscope to explore the microscopic world.

2-1 THE CELL THEORY

VOCABULARY

botanist
cell theory
zoologist

OBJECTIVES

- Describe the development of the cell theory.
- Summarize the cell theory.

You probably already know that your body and all other living things are made of cells (fig. 2-1). But, did you know that your knowledge of cells is far greater than that of even the best biologists living 200 years ago?

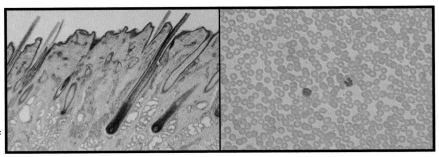

Fig. 2–1 Skin cells (left) and blood cells (right) are two types of cells that make up your body.

It is hard to imagine a time when scientists did not know about cells. But before the seventeenth century, this was the case. In the early 1600s no one really knew what made up humans or other living things. Scientists had learned about many body organs, but no one knew about cells (fig. 2-2).

DID YOU KNOW?
At birth, we have about 2 trillion cells. As adults, we have about 60 trillion cells.

Fig. 2-2 Scientists learned much about the human body by performing dissections on people who had died.

It is often true in the study of science that a new discovery can be used to help scientists learn about something else that is new. This happened with the cell. Anton Van Leeuwenhoek, a wealthy merchant who had a hobby of grinding lenses, developed a microscope that magnified things 200 times. This microscope allowed him to view a variety of things. He studied drops of pond water and discovered a host of tiny creatures he called "animalcules." He examined blood, scrapings from teeth, and other living things. Leeuwenhoek enjoyed sharing his microscope with others at dinners and parties (fig. 2-3). This helped to popularize the microscope and encouraged other scientists to develop similar instruments.

Fig. 2-3 Leeuwenhoek enjoyed showing friends his microscope.

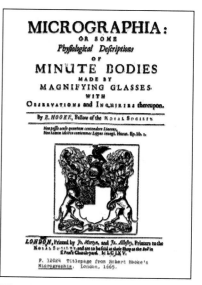

Fig. 2-4 Robert Hooke recorded his observations of cells in his book *Micrographia*.

The first person to use the word *cell* was Robert Hooke, an English scientist who made his own compound microscope in 1665. Hooke observed thin slices of cork from the bark of the cork oak tree and discovered they were made of hundreds of tiny walled spaces (fig. 2-4). To him, these looked much like the tiny rooms, or cells, monks lived in. Hooke used the word *cell* to describe the spaces that made up the cork. Hooke's discovery, along with that of Leeuwenhoek, spurred a chain of scientific discoveries.

For the next 100 years or more, microscopes continued to be improved. They became more powerful and easier to use. In 1824, René Dutrochet (Dü trô shĕ′), a French scientist, concluded from his observations that all living organisms were made of cells.

Fig. 2–5 The nucleus of an onion cell shows up as a small spot in the cell.

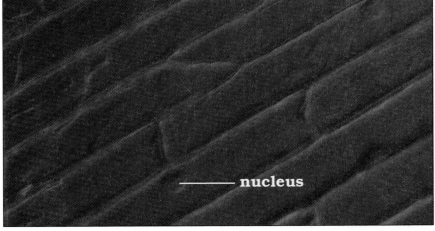

A few years later, in 1831, a Scottish scientist, Robert Brown, recognized that cells were made of still smaller structures. One structure, the central part of most cells, Brown called the nucleus (fig. 2-5).

Following Brown's discovery, Felix Dujardin, another French scientist, observed that cells were not hollow, but were filled with a jellylike substance (fig. 2-6).

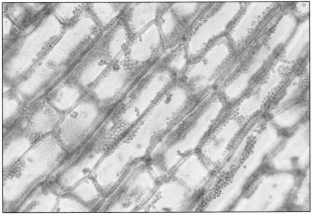

Fig. 2–6 The clear area in each of these cells is filled with cytoplasm.

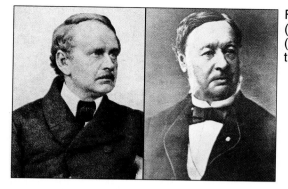

Fig. 2–7 Matthias Schleiden (left) and Theodor Schwann (right) discovered that all living things are made of cells.

More discoveries concerning the cell came in 1838-39, when two German scientists, Matthias Schleiden and Theodor Schwann, conducted extensive studies of living organisms (fig. 2-7). Schleiden, a plant scientist, or **botanist**, concentrated on plants. Schwann, a **zoologist**, or animal scientist, focused his research on animals. Their work resulted in two important ideas about cells: anything that is alive is made of cells, and the cell itself is alive.

THE DEVELOPMENT OF THE CELL THEORY			
Name	Date	Country	Contribution
Hooke	1665	England	• was first to observe and name cells.
Leeuwenhoek	1675	Holland	• was first to observe and describe living cells.
Dutrochet	1824	France	• discovered that various parts of organisms are made of cells.
Brown	1831	Scotland	• recognized that cells are made up of still smaller structures. • identified the central part of the cell as the nucleus.
Dujardin	1835	France	• discovered that cells are not hollow, but are filled with a jellylike substance.
Schleiden/ Schwann	1839	Germany	• discovered that all living organisms are made of cells. • discovered that cells are alive.
Virchow	1859	Germany	• discovered that cells come only from other living cells.

Fig. 2–8

Additional understanding of the cell came from the work of the German scientist Rudolf Virchow, who discovered that cells come only from other living cells.

The work of these scientists, outlined in figure 2-8, culminated in the formation of the cell theory. The **cell theory** states that all living things are made up of one or more cells, that cells are the basic units of life, and that cells come only from other living cells (fig. 2-9).

THE CELL THEORY
• All living organisms are made of one or more cells.
• Cells are the basic units of life.
• Cells come only from other living cells.

Fig. 2-9

REVIEW IT

1. Name seven scientists who helped contribute to the cell theory.
2. What is the cell theory?

2-2 CHARACTERISTICS OF THE CELL

OBJECTIVES

- Identify common characteristics of cells.
- Distinguish between eukaryotic and prokaryotic cells.
- Distinguish between plant and animal cells.

VOCABULARY
eukaryote cell
prokaryote cell

Today, cell biologists continue to study and learn about the cell. Modern technology continues to allow scientists to improve microscopes and develop better techniques for studying the structure and processes of the cell (fig. 2-10).

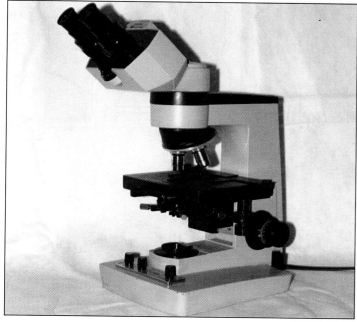

Fig. 2–10 Improvements made in microscopes enable us to see microorganisms in much greater detail.

Scientists recognize that cells are much more than the "tiny rooms" Hooke identified. They understand that cells are alive and that they respond to stimuli. They know that cells constantly change. They recognize that cells are able to manufacture new structures and produce new substances. Finally, they understand that cells often work together to form tissues, organs, and systems, which make living organisms.

CLASS ACTIVITY 2-2: Comparing Cells

Question: What do different kinds of cells look like?

Materials:

beaker (50 mL)	medicine dropper	microscope slides - 2
cork cells (prepared slide)	methylene blue	toothpick (flat)
cover slips - 2	microscope	water
Elodea leaf		

Procedure:
1. Place the prepared slide of cork cells on the microscope stage.
2. Observe the cells first under the low-power objective and then under the high-power objective. Indicate what parts of the cell are visible by writing *yes* or *no* on the data table. In the data section, draw a detailed picture of one of the cells you see.
3. Remove a leaf near the end of an *Elodea* plant. Place the leaf on the slide and add two drops of water. Cover the leaf and place the slide on the microscope stage. Repeat step 2.
4. Put a drop of methylene blue on the second microscope slide.
5. Use the toothpick's blunt end to gently scrape the inside of your cheek.
6. Stir the scrapings of the toothpick in the stain; then discard the toothpick.
7. Place the cover slip over the stain and place the slide on the stage of the microscope. Repeat step 2.

Data:

Cell	Cell Membrane	Cell Wall	Cytoplasm	Nucleus	Vacuole	Chloroplast
Cork						
Elodea						
Cheek						

Cork Cell	*Elodea* Cell	Cheek Cell

Questions:
1. What cell structure(s) did you see in all three cells?
2. What organelle(s) was visible in *Elodea*, but not in the cheek cell?
3. How is the shape of the cheek cell different from the *Elodea* cell?
4. Why aren't any organelles visible in the cork cells?

Conclusion: Write 3-5 sentences about what you learned from this activity.

Cells share several common characteristics:
- They are alive.
- They are enclosed in a membrane.
- They contain cytoplasm.
- They usually have one or more chromosomes.
- They can reproduce themselves.

Fig. 2–11 Bacteria cells lack a nucleus.

Cells can be divided into two distinct types. One group, the **prokaryote** (prō kar′ ē ōt) **cells**, do not have a true nucleus and lack membrane-bound structures (fig 2-11). The second group, the **eukaryote** (yōō kar′ ē ōt) **cells**, have both a nucleus and membrane-bound structures (fig. 2-12). Only bacteria have prokaryotic cells. All other organisms have eukaryotic cells.

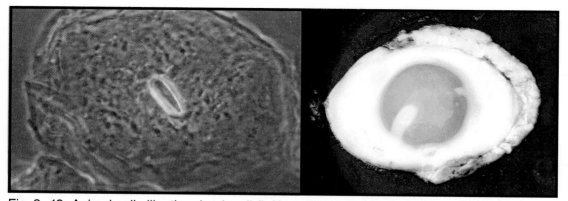

Fig. 2–12 Animal cells like the cheek cell (left) and the egg (right) have a nucleus and are called eukaryote cells.

41

There are also differences between animal and plant cells (fig. 2-13). One difference is that animal cells are surrounded only by a cell membrane, while plant cells are surrounded by an outer cell wall, in addition to the inner cell membrane. A second difference is that animal cells have small vacuoles, but plant cells have very large vacuoles that take up most of the space in the cell. Finally, most plant cells contain the green pigment, chlorophyll, which does not occur in animal cells.

Fig. 2–13

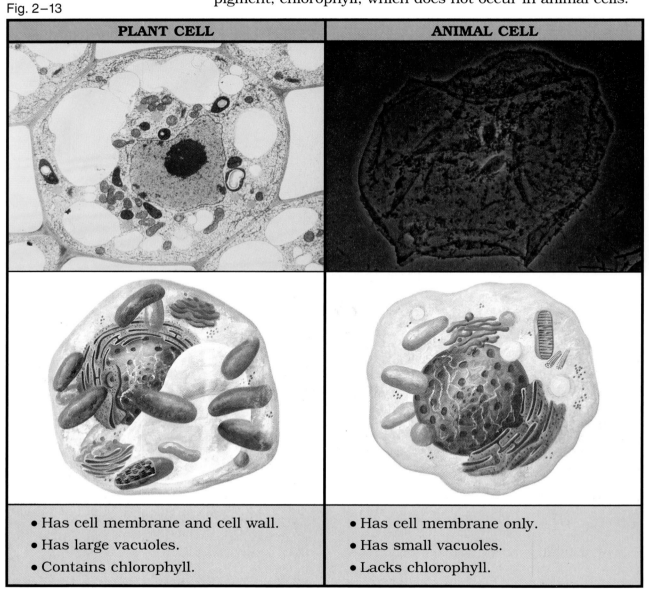

PLANT CELL	ANIMAL CELL
• Has cell membrane and cell wall. • Has large vacuoles. • Contains chlorophyll.	• Has cell membrane only. • Has small vacuoles. • Lacks chlorophyll.

REVIEW IT

1. What are the common characteristics of cells?
2. What is the difference between a prokaryotic cell and a eukaryotic cell?
3. How are plant cells different from animal cells?

Jewel Plummer Cobb

Jewel Plummer Cobb, the granddaughter of a freed slave, was born in 1924. After graduating from pharmacy school, she continued her education by completing a master's degree and a doctorate in cell physiology from New York University. Dr. Cobb has spent her life doing research on the effects of chemotherapy on the cell. In her research she compared the reactions of normal cells with the reactions of cancer cells to various chemicals. From her research she identified chemicals that destroy cancer cells but allow normal cells to live.

This amazing scientist has written more than 50 books and hundreds of articles and scientific reports. She continues to encourage women and minority students to choose careers in science. Because of her work to help students in science, she has been awarded eighteen honorary doctoral degrees from various universities. From 1981 to 1990, Dr. Cobb was President of California State University at Fullerton.

She still encourages students in the Black community to enter the field of science. She wants to be remembered as a Black female scientist who cared very much about what happened to young people, particularly young women going into science.

2-3 THE CYTOPLASM

electron microscope
organelle

- Identify organelles found in the cytoplasm.
- Describe the function of organelles.

What differences do you see when you compare the electron microscope shown in figure 2-14 with van Leeuwenhoek's microscope shown on page 32? While quite different in shape and size, the most important difference is in their magnification. Van Leeuwenhoek's microscope magnified about 200 times and allowed him to see only the larger cells. Modern **electron microscopes** use a beam of electrons, rather than light and lenses, to "see" specimens. These instruments magnify objects up to 1,000,000 times and have helped cell biologists get a better view of cells (fig. 2-15).

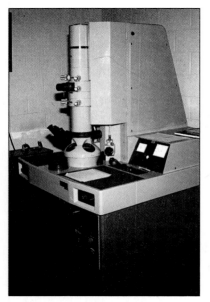

Fig. 2-14 Electron microscopes use a beam of electrons to "see" microscopic objects.

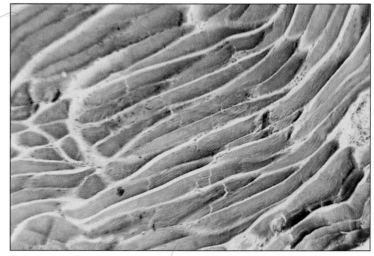

Fig. 2-15 Electron microscopes allow scientists to view very small objects more clearly and in three dimensions.

What are lipids, and how are they used by cells?

Improved microscopes and preparation techniques allow scientists to see many of the intricate parts that make up the cell. These parts, called **organelles**, give cells their various characteristics and are responsible for the many functions that cells perform. The organelles work together in a similar way to the organs and systems that make up your body (fig. 2-16).

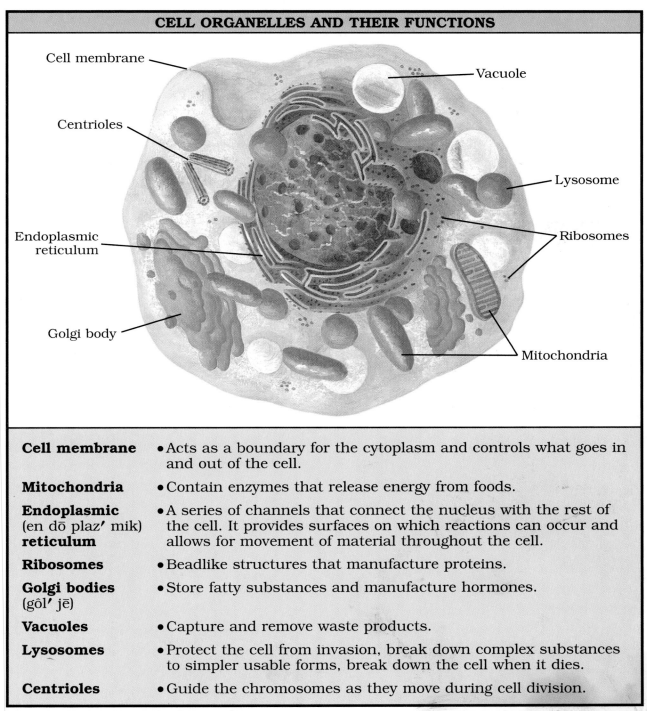

CELL ORGANELLES AND THEIR FUNCTIONS

Cell membrane
Centrioles
Endoplasmic reticulum
Golgi body
Vacuole
Lysosome
Ribosomes
Mitochondria

Cell membrane	• Acts as a boundary for the cytoplasm and controls what goes in and out of the cell.
Mitochondria	• Contain enzymes that release energy from foods.
Endoplasmic (en dō plaz′ mik) **reticulum**	• A series of channels that connect the nucleus with the rest of the cell. It provides surfaces on which reactions can occur and allows for movement of material throughout the cell.
Ribosomes	• Beadlike structures that manufacture proteins.
Golgi bodies (gôl′ jē)	• Store fatty substances and manufacture hormones.
Vacuoles	• Capture and remove waste products.
Lysosomes	• Protect the cell from invasion, break down complex substances to simpler usable forms, break down the cell when it dies.
Centrioles	• Guide the chromosomes as they move during cell division.

Fig. 2–16 The cell is made of many structures.

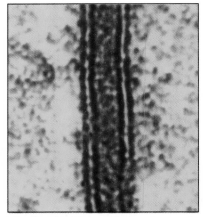

Fig. 2–17 The cell membrane is made of layers.

Suppose for a moment you could shrink as small as one of the millions of tiny glucose molecules that make up a sugar crystal. At this size you can easily enter a cell and take a look around. Imagine that you are inside the cell as you study figure 2-16 and learn about the cell and its organelles.

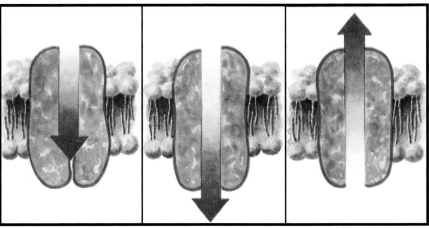

Fig. 2–18 Pores in the cell membrane allow material to enter and exit the cell.

To get inside the cell, you first must get through the cell membrane. The cell membrane is the covering of the cell and is made of three layers, giving it the appearance of a "sandwich" (fig. 2-17). The cell membrane serves as a fence around the cell. It controls what enters and exits the cell by opening and closing tiny passageways through the membrane (fig. 2-18). You enter the cell through one of these open pores.

Each liver cell has more than 1000 mitochondria working to produce energy.

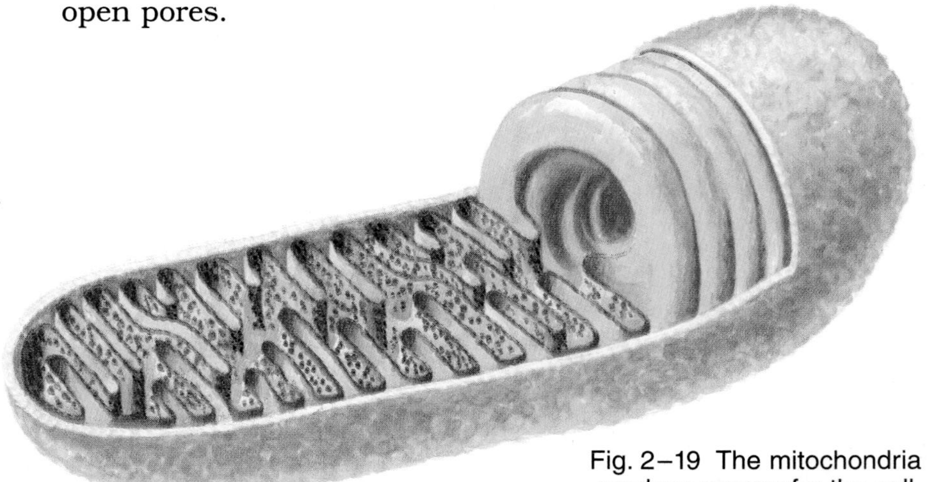

Fig. 2–19 The mitochondria produce energy for the cell.

TRY THIS 2-3: Fold It

Materials:

    metric ruler
    paper (8.5 x 11)

    pencil
    scissors

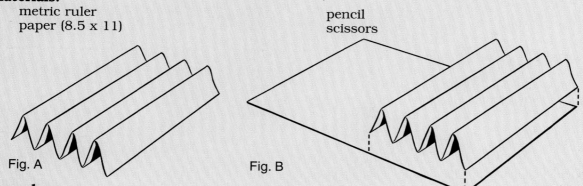

Fig. A   Fig. B

Procedure:

1. Use the scissors to cut a piece of paper in half. Label one half A and the other B.
2. Measure the length and width of A and determine its surface area.
   - What is the surface area of A?
3. Fold the piece as shown in figure A.
4. Lay the folded piece A on top of sheet B as shown in figure B. Mark the position occupied by A on sheet B. Cut off any part of B that was not covered by A.
5. Measure the length and width of sheet B and determine the area occupied by sheet A.
   - What is the area covered by the folded A?
   - Which is greater, the total area of the folded sheet or the area covered? What is the difference?
   - How could you make this difference larger?
   - Suppose pieces A and B represent the cristae of two mitochondria. Which mitochondria would probably supply more energy to the cell? Why?

Inside the cell you are immediately surrounded by a jelly-like substance called cytoplasm. This material fills most of the cell and acts as a factory. Located at various places throughout the cytoplasm are organelles, "machines" that carry out particular jobs.

Looking around, you see many unusual structures and a variety of activities taking place. One type of organelle you see looks like long French rolls. They are the mitochondria, the powerhouse of the cell. Mitochondria are surrounded by a double membrane (fig. 2-19). The inner membrane folds inward many times to form the cristae, which fill most of the inner space. This folded membrane is covered with enzymes that release energy from food. The energy produced by the mitochondria powers all cell activities.

Fig. 2–20 The endoplasmic reticulum is a series of channels present in the cytoplasm.

RESEARCH IT
Which organelle uses lipids, and how are the lipids used?

Fig. 2–21 The ribosomes manufacture proteins needed by the cell.

As you stand in the cell, you see in front of you a series of flattened channels running throughout the cytoplasm (fig. 2-20). These channels, called the endoplasmic reticulum (also called the ER), link the rest of the cell with the nucleus, or control center of the cell. In addition, the surface of the endoplasmic reticulum provides an area for reactions to occur and allows for movement of materials throughout the cell.

The surface of the endoplasmic reticulum is studded with thousands of tiny beadlike ribosomes (fig. 2-21). Other ribosomes float freely throughout the cytoplasm. Regardless of

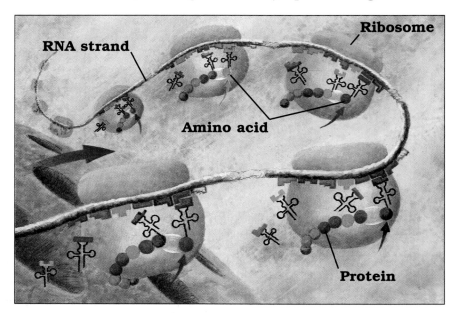

Fig. 2–22 RNA instructs the ribosomes to link specific amino acids to make protein chains.

48

where they are, ribosomes, under the direction of RNA, combine various amino acids to form proteins. These proteins, in turn, are used as building blocks of the cell (fig. 2-22).

As you continue to move through the cytoplasm, you see an organelle that looks like a stack of pancakes (fig. 2-23). This is a Golgi body, which stores fatty substances and helps to manufacture and package hormones.

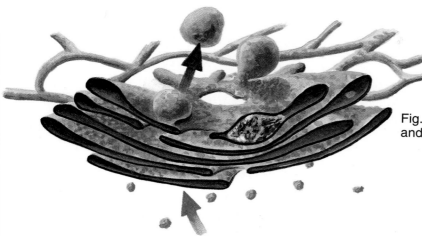

Fig. 2–23 The Golgi body manufactures and packages hormones.

Ahead you find a number of smaller organelles scattered throughout the cell. Some of these, the vacuoles, appear to be hollow. Vacuoles capture and remove the cell's waste products and are sometimes called the "garbage cans" of the cell. Vacuoles are most common in animal cells.

Farther ahead you see other small organelles, called plastids. These structures act as storage centers for cell products and also as manufacturing centers that produce products, such as carbohydrates, needed by the cell (fig. 2-24).

Fig. 2–24 Chloroplasts are present in plant cells and allow photosynthesis to take place.

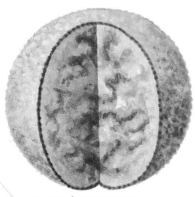

Fig. 2–25 Lysosomes contain digestive enzymes.

Fig. 2–26 This cross section of a centriole shows its internal structure. The centrioles are involved in cell division.

Plastids are most common in plant cells. One special plastid, called the chloroplast, contains the green pigment chlorophyll and manufactures sugar during photosynthesis.

Nearby are several ball-shaped lysosomes that contain digestive enzymes (fig. 2-25). They are important in protecting the cell from bacteria. They also help to break down and recycle the parts of the cell when it dies.

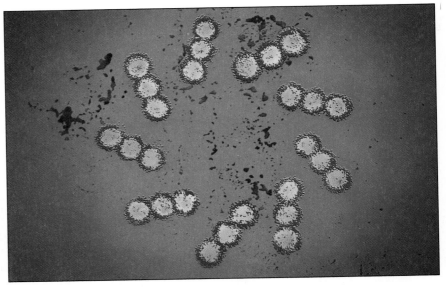

As you turn to enter the nucleus, you look to the right and see two centrioles, small barrellike structures positioned at right angles to each other (fig. 2-26). Most cells have these structures, which help guide the chromosomes apart when the cell divides.

REVIEW IT

1. Name the organelles that fit the five descriptions below:
   a. Protect the cell from invading bacteria.
   b. Stores fatty substances and manufactures and packages hormones.
   c. Contain enzymes that release energy from food.
   d. Connects the nucleus with the rest of the cell and allows for movement of materials throughout the cell.
   e. Beadlike structures that manufacture proteins.

2-4 THE NUCLEUS

OBJECTIVES

- Explain the function of the nucleus.
- Distinguish between chromosomes, genes, and DNA.
- Describe the relationship between DNA and RNA.

Having traveled to the center of the cell, you find a large, round structure. This is the nucleus. The nucleus controls and guides all cellular activities (fig. 2-27). As you get closer to the nucleus, you discover it is surrounded by a porous membrane. This nuclear membrane serves the same function for the nucleus as the cell membrane does for the cell. It controls what enters and exits the nucleus.

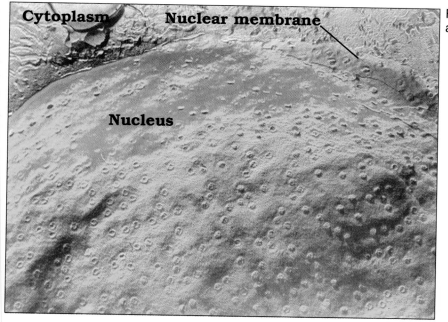

Cytoplasm Nuclear membrane

Nucleus

Fig. 2−27 The nucleus guides all the activities of the cell.

Fig. 2−28 The threadlike chromatin is actually the chromosomes stretched out.

As you enter the nucleus, you immediately become tangled in a mass of threadlike material called the chromatin (fig. 2-28). You untangle yourself and discover that the mass of threads is actually the cell's **chromosomes**, long ribbons of genetic material that direct cell activities. The chromosomes, which occur as pairs, are made up of packets of information called **genes**. The genes are actually segments of a complex

51

molecule called deoxyribonucleic acid, or DNA for short. **DNA** holds the specific instructions that direct all cell processes. The structure and function of DNA will be discussed in section 2-5.

In the nucleus you also see a spherical structure called the nucleolus. This structure manufactures ribosomes. Once a ribosome is manufactured in the nucleolus, it migrates out of the nucleus into the cytoplasm.

Adder's-tongue ferns (*Ophioglossum*), which have at least 630 pairs of chromosomes, hold the record for having the most chromosomes of any living organism. In contrast, a worker ant of an Australian species is made of cells that have only one chromosome each.

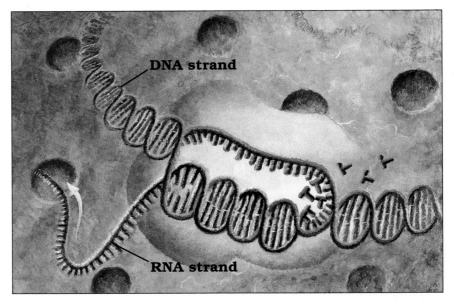

Fig. 2–29 RNA carries the instructions from the DNA out to the organelles of the cell.

The directions contained in DNA must be able to get out to the ribosomes in the nucleus. This is accomplished by ribonucleic acid, or RNA. **RNA** works as a messenger that picks up directions from DNA and carries them out to the cytoplasm (fig. 2-29). Once the ribosomes receive the directions, they make the desired product. This protein might become part of an organelle; or it might be used to repair a broken membrane.

REVIEW IT

1. What is the function of the nucleus?
2. What is the relationship between chromosomes, genes, and DNA?
3. How do DNA and RNA work together?

2-5 CELL ACTIVITIES AND PROCESSES

OBJECTIVES

- Identify the basic cell functions.
- Explain cell respiration.
- Distinguish between passive and active transport.
- Explain the difference between mitosis and meiosis.

VOCABULARY

active transport
ATP
cell division
cell respiration
cell transportation
diffusion
glucose
meiosis
mitosis
osmosis
passive transport
synthesis

Within any one cell, thousands of activities are constantly taking place. Mitochondria produce energy, material is moved in and out of the cell, vacuoles collect and store various products for use, and ribosomes manufacture proteins. These functions of the cell can be classed into four basic categories: respiration, transportation, **synthesis** (sin′ the sis), and reproduction. These functions are summarized below (fig. 2-30).

BASIC CELL FUNCTIONS	
Cell respiration	• the production of energy from food.
Cell transportation	• the movement of materials in and out of the cell.
Synthesis	• the production of new molecules and compounds.
Reproduction	• the production of new organelles.

Fig. 2–30

RESEARCH IT

What is a centromere, and on what structure is it located?

You have learned that oxygen is vital to life. Without it, most living organisms die. In humans and many other animals, oxygen is taken in during breathing. Once oxygen enters the body, it must travel to each cell. If cells are unable to get sufficient oxygen, they cannot produce energy. If this happens for very long, cells begin to die, and the organism itself may die.

The various functions of the cell are carried out by many different processes. Three of these are respiration, transportation, and cell division. Each of these processes is described in figure 2-31.

Fig. 2–31

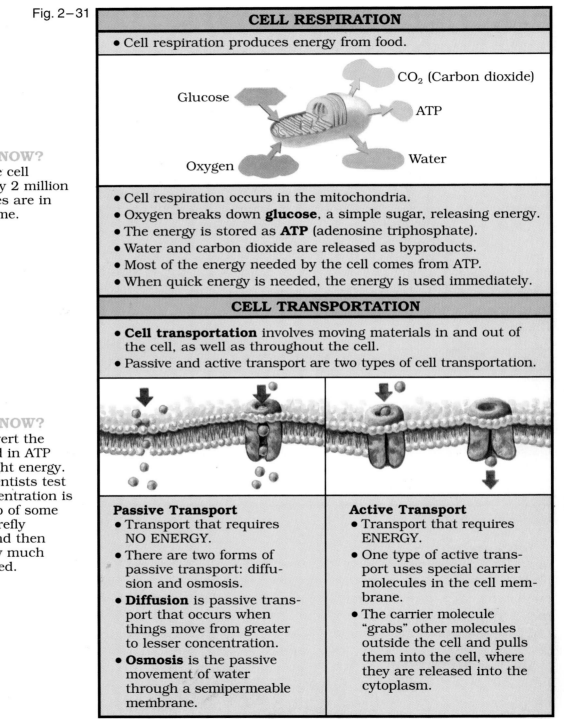

CELL RESPIRATION

- Cell respiration produces energy from food.

Glucose

CO_2 (Carbon dioxide)

ATP

Oxygen

Water

- Cell respiration occurs in the mitochondria.
- Oxygen breaks down **glucose**, a simple sugar, releasing energy.
- The energy is stored as **ATP** (adenosine triphosphate).
- Water and carbon dioxide are released as byproducts.
- Most of the energy needed by the cell comes from ATP.
- When quick energy is needed, the energy is used immediately.

CELL TRANSPORTATION

- **Cell transportation** involves moving materials in and out of the cell, as well as throughout the cell.
- Passive and active transport are two types of cell transportation.

Passive Transport
- Transport that requires NO ENERGY.
- There are two forms of passive transport: diffusion and osmosis.
- **Diffusion** is passive transport that occurs when things move from greater to lesser concentration.
- **Osmosis** is the passive movement of water through a semipermeable membrane.

Active Transport
- Transport that requires ENERGY.
- One type of active transport uses special carrier molecules in the cell membrane.
- The carrier molecule "grabs" other molecules outside the cell and pulls them into the cell, where they are released into the cytoplasm.

Fig. 2–31 continued

CELL DIVISION
• Cell division forms new cells. • Mitosis and meiosis are two types of cell division.

MITOSIS
• Produces two new cells, each having two sets of chromosomes. • Produces ALL CELLS EXCEPT REPRODUCTIVE CELLS. • Produces cells identical to the parent cell. • Results in the growth and repair of tissue. • Occurs in five stages.

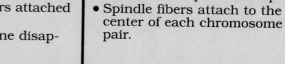

Interphase
- Cell involved in normal cell processes.

Prophase
- Each chromosome is copied.
- Chromosome pairs attached at middle.
- Nuclear membrane disappears.

Metaphase
- Chromosome pairs line up.
- Spindle fibers attach to the center of each chromosome pair.

Anaphase
- Spindle fibers pull apart the chromosome pairs.
- Two identical sets of chromosomes are pulled to either side of the cell.

Telophase
- Spindle fibers disappear.
- Nuclear membrane forms around each set of chromosomes.
- Cell membrane and cytoplasm pinch in to form two new identical cells.

Interphase
- Two new cells become involved in normal cell processes.

Fig. 2–31 continued

MEIOSIS (mī ō′ sis)

- Produces four new cells, each having only one set of chromosomes.
- Produces ONLY REPRODUCTIVE CELLS.
- Occurs in nine stages.

First meiotic division
- In the first stage of meiosis, the cell undergoes a simple mitotic division that produces two identical cells, each with a complete set of chromosomes.

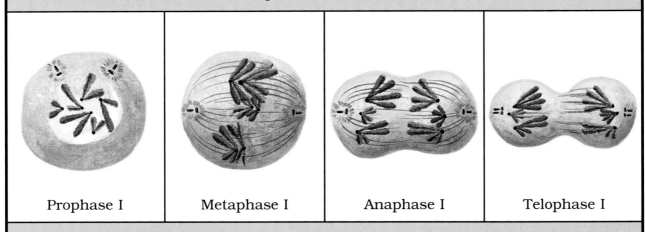

| Prophase I | Metaphase I | Anaphase I | Telophase I |

Second meiotic division
- In the second stage of meiosis, the two new identical cells produced in the first stage undergo reduction and division, producing two new cells with half of the complete set of chromosomes of the original parent cell.

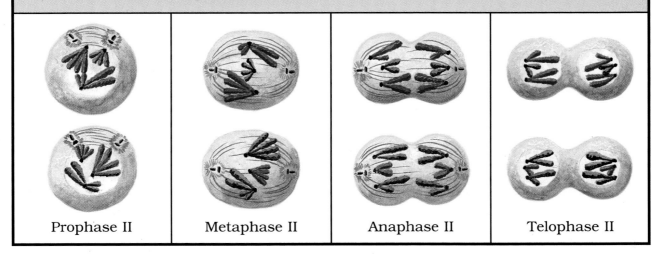

| Prophase II | Metaphase II | Anaphase II | Telophase II |

TRY THIS 2-5: Black Water

Materials:

    beaker (600 mL)
    cornstarch
    iodine (tincture)

    recloseable plastic bag (small)
    water

Procedure:

1. Make a cornstarch solution by mixing 200 mL of water with 1 tsp cornstarch. Stir until all the cornstarch is dissolved.

2. Pour the cornstarch solution into the plastic bag. Close the bag so no liquid can leak out or in.

3. Fill the beaker with about 300 mL of water. Add 10 drops of iodine to the water and mix thoroughly.

4. Submerge the bottom half of the plastic bag (the part of the bag that contains the cornstarch solution) in the beaker containing the iodine solution. Let the bag sit in the beaker for five minutes.

5. After five minutes observe any changes.
   - What happened to the solution in the bag?
   - Why did this change occur?
   - In this activity what does the plastic bag represent?

REVIEW IT

1. What are the basic cell functions?
2. What happens during cellular respiration?
3. What is the difference between active and passive transport?
4. How is meiosis different from mitosis?

DID YOU KNOW?
A cell spends about 5 percent of its time dividing and the other 95 percent resting.

2-6 DNA— THE BLUEPRINT

OBJECTIVES

- Describe the structure of DNA.
- Explain the function of DNA.
- Describe how DNA duplicates itself.

Fig. 2–32 Half the chromo-somes of the chick comes from the hen and the other half comes from the rooster.

About 28 days before the chick in figure 2-32 hatched, a rooster's sperm, containing one set of chromosomes, combined with an egg, containing one set of chromosomes, inside a hen. The fertilized cell now had two matching sets of chromosomes and began to undergo mitosis to produce new cells. These cells then divided many times to produce still more cells. The newly formed cells organized into tissues, organs, and systems. The chick grew and eventually hatched. This process of cell fertilization and division is repeated over and over in almost all living organisms, including humans.

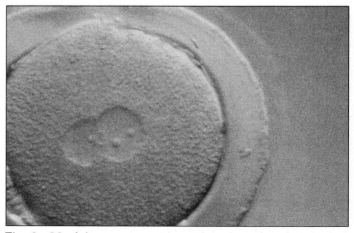

Fig. 2–33 A human zygote results when the chromo-somes in a sperm cell combine with the chromosomes in an egg cell.

Just as the chick did, you also started from one fertilized cell (fig. 2-33). In order to grow and develop, your body required a variety of materials. Some of these materials were absorbed ready to use. Other materials, such as proteins, had to be made inside the cell. For growth to occur correctly, your cells had to produce the proper proteins. The genes in your cells determined whether you would have big feet or small feet, brown eyes or blue eyes, and whether or not you could roll your tongue (fig. 2-34).

The instructions that direct the cells to create and use the various materials are contained in the DNA that makes up your chromosomes. That's why DNA is often called the "blueprint of life." Scientists estimate that if the DNA of one cell were stretched out, it would be more than 2 meters long.

Figure 2-35 shows a DNA molecule. As you can see, the DNA looks much like a long ladder that has been twisted. This arrangement is called a **double helix**. The sides of the DNA ladder are made up of alternating molecules of sugar and phosphate. Connecting the two sides of the ladder are "rungs" of pairs of special molecules called **nucleotide** (n$\overline{oo}'$ klē ō tīd) **bases**.

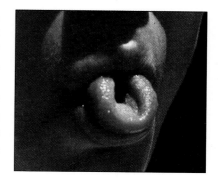

Fig. 2-34 The ability to roll your tongue is determined by the genes you receive.

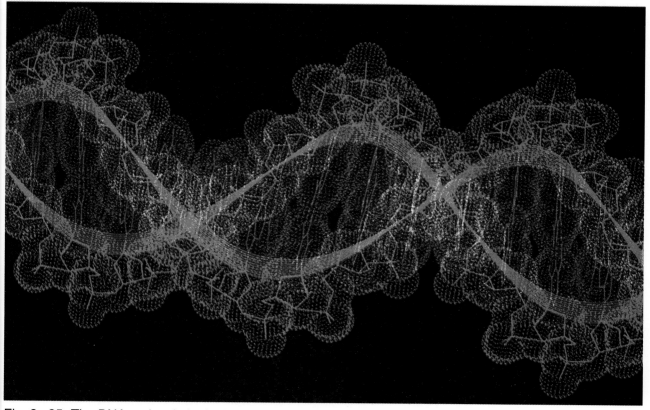

Fig. 2-35 The DNA molecule looks like a twisted ladder.

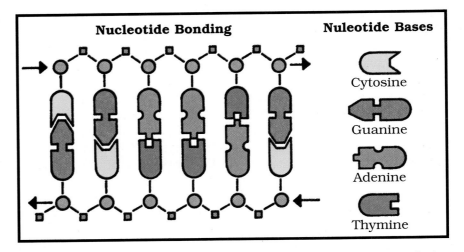

Only four nucleotide bases make up the rungs of the DNA molecule: adenine, cytosine, guanine, and thymine (fig. 2-36). They are often denoted by the letters A, C, G, and T. Look at several of the rungs. Do you see any pattern? You will notice that adenine always connects with thymine, and guanine always combines with cytosine. This happens because the structure of thymine and adenine

DID YOU KNOW?
A typical human cell has about 2000 times more DNA than a bacteria has.

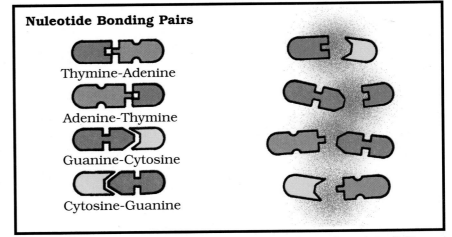

Fig. 2–37 The molecular shape of each base determines how it fits together with another to make a nucleotide base pair. Each base pair makes one rung of the DNA ladder.

permits them to fit together. Guanine and cytosine fit together for the same reason. Figure 2-37 shows the pair combinations that can be formed from these nucleotide bases. The sequence of the nucleotides along the DNA molecule determines the type of amino acids that will combine to produce a particular protein.

A sequence of three nucleotide base pairs is a code for a particular amino acid. A sequence of these amino acid codes represents the code for a particular protein. The more DNA in a cell, the more kinds of proteins can be produced.

Humans have 46 chromosomes (fig. 2-38). The DNA in these chromosomes contains codes for producing thousands of different proteins. Because the DNA is inside the nucleus while the ribosomes that manufacture the proteins are in the cytoplasm, the directions from the DNA must be taken out to the ribosomes. This task is performed by RNA. Each RNA molecule is a copy of a DNA code. When a segment of RNA reaches a ribosome, it is translated. The resulting translation is the protein (fig. 2-39).

When it is time for a cell to divide, all of the 46 chromo-

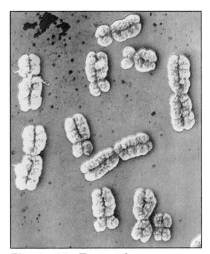

Fig. 2–38 Except for sperm and egg cells, every cell of your body contains 46 chromosomes.

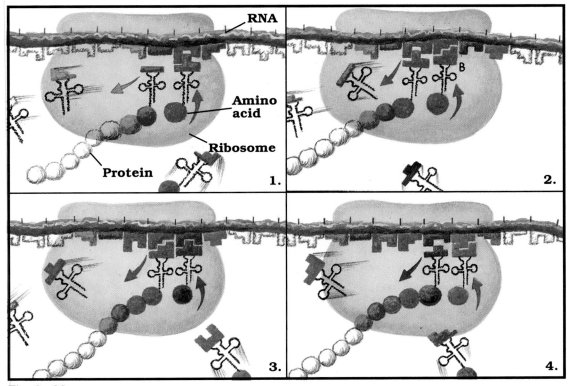

Fig. 2–39

61

somes must be copied exactly. This ensures that each new cell receives a complete set of chromosomes. The duplication of the chromosomes occurs when the cell is not dividing (fig. 2-40).

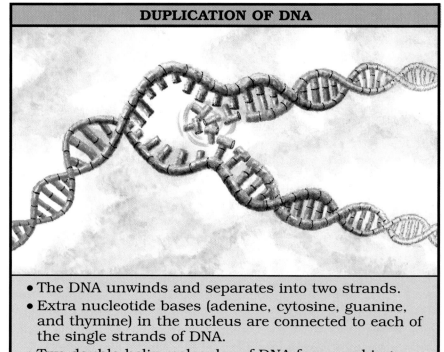

DUPLICATION OF DNA

- The DNA unwinds and separates into two strands.
- Extra nucleotide bases (adenine, cytosine, guanine, and thymine) in the nucleus are connected to each of the single strands of DNA.
- Two double-helix molecules of DNA form, making a copy of the original DNA.
- When the cell divides, one set of DNA goes into each new cell.

Fig. 2–40

REVIEW IT

1. Describe the structure of DNA.
2. Why doesn't thymine join with guanine, or adenine join with cytosine?
3. What is the function of DNA?
4. How does DNA duplicate itself?

James Watson

Have you ever worked on a jigsaw puzzle? How many pieces did it have? 200? 500? 1000? 10,000? One important work of scientists involves solving puzzles. While not exactly like the jigsaw puzzles you may have worked on, they are puzzles just the same. James D. Watson is a biologist who likes puzzles. In the early 1950s he began trying to solve one of the most difficult puzzles that confronted scientists. This puzzle involved discovering the structure of the substance that controls the cell. Working along with his colleague, Francis Crick, Watson studied models of large biological molecules made by Maurice Wilkins, a British biophysicist. Watson and Crick used X-ray diffraction to make three-dimensional images of these molecules.

After many years of frustrating work, James Watson and Francis Crick did something that no other scientists had done: they discovered the structure of deoxyribonucleic acid (DNA). DNA is the "code of life," the substance that directs all cell activities and that allows genetic information to pass from one generation to the next. The knowledge of this molecule led to great advances in the understanding of genetics. For their work Watson, Crick, and Wilkins received the 1962 Nobel Prize in physiology.

After being awarded the prize, Watson continued his research to discover more about DNA and genetics. Recently, James Watson has been working on another puzzle, the Human Genome Project, a project that is trying to map the entire sequence of DNA in our set of 46 chromosomes. Do you like puzzles? Keep working. Someday you may become like James D. Watson. You may solve a difficult puzzle of science.

CHAPTER 2 WRAP-UP

THINKING SKILLS: Making Models

Deoxyribonucleic acid (DNA) is the molecule responsible for directing all cell processes. Francis Crick and James D. Watson worked in the early 1950s to unravel the structure of this molecule. These researchers discovered that the DNA molecule is much like a "twisted" ladder. The sides are made up of phosphate and sugar molecules, while the rungs of the ladder are made up of pairs of nucleotide bases. The sequence of these nucleotide base pairs is what spells a particular code.

You are going to construct a two-dimensional model of the DNA molecule. Use the diagram in figure A and the materials listed to construct your model.

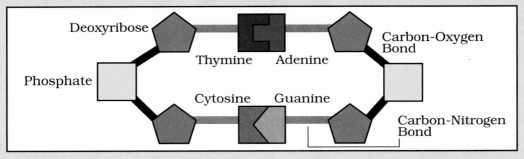

Materials:

    construction paper (black, blue, green, orange, pink, purple, red, yellow)
    glue stick   scissors
    poster board   Special Master R41

Procedure:

1. Use the patterns on the special master to trace and cut out the correct number of each piece. The number of each piece is indicated on the pattern.
2. Use the sample DNA molecule in figure A to construct a model of DNA. Glue the molecules onto the poster paper. Start your model like the pattern provided. Complete the molecule by adding pieces until you have a DNA molecule composed of 12 nucleotide base pairs.
3. Answer the questions below:
   a. Where in the cell is DNA found?
   b. What is the importance of the sequence of the base pairs?
   c. What makes up a nucleotide?
   d. How many nucleotides make up your DNA molecule?
   e. Which bases always join together?
   f. Why can't guanine and adenine join together?

QUESTIONS AND PROBLEMS

1. Why was little known about the cell before the mid-seventeenth century?
2. Although cells are similar in several ways, what are some general differences between cells?
3. Why are plant cells surrounded by cell walls?
4. Why are electron microscopes an advantage when studying cells?
5. List items that are absorbed into the cell.
6. Which happens faster, active or passive transport? Why?
7. In what type of body cells would you find the greatest number of mitochondria?
8. Cell organelles are similar in function to what body structure?
9. What structures cover the surface of the endoplasmic reticulum?
10. How does the cell membrane regulate what goes in and out of the cell?
11. Why doesn't thymine join with guanine?
12. How do lysosomes help keep the environment clean?
13. What is the difference between chromatin and chromosome?
14. What happens during meiosis that results in cells with half the genetic material of the parent cell?

RESEARCH

1. Use library resources to learn about the cell walls of plants. Find out what material makes up the walls and what uses have been found for it. Write a report on your findings.
2. Design a hands-on activity that can be used to teach students in grades K-3 about the structure of a cell. Present this activity to a group of lower-grade students. Make an oral presentation summarizing your experience.
3. Use butcher paper or continuous-sheet computer paper to make an illustrated time line that depicts the major events in the development of the cell theory.
4. Make a series of models that show what happens during each stage of mitosis. Be sure to label the parts of each model.
5. Develop a bulletin board that shows examples of diffusion and osmosis in everyday life.

REVIEW

HIGHLIGHTS

1. Several scientists developed an understanding of cells and their importance. Figure 2-8 lists these scientists and their contributions.
2. The cell theory states that all living organisms are made of one or more cells, cells are the basic units of life, and cells come only from other living cells.
3. Cells share several common characteristics: all cells are alive, all cells are enclosed in a membrane, all cells contain cytoplasm, and all cells have one or more chromosomes.
4. Eukaryote cells have a nucleus; prokaryote cells do not.

5. Animal and plant cell differences include: Animal cells are surrounded by only cell membranes; plant cells are surrounded by both cell membranes and cell walls; animal cells have small vacuoles; those in plant cells are very large.

6. Several organelles are found in a cell. These organelles and their functions are summarized in figure 2-16.

7. The nucleus controls and guides all cell activities.

8. Chromosomes are ribbons of genetic material. Many genes, packets of information, make up each chromosome. Each gene is made up of a segment of DNA that holds specific instructions for directing cellular activity.

9. DNA contains the codes for directing all cell processes. RNA picks up the information from DNA and carries it to the organelles of the cell.

10. Cell process can be classed into four basic categories: respiration, transportation, synthesis, and reproduction.

11. Cell respiration produces energy from food. The mechanism of how this is accomplished is summarized in figure 2-31.

12. Active and passive transport move materials in and out of cells. Active transport requires energy; passive transport does not.

13. Mitosis is simple cell division; it produces duplicates of the parent cell and occurs in body cells. Meiosis is reduction-division of cells; it produces cells that have half the genetic material of the parent cell and occurs only in the sex cells.

14. DNA is like a twisted ladder. The sides of the DNA are alternating molecules of sugar and phosphate, while the rungs (steps) are pairs of nucleotide bases. Nucleotide bases match up as follows: adenine with thymine and guanine with cytosine.

15. DNA directs all cellular activities, has the blueprint to make any part of any cell, and is the blueprint of life.

16. Duplication of DNA is summarized in figure 2-40.

VOCABULARY LIST

active transport	DNA	nucleotide base
ATP	double helix	organelle
botanist	electron microscope	osmosis
cell division	eukaryote cell	passive transport
cell respiration	gene	prokaryote cell
cell theory	glucose	RNA
cell transportation	meiosis	synthesis
chromosome	mitosis	zoologist
diffusion		

PRACTICE

Multiple Choice. Choose the best answer.

1. Which discovery about cells came last?
   - a. are alive
   - b. have organelles
   - c. have cytoplasm
   - d. came from living cells

2. How are prokaryote cells different from eukaryote cells?
    a. have a cell membrane   c. have a nucleus
    b. have no nucleus   d. none of these
3. What do plant cells have that animal cells do not have?
    a. a cell wall   c. cytoplasm
    b. chromosomes   d. a cell membrane
4. Which two are organelles?
    a. endoplasmic and reticulum   c. ribosomes and cytoplasm
    b. glucose and cristae   d. plastids and mitochondria
5. The job of the nucleus is to
    a. cause cell division   c. control cell activity
    b. mark the cell's center   d. make plastids
6. What is the main ingredient of a chromosome?
    a. DNA or genes   c. active transport materials
    b. genes and plastids   d. osmosis and nucleolus
7. The four cell processes are: transportation, reproduction,
    a. respiration and synthesis   c. excretion and respiration
    b. respiration and botany   d. conflagration and respiration
8. Mitosis causes growth, while meiosis creates the
    a. cell membrane   c. ATP
    b. sex cells   d. passive transport
9. DNA is shaped like a twisted ladder and is made of sugars,
    a. phosphate and cytoplasm   c. nucleotide bases and plastids
    b. RNA and thymine   d. phosphate and nucleotide bases
10. RNA carries directions to ribosomes so they can
    a. copy organelles   c. copy RNA
    b. make proteins   d. none of these

Matching. Match each word with its definition or description.
1. produces energy from food   a. cell respiration
2. holds instructions to direct the cell   b. cell theory
3. the powerhouse of the cell   c. chromosome
4. cell division that produces sex cells   d. cytosine
5. all living things are made of cells   e. DNA
6. a cell that has a nucleus   f. meiosis
7. long series of genes   g. mitochondria
8. cell division that causes only growth   h. mitosis
9. always joins with guanine   i. osmosis
10. a type of passive transport   j. eukaryote cell

CHAPTER 3

HEREDITY

Look at the people on the left. What similarities do you see? What differences do you see? Does this group look as though they are related? They are. These nine people are all first cousins. People who are related sometimes look similar. The more closely they are related, the more they may look alike. You may have been told you look like your mom or dad, a grandparent, or some other relative.

Why do people often resemble their parents or other relatives? Why do some people have blue eyes and others have brown, hazel, or green eyes? In this chapter you will study human heredity. You will examine how heredity works and learn why you have certain features.

SECTION TITLES

3–1 YOUR INHERITANCE

VOCABULARY

dominant
genetics
heredity
recessive

OBJECTIVES

- Explain the difference between heredity and genetics.
- Describe the importance of Gregor Mendel's contribution to our understanding of genetics.
- Distinguish between dominant and recessive traits.

Which of the characteristics in figure 3-1 do you have? These features and all your physical characteristics are the result of two packages of information you got when you were conceived. One package came in the sperm from your father; the other, in the egg of your mother. These packages combined to form your own unique set of inherited traits. Although the hereditary information in your cells is similar to your parents', it is also different. **Heredity** (hə red′ i tē), the transfer of traits or characteristics from one generation to the next, has interested people ever since they noticed that offspring are similar to their parents.

DID YOU KNOW?

Identical twins are usually thought of as being identical in every way, but slight differences in the genetic package of each twin do exist. These differences cause slight variations in body shape, hair color, skin color, and birthmarks, and may influence personality.

Fig. 3–1 Hair color and texture (left), hitchhiker's thumb (middle), and eye color (right) are examples of genetic traits.

Heredity is essential to successful farming (fig. 3-2). Years ago, farmers interested in improving their crops and livestock began to study what traits were inherited, how they were inherited, and what resulted from this inheritance. This study of traits and how they are inherited is called **genetics** (jə net′ iks). One of the first rules these farmers discovered was that high-quality plants and livestock usually produced high-quality offspring. By applying this rule, many domestic animals and crops were developed or improved (fig. 3-3). Today genetics involves much more than farm animals. Modern genetics studies the structure and effects of the genes in humans as well as in plants and animals.

While the development of farm animals and improved crops was valuable, much of the farmer's success was due to trial and error. No one really knew for sure how traits were inherited or exactly what would happen when two animals were bred or two plants crossed. This began to change in the mid-1800s due to the work of an Austrian monk named Gregor Mendel (fig. 3-4).

Fig. 3-2 Genetic principles are constantly used to improve crops.

Fig. 3-3 Domesticated fowl were developed by applying genetic principles.

Fig. 3-4 Gregor Mendel is called the "Father of Genetics."

DID YOU KNOW?
Anne Boleyn, the second wife of Henry VIII, had six fingers on one hand.

Mendel, often called the "Father of Genetics," was an avid gardener. He constantly tried to improve his vegetable and flower gardens. Mendel experimented and kept careful records of the results. He concentrated his study on certain traits, or characteristics, of pea plants. Mendel found that when a purebred tall plant was crossed with a purebred short plant, all of the resulting offspring were tall. When he crossed these offspring among themselves, the resulting plants showed a ratio of three tall plants to one short plant. This same principle held true with other characteristics, including the shape of seeds, the shape of the pods, and the color of the flowers. Figure 3-5 summarizes Mendel's findings.

Seed Shape	Seed Coat Color	Seed Color	Flower Position	Stem Length	Pod Shape	Pod Color
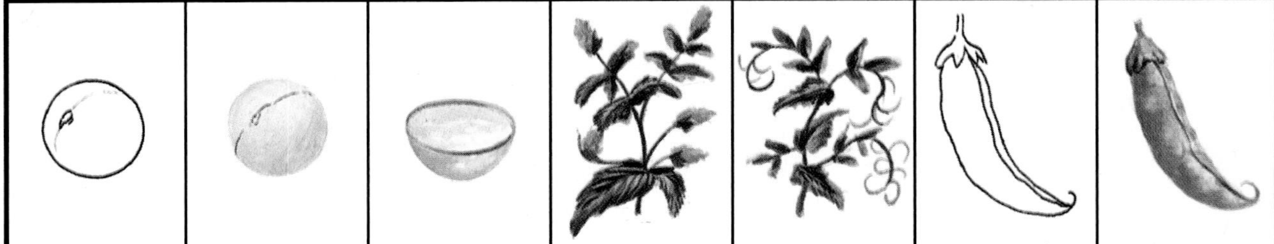						
Round 5474	Gray 705	Yellow 6022	Axial 651	Long 787	Smooth 882	Green 428
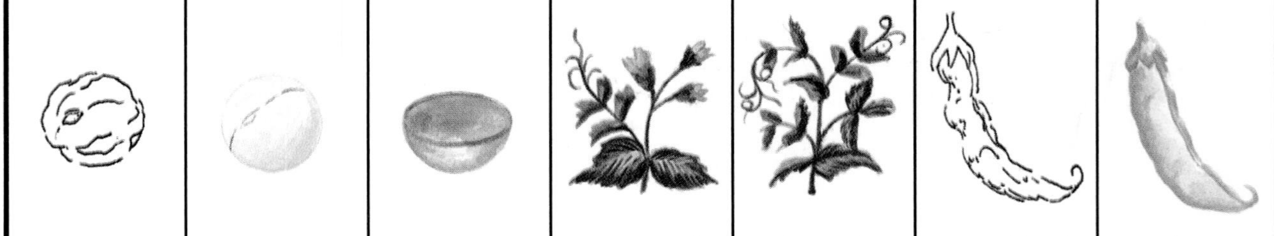						
Wrinkled 1850	White 224	Green 2001	Terminal 207	Short 277	Wrinkled 299	Yellow 152

Fig. 3–5 Mendel studied several traits of pea plants in developing his theory of heredity.

Based on his experiments, Mendel concluded that for these traits, one form seemed to dominate, while the other, even though it was present, was hidden. Mendel referred to the visible trait as **dominant**; the hidden trait he called **recessive**. In Mendel's experiments tall plants, smooth seeds, and red flowers were all dominant traits. Recessive traits included shortness, wrinkled seeds, and white flowers.

TRY THIS 3-1: Chances Are

Materials:
   pennies - 2

Procedure:
1. Flip the penny in the air 50 times. Keep track of how many times the coin landed "heads" and how many times it landed "tails."
   - What is the chance of "heads" when the coin is flipped?
   - What is the chance of "tails" when the coin is flipped?
   - How many times did "heads" show in the 50 tosses?
   - How many times did "tails" show in the 50 tosses?
   - How did your data compare to the theoretical probability?
2. Repeat step 1. This time flip two coins, and keep track of the resulting combinations.
   - What is the probability for each combination?
   a. head-head
   b. head-tail
   c. tail-tail
   - How did your data compare to the theoretical probability?
3. Combine your data from step 2 with that of your classmates.
   - How did the combined data compare with the theoretical probability?
   - How does the data compare to the theoretical probability as the number of trials increases?
   - How is tossing two coins together similar to a hybrid cross?

REVIEW IT

1. What is the difference between heredity and genetics?
2. Who was Gregor Mendel? Why is his work important?
3. What is the difference between dominant and recessive traits?

3-2 HOW INHERITANCE WORKS

OBJECTIVES

- Explain the law of inheritance.
- Distinguish between genotype and phenotype.
- Explain how traits are inherited.
- Explain how sex is determined in humans.

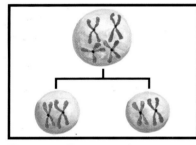

Fig. 3-6 Because chromosomes occur in pairs, genes do also.

Mendel's principles of heredity and the many discoveries that followed led to the discovery of the law of inheritance. This law states that all inherited traits are determined by genes. Let's see how this works.

In section 2-4 you learned that chromosomes occur in pairs. This means that genes also occur in pairs (fig. 3-6). The two members of a gene pair may be identical, or they may be different. If both genes are identical, the individual is said to be **homozygous** (hō mō zī′ gəs) for that trait. If they are different, the individual is **heterozygous** (het ər ō zī′ gəs) for the trait (fig. 3-7). The set of genes an organism inherits makes up its **genotype** (jen′ ə tīp). An organism's

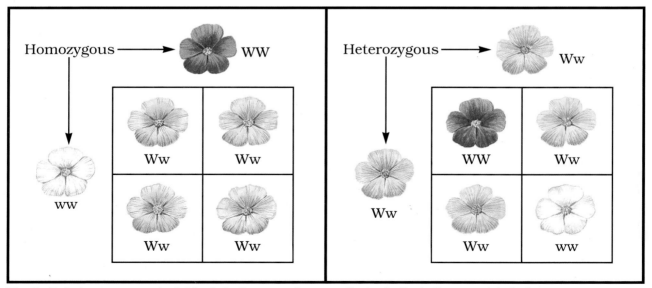

Fig. 3-7 In homozygous individuals both genes for a particular trait are the same. In heterozygous individuals the two genes for a particular trait are different.

Fig. 3–8 Guinea pigs show a variety of color combinations or phenotypes.

genotype contains all the DNA that directs the activities in the cells, regulates body processes, and influences the organism's behavior and appearance.

It is difficult to see an organism's actual genotype. Because of this, the organism's outward appearance, or **phenotype** (fē′ nō tīp), is sometimes used to determine genotype (fig. 3-8). But phenotype is not always an accurate guide. A recessive gene may be part of a genotype, but the recessive trait is not visible because it is masked by the dominant trait. For example, a tall pea plant may have two "tall" genes, or it may have one "tall" gene and one "short" gene.

Scientists use a coding system to identify the genotype for a particular trait. In this system, capital letters are used to represent dominant genes, and small letters are used for recessive genes (fig. 3-9). For example, the symbol for a homozygous (same genes) yellow-seeded pea plant is "YY." A homozygous green-seeded plant is "yy," and a heterozygous (different genes) pea plant is "Yy" or "yY." Two symbols are

Gametes	Y	y
Y yellow seed	YY	Yy
y green seed	yY	yy

Fig. 3–9 Capital letters are used to identify dominant genes; lowercase letters are used to identify recessive genes.

75

used for each trait because there are two gene possibilities for each trait. Offspring receive one gene for each trait from each parent (fig. 3-10).

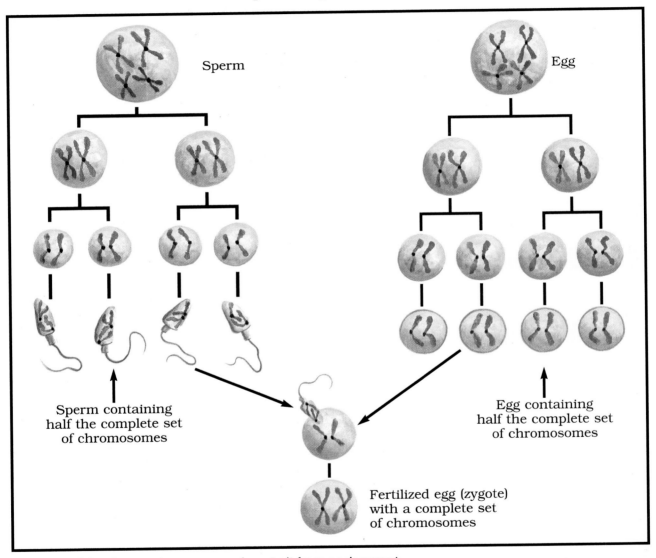

Fig. 3–10 Offspring receive one gene for a trait from each parent.

A homozygous yellow-seeded pea plant can pass only a "yellow" gene to its offspring, and a homozygous green-seeded pea plant can pass only a "green" gene. But a heterozygous pea plant can pass either a "yellow" gene or a "green" gene on to the next generation.

Traits are inherited when genes are passed from parent to offspring. To understand how this occurs, it is helpful to use a Punnett square (fig. 3-11). This is a table that organizes and displays genotypes of parents and helps predict the genotype and phenotype of offspring. To complete a Punnett square for one trait, study figure 3-12. In this Punett square we will look at plant height (T=tall, t=short) and heterozygous parents for the trait. First, write possible genes that can be inherited from the female on the left side. Write the possible genes that can be inherited from the male across the top of the square. Then, take one gene from each parent and write it in the squares. The genotypes that appear in the squares represent the possible genotypes of the offspring of the cross.

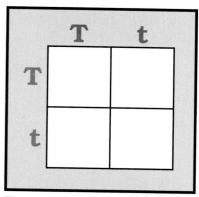

Fig. 3–11 A Punnett square is useful in showing how particular genes are inherited.

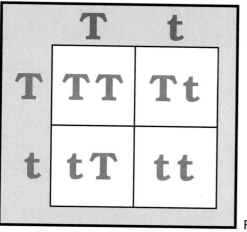

Fig. 3–12

RESEARCH IT
Find out why calico cats are almost always female.

Figure 3-13 shows that if a homozygous tall (TT) plant is crossed with a homozygous short (tt) plant, the only genotype possible for the offspring is heterozygous tall (Tt). Since the gene for tall is dominant over the gene for short, all of these plants will be tall, even though they each carry a gene for short. If, however, two heterozygous plants are crossed, the offspring have a 3-to-1 (3:1) chance of being tall.

One of the most obvious genetic traits organisms inherit is sex. Sex is determined in different ways in different organisms. In turtles the temperature at which the eggs are incubated determines the sex of the baby turtles. If the eggs are kept warm, females develop; if the eggs are kept cool, males develop. The sex of some fish changes, depending on conditions. In humans and most mammals, sex is determined by a pair of chromosomes called the **sex chromosomes**.

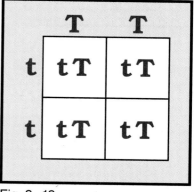

Fig. 3–13

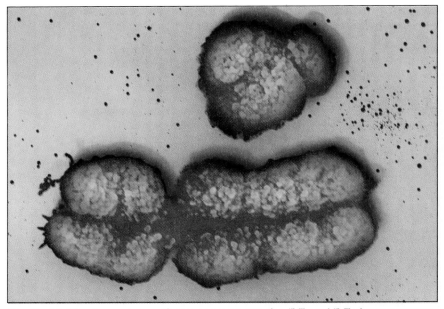

Fig. 3–14 The human sex chromosomes are the "X" and "Y" chromosomes.

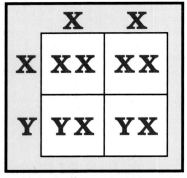

Fig. 3–15 In humans there is an equal chance that a zygote will be male or female.

In humans these chromosomes are called the "X" and "Y" chromosomes (fig. 3-14). The cells of females carry two "X" chromosomes, while the cells of males carry one "X" and one "Y" chromosome. During meiosis, when egg and sperm cells are developing, the sex chromosomes separate. Each egg receives one "X" chromosome. Each sperm receives either an "X" or a "Y" chromosome. The Punnett square in figure 3-15 shows how sex is determined. If a sperm containing an "X" chromosome combines with the egg, the genotype of the fertilized egg is "XX," and it will develop into a female. If a sperm carrying a "Y" chromosome combines with the egg, the genotype of the fertilized egg is "XY," and it will develop into a male. Since there is an equal chance for a sperm to have either an "X" or "Y" chromosome, male and female offspring are produced in about equal numbers.

REVIEW IT

1. What is the law of inheritance?
2. What is the difference between the phenotype and genotype of an individual?
3. Explain how a trait is inherited.
4. Explain how sex is determined in humans.

3-3 PATTERNS OF INHERITANCE

OBJECTIVES

- Distinguish between dominant and recessive inheritance.
- Explain incomplete dominance.
- Identify traits that are related to sex.

Have you ever tried to roll your tongue (fig. 3-16)? Many people are able to roll their tongues, but no matter how hard others try, they cannot. Did you know that tongue rolling is a genetic trait? It is, and so are all other traits. Whether your earlobes are attached or unattached, whether you have hitchhiker's thumb, whether your hair is curly or straight, and even whether you can taste certain things are all examples of genetic traits (fig. 3-17).

Fig. 3–16 The ability to roll your tongue is determined by the genes you inherit.

Geneticists, scientists who specialize in the study of heredity, have discovered several patterns of **inheritance**, or how traits are passed from one generation to another. Each genetic trait follows a particular pattern of inheritance. These paterns include: dominant, recessive, incomplete-dominance, sex-linked, and sex-influenced inheritance.

VOCABULARY

carrier
dominant inheritance
geneticist
incomplete-dominance
    inheritance
inheritance
recessive inheritance

RESEARCH IT
What is polydactylism? What character of the Old Testament is mentioned as having this condition?

DID YOU KNOW?
Cleft palate and gout are sex-influenced traits that are more common in men than in women. The genetic disorder spina bifida is more common in women.

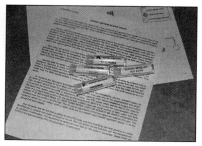

Fig. 3–17 Your ability to taste certain things is determined by the genes you inherit.

DOMINANT AND RECESSIVE INHERITANCE

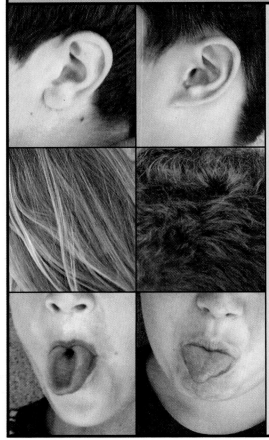

Dominant inheritance—one gene is dominant and determines the trait.

- If an organism is homozygous for a dominant trait, all its offspring will exhibit the trait.

- If an organism is heterozygous for a dominant trait, each of its offspring has a 50 percent chance of inheriting the trait.

- Examples: curly hair, tongue rolling, hitchhiker's thumb, unattached earlobes.

Recessive inheritance—one gene is recessive and is hidden by the dominant trait.

- A recessive trait is exhibited only if both recessive genes are present.

- Organisms that carry recessive genes but do not exhibit them are called **carriers**.

- Examples: straight hair, inability to roll tongue, straight thumb, attached earlobes, and many genetic diseases.

INCOMPLETE-DOMINANCE INHERITANCE

- Traits in which neither gene is dominant.
- Results in a blending of traits.
- Example: impatiens flowers.

1. Crosses involving homozygous red (RR) flowers always produce plants that bear red flowers.
2. Crosses involving homozygous white (rr) flowers always produce plants that bear white flowers.
3. Crosses that involve red (RR) and white (rr) flowers produce heterozygous offspring (Rr) that are pink.

TRY THIS 3-3A: The Genetic Package

Materials:
   none needed

Procedure:
1. The box below represents the genetic package a baby boy received from his father and mother. Examine the package and complete the table.
   - Describe the boy's phenotype.

$$X : B - c - r - t - W - P \qquad Y : b - c - R - T - w - P$$

KEY:

Eye color . . . . . brown (B)/blue (b)
Hair texture. . . . curly (C)/straight (c)
Tongue rolling . . roller (R)/non-roller (r)

Height . . . . tall (T)/short (t)
Widow's peak . . peak present (W)/peak absent (w)
PTC . . . . taster (P)/non-taster (p)

	GENETIC TRAITS					
	Eye Color	Hair Texture	Tongue Rolling	Height	Widow's Peak	PTC Taster
Gene inherited from father						
Gene inherited from mother						
Boy's genotype						

TRY THIS 3-3B: Boy or Girl?

Materials:
   large plastic cups - 2
   red beans - 25

   shoe box
   white beans - 75

Procedure:
1. Label one cup *Male* and the other *Female*.
2. In the cup labeled Female, put 50 white beans. In the cup labeled Male, place 25 white beans and 25 red beans.
   - Which combination of beans represents a female? Which represents a male?
3. Make a data table by numbering 1 to 50 on a sheet of paper.
4. Without looking, take a bean from each cup. Look at the beans and determine the sex of this combination. Record this on a data table. Place the pair of beans in the shoe box.
5. Repeat step 4 until all beans have been removed from each cup.
   - What is the chance of a child being male? Being female?
6. Look only at the sex of the first four trials (numbers 1 to 4).
   - What is the ratio of females to males in the small sample? In the large group?
   - Why is it important to use large samples when analyzing patterns of inheritance?

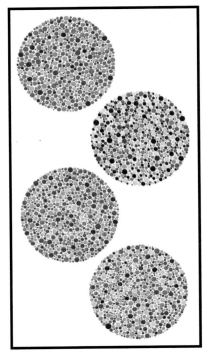

Fig. 3–18 People who are color-blind see things differently from those who are not colorblind.

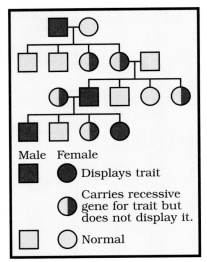

Male   Female

■ ● Displays trait

◐ Carries recessive gene for trait but does not display it.

☐ ○ Normal

Fig. 3–19 Hemophilia is an inherited disease carried on the X-chromosome.

While many traits follow dominant, recessive, or incomplete-dominance patterns, other traits appear to be related to whether an organism is male or female. This may occur because the trait is carried on the "X" and not on the "Y" chromosome, or it may result when the trait is expressed in one sex but not the other.

Colorblindness is an example of a trait related to sex. This trait, carried on the "X" chromosome, affects how a person perceives certain colors (usually red and green) (fig. 3-18). When men, who have only one "X" chromosome, inherit the colorblind gene, there is no gene on the "Y" chromosome to counter it—and the individual is colorblind. But since women have two "X" chromosomes, they must inherit two genes for colorblindness in order for them to be colorblind. For this reason, colorblindness is more common in men than in women. The genetic disease hemophilia, which prevents the blood from clotting, follows a similar pattern of inheritance and is also more common in men than in women (fig. 3-19).

Some traits, such as baldness, are related to sex because they are influenced by the presence of certain hormones. The gene for baldness can be represented by "B," and the gene for keeping hair, by "b." Both men and women with the genotype "BB" begin to lose their hair about age 30. Men and women with the genotype "bb" keep their hair. However, what happens to people with the heterozygous genotype "Bb" depends on the sex of the individual. Women with Bb tend to keep their hair, while men with the same genotype become bald. This happens because of the influence of the male and female sex hormones. In men, "B" is expressed over "b," while in women the situation is reversed.

REVIEW IT

1. How is dominant inheritance different from recessive inheritance?
2. What is incomplete dominance?
3. List two traits related to the sex of an organism.

CLASS ACTIVITY 3-3: Uniquely U

Question: Which common traits do you show?

Materials:

Special Master R63

Procedure:

1. Obtain a Special Master.
2. Determine whether you show the dominant form or the recessive form of each trait. Record your observation in the first column of the data sheet.
3. Start at the center of the Genetic Wheel (Special Master), and shade the section that fits your characteristics for each trait.
4. Continue to work out from the center to the edge of the wheel, each time shading the appropriate section for each trait.
5. Determine your genetic number. Record.
6. Complete the data chart based on your class.

Data:

TRAIT	YOU YES	CLASS percent YES
Long ear lobe (L-)		
Short ear lobe (ll)		
Tongue roller (R)		
Non–tongue roller (rr)		
Curly hair (C-)		
Straight hair (cc)		
Digital hair (M-)		
No digital hair (mm)		
Hitchhiker's thumb (T)		
Normal thumb (tt)		
Widow's peak (W-)		
No widow's peak (ww)		
Brown eyes (B-)		
Blue eyes (bb)		

My Genetic Number = _____

Questions:

1. Which dominant traits and which recessive traits do you have?
2. Based on the class data, which traits are dominant? Which are recessive?
3. How many combinations are possible for these traits?
4. How many classmates have the same genetic number as you?
5. What is the chance of fraternal twins having the same genetic number? Explain.

Conclusion: Write 3–5 sentences about what you learned from this activity.

3-4 MUTATIONS

genetic disease
mutation

OBJECTIVES

- Explain a mutation.
- Distinguish between gene mutations and chromosome mutations.
- Describe factors that can cause mutations.

Suppose you examined a hundred monarch butterflies, a hundred field mice, or a hundred seventh graders (fig. 3-20). In each group you would find tremendous diversity. To understand how this diversity develops, remember that thousands of genes make up your chromosomes. During cell division the DNA molecule that makes up each chromosome duplicates itself. The DNA is supposed to copy itself exactly, but this does not always happen. Sometimes

Fig. 3-20 A group of seventh and eighth graders shows diversity.

nucleotide bases may get out of sequence, small pieces of DNA may break off and reattach out of order, or chromosomes may break and reattach in a new way (fig. 3-21). As a result, the gene or chromosome may be altered permanently and passed on to the new cells. Permanent changes in DNA, called **mutations**, can occur in body cells or in sperm- and egg-producing cells.

Gene mutations occur when DNA is not copied correctly or when pieces of DNA are lost or gained. These mutations are

RESEARCH IT

Find out the symptoms and the type of inheritance exhibited by each of the following conditions: Marfan's syndrome, cystic fibrosis, and Lou Gehrig's disease.

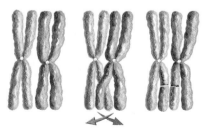

Fig. 3-21 When chromosome pairs separate during cell division, pieces may switch places, making new combinations of genetic traits.

84

responsible for many forms of cancer and for the aging of tissue. They are also responsible for several inherited, or **genetic diseases**, including muscular dystrophy (mus′ kyōo lər dis′ trə fē), sickle-cell anemia (ə nē′ mē ə), and cystic fibrosis (sis′ tik fī brō′ sis). Sometimes dogs, cats, and even humans have two different colored eyes (fig. 3-22). This condition occurs because a gene that produces eye color mutated while one of the eyes was developing.

Chromosome mutations occur when a chromosome breaks and pieces are lost, new pieces are gained, or the original pieces rejoin in a new way. In humans these changes are responsible for some genetic diseases.

Fig. 3−22 Gene mutations can produce unusual eye color in animals.

Mutations can occur naturally through cell division. They can also occur, for example, from drug abuse and by exposure to solar radiation, radioactive elements, certain chemicals in foods and manufacturing, and pollution (fig. 3-23). Whatever the cause, these mutations may be passed on to offspring.

REVIEW IT

1. How does a mutation occur?
2. What is the difference between a gene mutation and a chromosome mutation?
3. List several factors that can cause mutations.

Fig. 3−23 Cigarette smoking can cause mutations that result in lung cancer.

Sally Fox

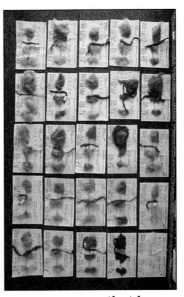

For thousands of years colored cotton has been raised around the world, but its short fibers could not be machine-spun into thread. Because little cotton thread or cloth is made by hand, this cotton was considered unusable until 1982.

Then came Sally Fox, an entomologist, who was working for a California farmer, trying to develop new varieties of cotton that naturally resisted insects. While conducting her research, she acquired some colored cotton and grew it for fun. Her interest increased as her plants produced beige, pale pink, mint green, and mahogany bolls. Spurred on by what she found, Sally began to develop long-fiber varieties of the colored cotton.

For five years Sally Fox worked, selecting and crossbreeding long-fiber white cotton with her colored varieties. She found that the colors in her cotton did not fade with washing, but rather became darker. Her cotton was also much more resistant to fire than regular cotton and held hope for use in less-flammable types of clothing. In addition, she found that her colored cotton was more resistant than white cotton to insects, so it could be grown with less use of pesticides.

In 1988 Sally demonstrated that her new varieties of long-fiber colored cotton could be machine spun into thread. This instantly made her cotton valuable, and a Japanese mill purchased half of her crop. In 1989, Levi Strauss began making colored denim, using the colored cotton she had developed. Since that time other clothing manufacturers have used Sally Fox's colored cotton in their clothing.

Sally Fox was forced to leave California when cotton farmers became alarmed that her cotton might mix with their white cotton. So she is developing yellow, orange, and several other new colors at her farm in Arizona. Sally's trademarked product, Fox Fibre, is currently available in coyote brown, sage, coffee brown, and leaf green and is grown in Arizona and Texas.

3-5 GENETIC ENGINEERING

- Explain genetic engineering.
- Analyze the impact of genetic engineering.

gene therapy
genetic engineering
selective breeding

Both plants in figure 3-24 are strawberries. The ones on the bottom are wild strawberries found in the mountains of California. The ones on top are grown commercially. Commercial strawberry plants produce berries that are larger, sweeter, and more resistant to disease. Commercial plants also produce more berries than the wild variety.

The food crops produced today have all descended from wild species. By crossing and recrossing plants that had desirable traits, horticulturists have developed crops that produce better harvests. This process, called **selective breeding**, was also used to produce the many varieties of domestic animals (fig. 3-25). Selective breeding is still used to produce better varieties of plants and animals. Another breeding technique, however, is receiving increasing attention.

Fig. 3-24 The commercial variety of strawberry (top) was developed from wild strawberries similar to the ones below.

Scientists using recombinant DNA technology have successfully implanted into tobacco plants the firefly gene that enables the insect to glow. The result—a plant that glows in the dark.

Fig. 3-25 The shar-pei, like most other varieties of domestic dogs, was developed by selective breeding.

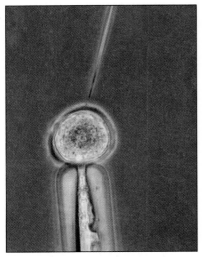

Fig. 3–26 The first successful attempt at gene splicing occurred between a toad and a bacterium.

This technique, called **genetic engineering**, involves transferring the genes from one organism to another. This technology began in the early 1970s as scientists learned that certain bacteria produced special enzymes that cut DNA. These enzymes were very specific as to where they cut the DNA. The fragments of DNA had "sticky" ends that allowed them to reattach to other DNA fragments. In 1973 the first successful attempt to perform genetic engineering occurred when a gene from a toad and one from a bacterium were stuck together (fig. 3-26).

There are several uses of genetic engineering. The most common use of this technology has been in plants. Geneticists have been able to replace natural genes with improved genes. These genes have enabled scientists to produce special plants such as rot-resistant tomatoes, plants that are drought- and disease-resistant, and even plants in special shapes that make them easier to harvest (fig. 3-27).

RESEARCH IT
In Hitler's Germany what traits were considered most desirable? What was the destiny of those individuals who had other than the desirable traits?

Fig. 3–27 This azalea was genetically engineered.

A second application of genetic engineering involves the use of bacteria to produce enzymes and proteins that can be used in the treatment of certain diseases or disorders. Figure 3-28 shows how this is done.

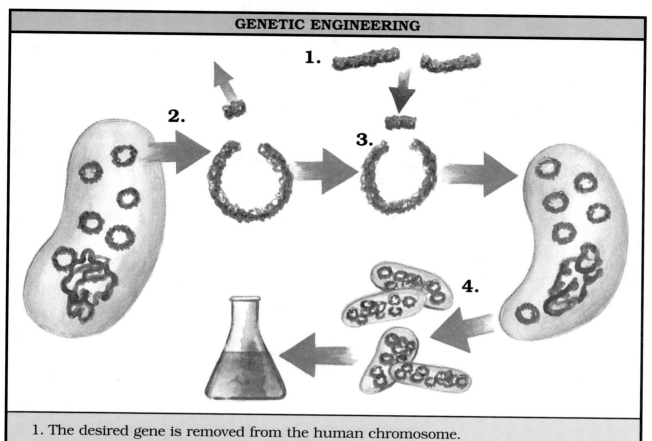

GENETIC ENGINEERING

1. The desired gene is removed from the human chromosome.
2. The chromosome of a bacterial cell is removed and split open.
3. The human gene is inserted into the bacterial chromosome, which is then placed back into the bacterial cell, causing the bacteria to produce the desired product.
4. Each time the bacterial cell divides, it copies the human gene along with its own chromosome. All successive bacteria also produce the desired product.

Fig. 3–28 Genetic engineering modifies certain bacteria to produce needed enzymes or proteins.

In this process, bacteria are used to produce human growth hormone, insulin, cancer-fighting proteins, and interferon (in tər fir′ än), a protein effective in fighting viral infections.

Another area of genetic engineering involves replacing defective genes with healthy ones. This process, called **gene therapy**, is currently being used to treat victims of severe combined immunodeficiency (im′ myōō nō dē fish′ ən sē), or SCID, a disease that makes a person defenseless against infection. In the past, victims of this disease had to live in

Fig. 3–29 In the past, victims of SCID had to wear protective gear whenever they left a sterile environment.

special environments that were free of any infectious organisms (fig. 3-29). Using genetic engineering, scientists have been able to manufacture healthy genes and successfully transplant them back into the body of SCID patients. Individuals who have received this treatment have been able to live fairly normal lives (fig. 3-30). With improved testing techniques, more and more genes will be identified, allowing scientists to better treat many diseases.

While genetic engineering has produced many benefits, some people are concerned that this technology poses serious problems. They worry that genetically altered bacteria may spread out of laboratories and create disaster, and that disease-causing bacteria and viruses may be developed for which there is no cure. Others are troubled that genetically altered plants or animals may drive native species out of the environment. Some even worry that this technology may be used to create individuals that show only certain "desirable" traits.

These concerns raise the crucial question, "Will the benefits of genetic engineering outweigh the risks?" The answer will only come in the years ahead as researchers continue to learn more about chromosomes and genes.

Fig. 3–30 Advances in gene therapy enable many individuals to live normal lives.

REVIEW IT

1. What is genetic engineering?
2. What benefits have come from genetic engineering?
3. What are the potential risks of genetic engineering?

On May 18, 1994, a long-awaited announcement was made by the U.S. Food and Drug Administration (FDA). The announcement gave Calgene Inc., of Davis, California, permission to begin marketing their newly developed Flavr Savr tomato. The Flavr Savr tomato is a genetically engineered fruit designed to resist softening, the primary cause of tomato spoilage. It is hoped that the new tomato will make it easier for tomato lovers to find ripe tomatoes throughout the year instead of only during the prime growing season.

Since the beginning of agriculture, farmers have worked to improve their products. Until recently, the changes were slow and accomplished only by selective breeding, a trial-and-error method of genetic change. With advances in genetics and improved technology, changes that once took months or years can now be done almost immediately. This advance was made possible by genetic engineering, in which genes with clearly defined functions are inserted into plants.

While it may appear that the Flavr Savr tomato should only increase the number of happy tomato consumers, it represents a heated controversy. This debate exists between companies and scientists who develop such "designer foods" and individuals who claim genetically altered crops pose more risk than benefit to society.

Supporters of genetically engineered food plants point to their potential benefits. These benefits include natural resistance to disease and pests, easier handling and storage, improved nutrition, greater availability, and increased production.

While the benefits of Flavr Savr tomatoes and similar foods seem to justify continued research and development, opponents point out several problems. Concerns include the fear that genetically engineered plants may produce allergy-producing proteins. Also, some fear that designer foods may be "contaminated" by genes from foods prohibited by religious beliefs (pig genes in fish, for example). Some opponents worry that some genes used in the bio-engineering process may cause consumers to become resistant to certain antibiotics. Finally, environmental groups fear that genetically engineered plants may escape into the environment and take over the natural environment.

Undoubtedly the controversy will continue. In the meantime, it is sure that companies like Calgene will continue to produce foods that appeal to producers and consumers alike. As Roger Salquist, CEO and Chairman of Calgene, stated, "We're offering consumers a choice and a better product, and they are responding with purchases and praise."

Questions:

1. How are Flavr Savr tomatoes different from other tomatoes?
2. How is genetic engineering being used to develop new crops?
3. What are potential benefits of genetically altered plants? What are the dangers?

CHAPTER 3 WRAP-UP

SKILLS DEVELOPMENT

THINKING SKILLS: Collecting Data

Scientists collect and analyze a variety of data. Often the data is collected by making field observations or by observing the results of experiments. When the collected data is analyzed, scientists form conclusions that help them understand how and why things happen the way they do.

Look over the classroom below. Determine the number of students having each type of hair. Complete the table and answer the questions.

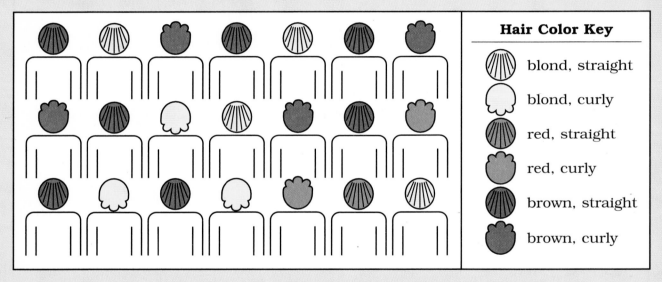

Hair Color	Straight	Curly	Total
Blond			
Red			
Brown			

1. What percentage of the class has each hair type?
   - a. blond straight -
   - b. blond curly -
   - c. red straight -
   - d. red curly -
   - e. brown straight -
   - f. brown curly -
2. Based on your data, what hair type do you think is most dominant? What kind is most recessive?
3. How do you think your data would change if you investigated a classroom in Norway? What about a classroom in Argentina?

QUESTIONS AND PROBLEMS

1. How is DNA used by investigators when solving a crime?
2. Why do people who are exposed to radiation often suffer gene and chromosome mutations?
3. Why does a child looks like one parent, while a brother or sister looks like the other parent?
4. Why do some older women grow heavier facial hair? How could this be treated?
5. How does selective breeding work?
6. Each of the following crosses of snapdragon plants produces 100 offspring. For each cross determine the approximate number of offspring that will have white flowers, red flowers, or pink flowers.
   - a. white crossed with pink
   - b. white crossed with red
   - c. red crossed with pink
   - d. pink crossed with pink
7. In humans, which parent determines the sex of a baby?
8. Suppose both of your parents can roll their tongue, and you can't. What can you be sure of regarding the genotype of your parents for this trait?
9. What is a carrier?
10. Why are most colorblind people males?
11. Why are bacteria used to produce human enzymes and proteins?

RESEARCH

1. Use library resources to find out what human traits are determined by multiple genes. Write a two-page report on your findings and include a poster that shows how multiple-gene inheritance works.
2. Form teams with two or three other classmates and conduct research to support the statement "Genetic engineering poses many dangers to society and should be made illegal" or the statement "Genetic engineering offers many benefits to humanity and should be encouraged." Give an oral presentation summarizing your research.
3. Pick one of the genetic diseases listed below and do library research to find its cause, how it is inherited, its symptoms, current treatment, and current research that is being conducted. Develop a set of posters that display your findings.

asthma	Huntington's disease	sickle cell anemia
cystic fibrosis	muscular dystrophy	Tay-Sachs disease
Down's syndrome	phenylketonuria (PKU)	Type II diabetes

4. Make a chart that traces a particular genetic trait through several generations of your family.
5. Develop a bulletin board that displays basic information about human genetics.

REVIEW

HIGHLIGHTS

1. Heredity is the transfer of traits from one generation to another. Genetics is the study of how heredity occurs.

2. Gregor Mendel was the first to identify specific traits and describe how they were inherited.
3. Dominant traits are usually visible and mask the presence of recessive traits. Recessive traits are the hidden forms, visible only when the dominant forms are absent.
4. The law of inheritance states that all inherited traits are determined by genes.
5. Genotype refers to the genes an organism has for a particular trait. Phenotype refers to the outward appearance regarding the trait.
6. An organism inherits one gene for a particular trait from each parent.
7. In humans, sex is determined by the sex chromosomes. Females have two X-chromosomes; males have one X-chromosome and one Y-chromosome.
8. In dominant inheritance one gene is dominant and determines the trait. In recessive inheritance one gene is recessive and is hidden by the dominant gene. These two forms of inheritance are summarized in 3-17.
9. Incomplete-dominance inheritance involves traits in which neither gene is dominant. In these traits there is often a blending of the feature.
10. In humans, traits related to sex include hemophilia, colorblindness, and baldness.
11. A mutation is a sudden permanent change in the DNA of genes.
12. Gene mutations involve lost, gained, or improperly copied DNA; chromosome mutations occur when a chromosome breaks, pieces are lost, or new pieces are gained.
13. Some mutations occur naturally at cell division. Others are the result of solar radiation, chemicals, pollution, or drug abuse.
14. Genetic engineering is the transfer of genes from one organism to another.
15. Genetic engineering has produced disease- and rot-resistant plants, proteins and enzymes, insulin, and interferon. It has also been used to fight various diseases, including ADA.

VOCABULARY LIST

carrier	genetics	inheritance
dominant	genotype	mutation
dominant inheritance	heredity	phenotype
gene therapy	heterozygous	recessive
genetic disease	homozygous	recessive inheritance
genetic engineering	incomplete-dominance	selective breeding
geneticist	inheritance	sex chromosome

PRACTICE
Multiple Choice. Choose the best answer.
  1. The transfer of traits is called
      a. inheritance
      b. heredity
      c. incomplete dominance
      d. gene copying

2. Genetics is the study of
   a. mutations
   b. recessive/dominant genes
   c. inheritance
   d. all of these
3. When two genes are present, the hidden one is called
   a. dominant
   b. dominant/recessive
   c. recessive
   d. none of these
4. All inherited traits are determined by
   a. genes
   b. sex chromosomes
   c. mutations
   d. one gene
5. In humans, a person's sex is determined by
   a. one gene
   b. X and Y chromosomes
   c. only the X chromosome
   d. recessive inheritance
6. When traits blend together it is called
   a. blending genes
   b. semi-dominance
   c. averaging
   d. incomplete dominance
7. If a gene is strong and determines a trait, it is called
   a. dominant inheritance
   b. heterozygous genes
   c. recessive inheritance
   d. homozygous genes
8. Permanent changes to DNA are
   a. lethal
   b. mutations
   c. dominant
   d. phenotypes
9. Selective breeding has been used to produce
   a. varieties of dogs and cats
   b. tomatoes
   c. new kinds of plants
   d. all of these
10. Transferring genes from one organism to another is
   a. illegal
   b. selective breeding
   c. genetic disease
   d. genetic engineering

Matching. Match each word with its definition or description.
   1. the study of inheritance
   2. the stronger gene
   3. an organism that has but does not show recessive genes
   4. the transfer of traits to another generation
   5. results in improved varieties
   6. a permanent change in a gene
   7. one dominant gene determining a trait
   8. an organism's outward appearance
   9. a trait hidden by dominance
   10. the X and Y chromosomes

   a. carrier
   b. dominant
   c. dominant inheritance
   d. heredity
   e. genetics
   f. mutation
   g. phenotype
   h. recessive
   i. selective breeding
   j. sex chromosomes

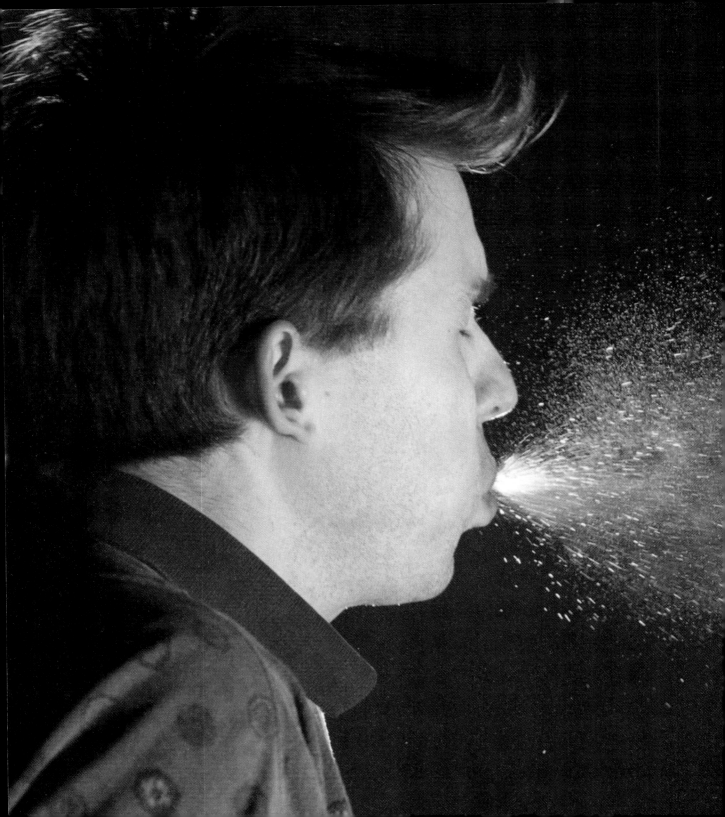

CHAPTER 4

VIRUSES

INTRODUCTION

Have you ever had to sneeze when you really didn't want to? Perhaps you were in a crowd or with someone you wanted to impress, and your sneeze embarrassed you. A sneeze is your body's response to an irritation in your nose. This reflex makes you take a large breath. Your larynx is closed off by the glottis so that pressure in your lungs builds as you try to exhale. The glottis suddenly opens, allowing an explosive rush of air to pass through your nose and blow out the irritation. The spray from a sneeze can reach a speed of more than 100 mph!

Sneezing is a common way by which disease-causing microorganisms, such as viruses, spread from person to person. Millions of these microorganisms can be released in the spray of a single sneeze. Once released, they are ready to infect other people.

What exactly are viruses? How do they harm us? How do they benefit us? You will explore these and other questions as you study this chapter.

SECTION TITLES

Sneezing and coughing help spread viruses and other microorganisms.

4-1 CHARACTERISTICS OF VIRUSES

VOCABULARY
capsid
envelope
host cell
retrovirus
virus

OBJECTIVES

- Identify the characteristics of viruses.
- Describe the basic structure of viruses.
- Describe how viruses are classified.
- Explain how viruses reproduce.

The objects in figure 4-1 look like some type of fictional spacecraft, but they are not. What you see are **viruses**, non-cellular structures that can reproduce only inside other living cells. The virus on the left is a bacteriophage that attacks bacterial cells. The virus in the middle is HIV, the virus that cause AIDS. The one on the right, an influenza virus, is responsible for causing the flu and may be present in your body right now as you read this page.

Fig. 4-1

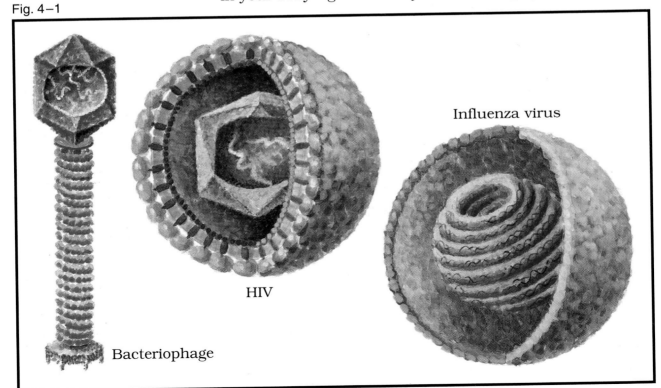

Influenza virus

HIV

Bacteriophage

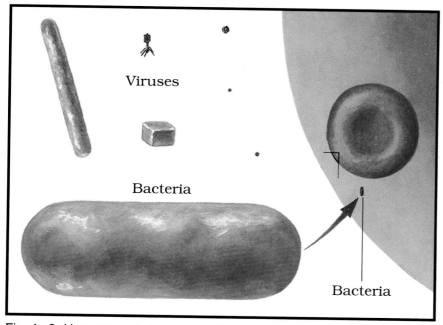

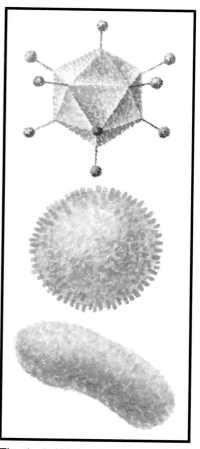

Fig. 4−2 Here several viruses are shown in comparison to a bacterium and a red blood cell.

Viruses were first discovered in the early 1900s. Because they were so small, not much was known about them at first. But with the invention of the electron microscope in 1935, scientists were able to see and study these tiny structures much more easily. Figure 4-2 shows the size of several viruses in comparison to bacteria and red blood cells.

The three viruses in Figure 4-3 appear very different from each other, but they share several characteristics:

- They are usually considered to be nonliving.
- They are made of either DNA or RNA. Viruses made of RNA are called **retroviruses**.
- They are covered by a protective capsid.
- They reproduce only by invading cells called **host cells**.
- They cause host cells to manufacture more viruses.

Fig. 4−3 While viruses may look different from each other, they share several characteristics.

All viruses share the same basic structure (fig. 4-4). Each virus consists of two basic components, a strand of DNA or RNA surrounded by a protein coat called a **capsid**. In some viruses, including HIV (the virus that causes AIDS), the cap-

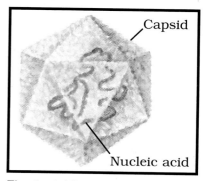

Fig. 4−4 Viruses are made of a nucleic acid core and a protecting capsid.

TRY THIS 4-1: That's Pretty Small

Materials:

chalk

kite string - 1 m

paper dots - 100

scissors

Procedure:

1. Find a sidewalk area and use the 1 m kite string to draw a circle 2 m in diameter. This 2 m circle represents a red blood cell (one of the smallest cells in your body).

2. Spread out the 100 paper dots on the 2 m red blood cell. Each paper dot represents a virus.

   - How does the size of a virus compare to the size of a red blood cell?
   - About how much area is covered by the paper dots?
   - How many dots do you think it would take to fill the 2 m circle?
   - What problems are created by the small size of viruses?

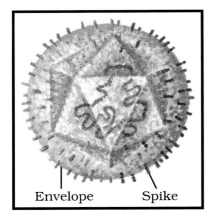

Fig. 4–5 In addition to the capsid, many viruses have an envelope, which may contain spikes that extend outward.

sid is surrounded by another layer called an **envelope** (fig. 4-5). Often extending out from this envelope are spikes, which help the virus attach to a host cell.

Viruses are classified by their shape (fig. 4-6). Some are rod shaped, others are shaped like a polyhedron (a many-sided structure), still others are covered by an envelope. Finally, some viruses, called complex viruses, look much like satellites or spaceships.

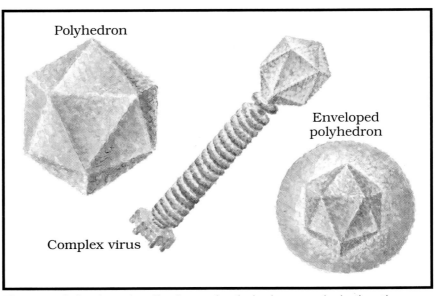

Fig. 4–6 Scientists classify viruses by their shape and whether they are covered by an envelope.

You have learned that a virus can reproduce only inside a living cell. It does this in two ways. One method requires the virus to attach to a receptor on the surface of the cell. Then it injects its nucleic acid, DNA or RNA, into the host cell. The second method occurs when the virus is engulfed by the cell membrane and taken into the cell. Whatever way the virus enters the cell, the virus's nucleic acid directs the cell to make new viruses. After making many new viruses, the cell bursts open and releases the newly manufactured viruses. These new viruses move out to attack other cells. Figure 4-7 summarizes this process.

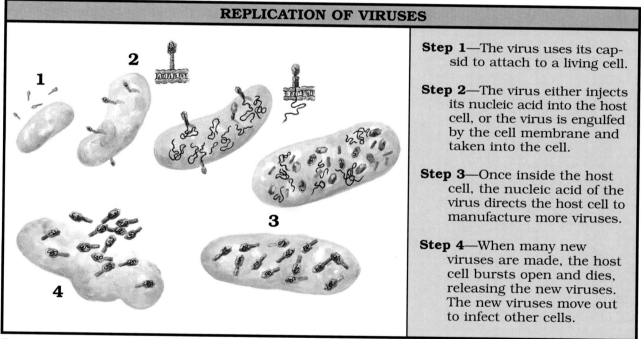

REPLICATION OF VIRUSES

Step 1—The virus uses its capsid to attach to a living cell.

Step 2—The virus either injects its nucleic acid into the host cell, or the virus is engulfed by the cell membrane and taken into the cell.

Step 3—Once inside the host cell, the nucleic acid of the virus directs the host cell to manufacture more viruses.

Step 4—When many new viruses are made, the host cell bursts open and dies, releasing the new viruses. The new viruses move out to infect other cells.

Fig. 4-7

REVIEW IT

1. What characteristics are common to all viruses?
2. What are the basic parts of a virus?
3. How are viruses classified?
4. How do viruses reproduce?

4-2 VIRUSES AND DISEASE

pathogen
vaccine

One method of treating warts caused by the papillomarviruses is the use of lasers. The laser is used to burn away the wart tissue. In the process, virus-laden smoke is produced. This smoke has caused some physicians who use this procedure to contract warts themselves, especially in their nostrils.

OBJECTIVES

- Explain how viruses cause disease.
- Explain how vaccines prevent some diseases caused by viruses.

You now know that viruses reproduce inside of cells. But how do people get infected by a virus, such as a cold virus, in the first place? Look again at the picture on page 96. Each time an infected person sneezes or coughs, millions of viruses are released. Viruses sneezed or coughed into the air may land on you or some object, such as a desk or counter. You may breathe the viruses in, or you may pick up viruses by coming in contact with the object on which the viruses fell (fig. 4-8). In either case, viruses enter your body, usually through your mouth or nose (fig. 4-9). Once inside, they start invading cells.

Fig. 4-8 Viruses get on your hand when it comes in contact with another surface, such as a desktop.

Fig. 4-9 Once on your hand, viruses get into your body when you bite your fingernails.

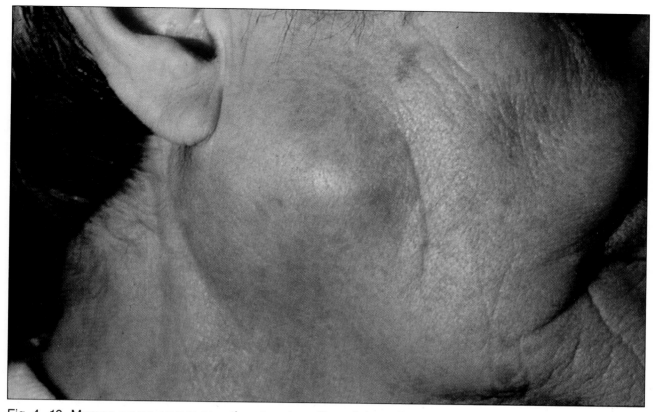

Fig. 4–10 Mumps cause severe sore throat and swelling of the salivary glands.

New viruses released from the host cells quickly infect other cells. Once inside the newly infected cells, the virus reproduces to produce still more viruses, which can then infect other cells. While not all viruses cause disease, many do. An agent, such as a virus, that causes disease is called a **pathogen**. Virus pathogens cause disease by destroying healthy cells. When enough of a particular type of cell is destroyed, that part of the body does not function as it should, and symptoms of disease appear.

Different viruses act in different ways. Cold viruses attack the cells that line the nose and throat, causing sneezing and coughing. Mumps viruses focus their attack on the salivary glands, causing swelling, fever, and a sore throat (fig. 4-10). The chickenpox virus attacks the cells of the nervous system and causes fever, headaches, and skin blisters. Cancer may be caused by a virus that attacks cells and causes them to grow abnormally rather than die.

RESEARCH IT

Find out the vaccine developed by each of the following scientists:

Louis Pasteur
Edward Jenner
Emil von Behring
Shibasaburo Kitazato
Jonas Salk
John Enders
Thomas Weller

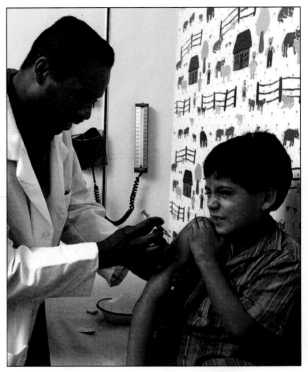

Fig. 4–11 Vaccines help protect people from many diseases.

RESEARCH IT
Find out about the Hantavirus and the virus that causes Lyme disease:
- What kind of virus is it?
- What are the symptoms of infection?
- How is it spread?
- What is the treatment for the infection?

Fortunately, most young people in Canada and the United States don't have to worry about getting sick from diseases caused by certain viruses, because they have received vaccines against them (fig. 4-11). A **vaccine** is a substance that contains inactive or weakened pathogens. The viruses in the vaccine can no longer cause disease.

When injected into the body, a vaccine stimulates the immune system to produce antibodies. Antibodies are proteins that destroy viruses and other pathogens and protect you from disease. If active viruses for the particular disease should enter your body in the future, the immune system will attack and destroy the virus and keep you from getting the disease.

REVIEW IT

1. How do viruses cause disease?
2. What is a vaccine?
3. How do vaccines prevent disease?

CLASS ACTIVITY 4-2: Stick Together

Question: What factors affect a virus's ability to attack a cell?

Materials:

fabric samples (60 x 60 cm)   transparent tape
    cotton   Velcro Ping-Pong ball
    felt
    sweat shirt
    terry cloth
    T-shirt
    Velcro

Procedure:
1. Form groups of two or three.
2. Tape the cotton sample securely to a wall.
3. Stand about 2 meters from the wall and toss the ball so it hits the cotton sample. Record whether or not the ball sticks to the cotton.
4. Repeat step 2 nine more times.
5. Repeat steps 2 and 3 with each sample of fabric.

Data:

Fabric	Number of Times Ball Stuck	Number of Times Ball Didn't Stick
cotton		
felt		
sweat shirt		
terry cloth		
T-shirt		
Velcro		

Questions:
1. Which fabric did the ball stick to the least number of times?
2. Which fabric did the ball stick to the greatest number of times?
3. Why did the ball stick more to one type of fabric than to another?
4. In this demonstration, what does the ball represent? What does the fabric sample represent?
5. What could be done to make the ball stick to the cotton more frequently? This change would be similar to what event in a cell or virus?

Conclusion: Write 3-5 sentences about what you learned from this activity.

4-3 VIRUSES AND THE IMMUNE SYSTEM

OBJECTIVES

- Describe the body's immune system.
- Explain how HIV attacks the immune system.
- Explain how HIV causes AIDS.

People often take for granted the fact that most of the time they enjoy good health. Oh, they may suffer with a cold or the flu for a few days, but usually the body is successful in preventing pathogens from causing unpleasant infections. You may remember that the body's defense system consists of the protective covering of the skin, the mucous membranes, and the immune system (fig. 4-12).

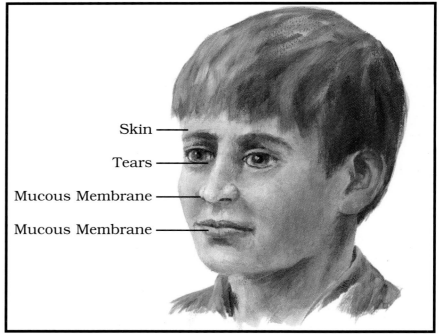

Skin

Tears

Mucous Membrane

Mucous Membrane

Fig. 4–12 The skin and mucous membranes are part of the body's defense against disease.

The **immune system** is designed to protect the body from disease once pathogens have entered the body. It is a body system made of several components: macrophages, lymphocytes (lim′ fō sīt), and interferon (fig. 4-13).

106

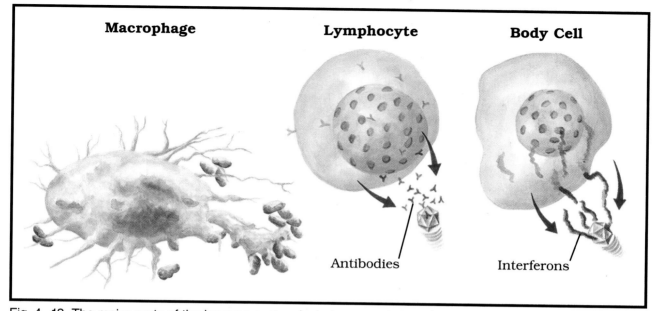

Macrophage **Lymphocyte** **Body Cell**

Antibodies Interferons

Fig. 4–13 The major parts of the immune system include macrophages, lymphocytes, and regular body cells.

Macrophages and lymphocytes are specialized cells that combat pathogens in a variety of ways. **Macrophages** are white blood cells designed to destroy invading pathogens by engulfing them. **Lymphocytes** are immune cells produced by the lymph system, a part of the circulatory system.

Scientists classify lymphocytes as either B-lymphocytes or T-lymphocytes. The **B-lymphocytes** are produced in the bone marrow and are programmed to produce antibodies. **Antibodies** are protein substances that attach to the surfaces of pathogens, making it difficult for them to attach to healthy cells.

The second group of lymphocytes, the **T-lymphocytes**, are also produced in the bone marrow but travel to the thymus gland in the neck to be programmed as either T-helper cells or T-suppressor cells. The **T-helper cells** are called the master cells of the immune system because they activate the other immune cells. **T-suppressor cells** help maintain a balance of T-helper cells in the system and turn off the immune response after an infection.

The final component of the immune system is interferon. **Interferon** is a protein produced by special cells. It is designed to prevent viruses from entering host cells, where they could multiply.

Most of the time, your immune system protects you from infection and disease. The immune system can become weakened, however, so that it no longer protects you from pathogens, and you are unable to fight disease.

One virus, called human immunodeficiency virus, or **HIV**, actually attacks the cells of the immune system. When this virus destroys the immune system, the resulting disease is called acquired immune deficiency syndrome, or **AIDS**.

When the HIV enters the body, its spikes attach to cells that have specific receptor sites. These cells include T-helper cells, white blood cells, cells in the brain, and cells that line the anus. The viral spikes attach in much the same way as Velcro strips attach to each other (fig. 4-14). Once HIV attaches to the host cell, it injects its RNA into the host cell. The virus RNA is converted to DNA, which then combines with the host's own DNA. This results in the host cell making copies of the HIV. New viruses then burst out from the host cell.

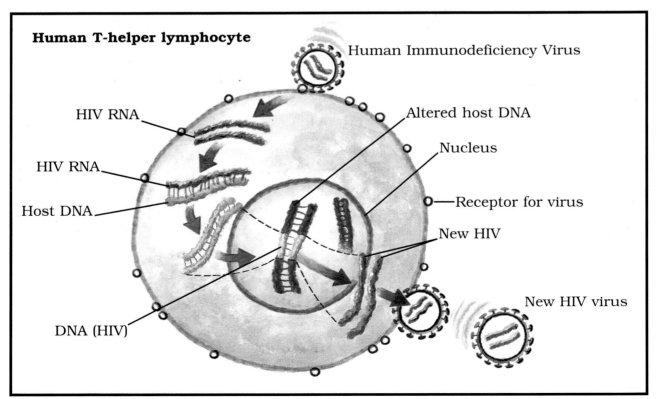

Human T-helper lymphocyte

Human Immunodeficiency Virus

HIV RNA

HIV RNA

Host DNA

DNA (HIV)

Altered host DNA

Nucleus

Receptor for virus

New HIV

New HIV virus

Fig. 4–14 HIV attacks the body by attacking the T-helper cells, causing them to produce copies of HIV virus.

OPPORTUNISTIC INFECTIONS OF HIV
Pneumocystis carinii pneumonia
Candidiasis
Histoplasmosis
Hairy leukoplakia
Tuberculosis
Kaposi's sarcoma
Non-Hodgkin's lymphoma

Fig. 4-15

The HIV grows quietly in the cells of the lymph system, gradually destroying the T-helper cells. When enough of these cells die, the immune system can no longer defend the infected person against infection, and the person begins to show the symptoms of AIDS.

The virus is transmitted from one person to another, primarily through direct contact with body fluids: blood, semen, and vaginal fluid. These body fluids contain high numbers of lymphocytes and other white blood cells.

The collapsed immune system exposes the person to a variety of infections. These infections, called **opportunistic infections**, attack the body when the immune system has been weakened (fig. 4-15). Pneumonia and tuberculosis are examples of opportunistic infections. A fungus infection, commonly called thrush, often alerts the physician that the person may be HIV infected. The destruction of brain cells may affect the person's ability to think or to walk. Persons with AIDS may get many other diseases caused by other pathogens commonly found in the environment, but which people with healthy immune systems fight off. AIDS is a fatal disease.

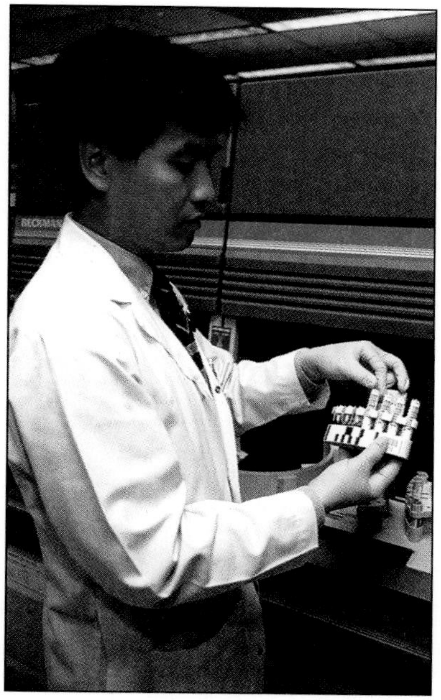

Fig. 4–16 Scientists search for ways to prevent HIV from damaging the body's immune system.

Scientists continue to search for ways to prevent HIV from entering the cell or from multiplying and damaging the immune system (fig. 4-16). They are working to develop a vaccine to prevent the HIV infection and medicines to treat HIV infection.

REVIEW IT

1. What are the main parts of the immune system?
2. How does HIV attack the immune system?
3. What results when HIV destroys T-helper cells?

CHAPTER 4 WRAP-UP

THINKING SKILLS: Classifying

Biologists classify things to make them easier to study, to understand their inter-relationships, and to make it easier to talk to others about the things they study. Scientists have developed a system for classifying viruses that identifies the type of cells a virus attacks, its composition, and structure.

Study the Special Master R95 and complete the table by marking an X in the boxes of the correct characteristics.

Virus	Animal	Bacteria	Plant	DNA	RNA	Enveloped	Naked
Adenovirus							
Cancer virus							
Cauliflower virus							
Corn virus							
Corona virus							
Cucumber virus							
Cystovirus							
Flu virus							
Herpes virus							
Lettuce virus							
Levivirus							
Parvovirus							
Plasmavirus							
Podovirus							
Poliovirus							
Potatovirus							
Poxvirus							
Stylovirus							
Tectivirus							
Tobacco virus							
Tomato virus							

QUESTIONS AND PROBLEMS

1. What is the difference between a B-lymphocyte and a T-lymphocyte?
2. Why is it a good idea to wash your hands several times a day?
3. What are opportunistic diseases?
4. Are all viruses pathogens? Explain.
5. Why wasn't there much knowledge about viruses before 1935?
6. Why are viruses usually considered nonliving?
7. Why are elderly people more susceptible to the flu virus than are young people?
8. What specific cells does each virus attack?
   a. chickenpox
   b. cold
   c. mumps
   d. HIV
9. How do RNA viruses behave differently from DNA viruses?
10. Why is it rare for a person without AIDS to show symptoms of Kaposi's sarcoma or thrush?
11. What is the advantage of an envelope for some viruses?

RESEARCH

1. Use library resources to discover viruses that attack domestic animals. Find out how the virus is transmitted, the symptoms of the disease, and current treatment. Develop a bulletin board that summarizes your findings.
2. Create a series of colored overhead transparencies that teach the steps of viral infection. If possible, use the transparencies to teach a group of students.
3. Make a list of viruses that humans are vaccinated against. Describe the disease caused by each virus and identify when a person should first be vaccinated for the disease and how often follow-up vaccinations should occur. Write a report on your findings.
4. Obtain books on biology or microbiology and find pictures of several complex viruses. Make a three-dimensional model of one or two of these.
5. Use library resources to discover how scientists are using viruses in the treatment of various diseases. Make an oral presentation to the class. Be sure to include visual aids.

REVIEW

HIGHLIGHTS

1. Viruses share several common characteristics: They are usually considered to be nonliving, they are made of either DNA or RNA, they are covered by a protective coat, they reproduce only by invading other cells, they cause the cells they invade to manufacture more viruses.
2. A virus is basically a molecule of RNA or DNA surrounded by a protein coat called a capsid.

3. Viruses are classified by their shape.
4. Viruses reproduce by attaching to host cells and injecting their RNA or DNA. The host cell then manufactures new viruses, bursts and releases new viruses. Figure 4-7 summarizes this process.
5. Viruses cause diseases by destroying healthy cells.
6. Vaccines are inactive or weakened pathogens that stimulate the body to produce antibodies to resist disease.
7. The immune system is composed of the lymph system, white blood cells, and the thymus gland.
8. HIV weakens the immune system by attacking and destroying lymphocytes; specifically HIV destroys T-helper cells and other white blood cells.
10. HIV causes AIDS by destroying the immune system, which allows opportunistic infections to cause illness and death.

VOCABULARY LIST

AIDS	immune system	retrovirus
antibody	interferon	T-helper cell
B-lymphocyte	lymphocyte	T-lymphocyte
capsid	macrophage	T-suppressor cell
envelope	opportunistic infection	vaccine
HIV	pathogen	virus
host cell		

PRACTICE

Multiple Choice. Choose the best answer.

1. Viruses are not
   a. covered by a capsid
   b. considered to be alive
   c. made of RNA or DNA
   d. none of these

2. A virus basically is a protein coat that contains
   a. host cells
   b. organelles
   c. DNA or RNA
   d. living cytoplasm

3. Viruses are classified into
   a. a rod-shaped group
   b. a polyhedron-shaped group
   c. an envelope-shaped group
   d. all of these

4. Viruses reproduce by injecting
   a. DNA or RNA into a host
   b. mitosis-causing chemicals
   c. vaccines
   d. none of these

5. Viruses cause disease by
   a. invading cells
   b. making dangerous chemicals
   c. weakening the muscles
   d. causing high fever

6. Vaccines are usually dead or weakened
   a. capsids
   b. polyhedrons
   c. lymphocytes
   d. pathogens
7. The human immune system is made up of white blood cells and
   a. lymph system and thymus
   b. lymphocytes and mumps
   c. vaccines and pathogens
   d. all of these
8. Viruses weaken the immune system by destroying
   a. pathogens
   b. white blood cells
   c. strong chemicals
   d. dead lymphocytes
9. HIV attacks
   a. red blood cells
   b. bone cells
   c. T-helper cells
   d. all of these
10. HIV causes AIDS by weakening
   a. all vaccines
   b. the immune system
   c. all white blood cells
   d. several host cells

Matching. Match each word with its definition or description.
1. produce antibodies
2. where viruses reproduce
3. virus protein coat
4. dead or weakened pathogens
5. usually considered nonliving
6. AIDS
7. occurs when the immune system is damaged
8. surrounds the protein coat
9. either a "suppressor" or a "helper" cell
10. any virus that causes a disease

a. acquired immuno-
   deficiency syndrome
b. B-lymphocyte
c. capsid
d. envelope
e. host cell
f. opportunistic infection
g. pathogen
h. T-lymphocyte
i. vaccine
j. virus

CHAPTER 5

MONERA, PROTISTA, AND FUNGI

INTRODUCTION

Termites eat wood—fallen trees, wood scraps, and lumber in buildings. Just about any type of wood looks like lunch to a termite. Every year these destructive insects cause hundreds of millions of dollars worth of damage to buildings. But did you know that termites cannot digest the wood they eat? They rely on small organisms called protists living in their intestines to break down the wood so it can be used. Without these tiny organisms, termites would die.

Are protists animals or plants? They are neither. They represent another kingdom of living things that you will investigate in this chapter.

SECTION TITLES

Tiny intestinal protists help termites digest the wood they eat.

5-1 THE KINGDOM MONERA

bacteria
cyanobacteria
Monera

OBJECTIVES

- Identify the characteristics of monerans.
- Distinguish between cyanobacteria and other monerans.

You have learned that scientists classify living organisms into five different kingdoms (fig. 5-1). Two of these kingdoms, animals and plants, are familiar to you. The other three, Monera, Protista, and Fungi, may be new to you.

At one time all living things were classed as either plant or animal, but many organisms did not seem to fit well into either of these two kingdoms (fig. 5-2). As a result, three new kingdoms were added, allowing scientists to classify organisms more consistently.

RESEARCH IT

Since monerans and protists lack any type of muscular system, explain how their cilia or flagella are able to move.

Fig. 5-1 Living organisms are classified into five different kingdoms.

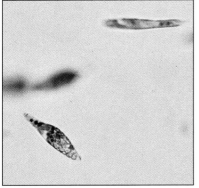

Fig. 5-2 *Euglena* have characteristics of both plants and animals.

116

Unlike viruses that lack cell organelles and are considered nonliving, organisms in the kingdom **Monera** (mə nir′ ə) are made of cells that have organelles and are considered alive. The organisms that make up this kingdom represent the smallest living things.

Monerans share several common characteristics summarized in figure 5-3.

CHARACTERISTICS OF MONERANS	
	• Prokaryotic, lack the nuclear membrane. • Chromosomes spread throughout the cytoplasm. • Have a cell wall and cell membrane. • Lack most cell organelles. • Some have capsules, protective protein coats. • Move by flagella.

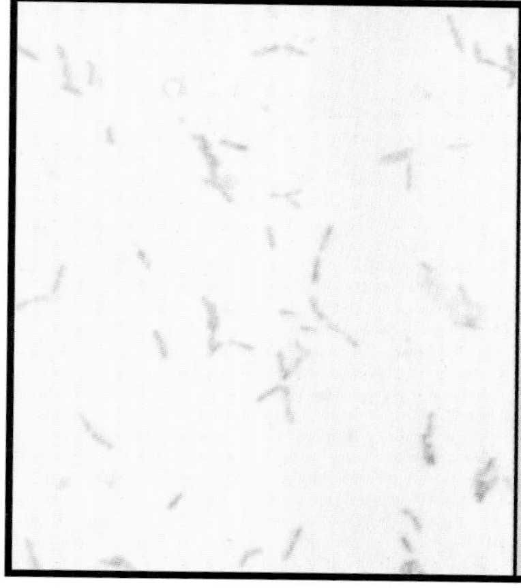

Fig. 5-3

Monerans are found just about everywhere on Earth. They live in your mouth, in your intestines, under your fingernails, and between your teeth (fig. 5-4). They live in glaciers, in desert sand, and even in the volcanic vents on the ocean floor, where there is no oxygen (fig. 5-5).

Fig. 5-4 Having your teeth thoroughly cleaned removes many harmful bacteria that cause cavities.

Fig. 5-5 One species of bacteria is able to survive the harsh environment of volcanic vents deep on the ocean floor.

Scientists classify monerans into several groups. Two of the most common are the cyanobacteria (sī ə nō bak tir′ ē ə) and bacteria (fig. 5-6).

DID YOU KNOW?
More than a dozen types of bacteria make their homes on or in the human body. The skin of the armpits can harbor up to 516,000 bacteria per square inch.

CHARACTERISTICS OF CYANOBACTERIA	
	• Contain chlorophyll.
	• Are able to photosynthesize and produce their own food.
	• Are classed as producers.
	• Are primary food of zooplankton (zō ō plaŋk′ tən).
	• Help scientists determine water quality.

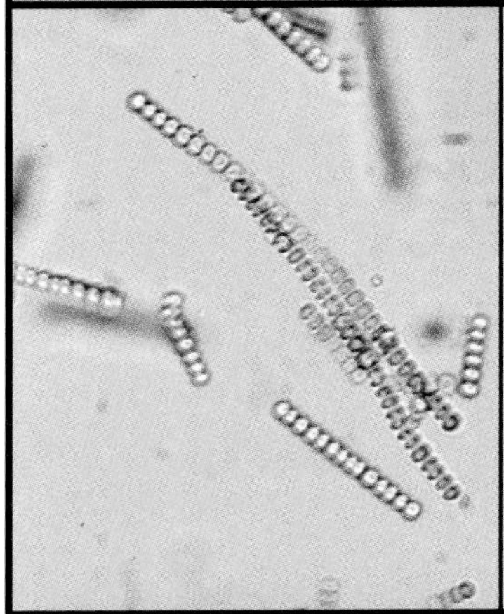

CHARACTERISTICS OF BACTERIA	
	• Usually lack chlorophyll.
	• Usually are unable to photosynthesize and must get their food from other organisms.
	• Are consumers and decomposers.
	• Sometimes have a capsule for extra protection.
	• Live in a variety of habitats.

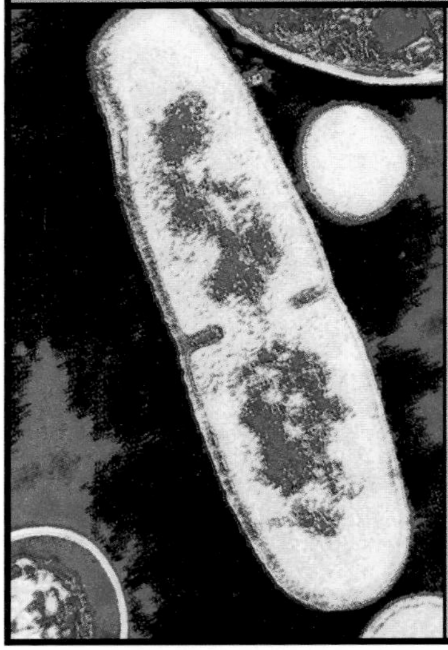

Fig. 5–6

REVIEW IT

1. What are the characteristics of the kingdom Monera?
2. How do cyanobacteria differ from other bacteria?

CLASS ACTIVITY 5-1: That's Rotten!

Question: Why do things decompose faster in some soils than in others?

Materials:

dirt
humus
paper strips—4
plastic cups—4

potting soil
sand
water

Procedure:

1. Label one cup "dirt," label a second cup "humus," a third cup "potting soil," and a fourth "sand."
2. Place a strip of paper on one side of each cup so about half of the strip is buried when the soil sample is added.
3. Fill each cup about three-fourths full with the appropriate soil sample. Be sure the sample is moist but not wet.
4. Place the cups in a dark area that stays at a constant temperature.
5. After three days observe the strip in each cup. Record.
6. Repeat step 5 after five days and after seven days.

Data:

Sample/Day		Amount of Decomposition			
		None	Minor	Moderate	Excessive
Dirt	Day 3				
	Day 5				
	Day 7				
Humus	Day 3				
	Day 5				
	Day 7				
Potting Soil	Day 3				
	Day 5				
	Day 7				
Sand	Day 3				
	Day 5				
	Day 7				

Questions:

1. Which sample showed the most decomposition? Which showed the least?
2. Why did the paper strip rot faster in some samples than in others?
3. What effect would a warmer temperature have on the decomposition rate? Explain.
4. What caused the decomposition of the paper strips?
5. Which soil sample do you think had the most microorganisms living in it? Why?

Conclusion: Write 3-5 sentences about what you learned from this activity.

5-2 BACTERIA

aerobic bacteria
anaerobic bacteria
botulism
fission
pasteurization
salmonella
toxin

OBJECTIVES

- Describe the main groups of bacteria.
- Explain how bacteria reproduce.
- Identify conditions that influence bacterial growth.
- Describe the harmful and beneficial effects of bacteria.

Although bacteria share several common characteristics, they also display important differences. One of these differences, shape, is used by scientists to classify bacteria into three main groups: cocci, bacilli, and spirilla (fig. 5-7).

Fig. 5—7

TYPES OF BACTERIA	
	Cocci (käk′ sī) • Spherical shaped. • Occur singly, in pairs, or in chains. • Importance: cause pneumonia, sore throat, and gonorrhea; also used to make yogurt, buttermilk, and cheese.
	Bacilli (bə sil′ ī) • Rod shaped. • Occur singly or in pairs. • Importance: live in the human intestine; some cause food poisoning, cholera, and whooping cough; also important in the decay and recycling of nutrients.
	Spirilla (spī ril′ ə) • Spiral shaped. • Occur only singly. • Importance: causes Lyme disease and syphilis; live as parasites on other bacteria.

Bacteria, like all living things, are able to reproduce. This usually occurs by **fission**, a form of asexual reproduction (fig. 5-8). Fission begins when the chromosomes of the cell are copied (1). Next, the cell membrane and cell wall pinch in at the middle, dividing the cell into two new cells (2). A new cell membrane and cell wall form between the two cells as they separate (3). Finally, the cells separate (4). This

For what did Joseph Lister use carbolic acid?

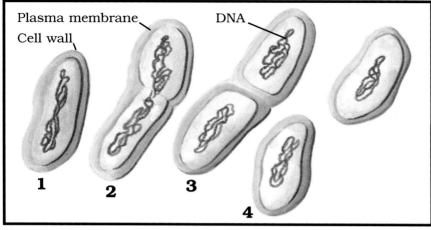

Fig. 5−8 Most bacteria reproduce by fission.

process takes 20 to 30 minutes and can lead to more than 200,000 descendants in six hours. Fortunately, this doesn't usually happen, because conditions do not allow it.

Bacteria require specific conditions for optimum growth and reproduction. Conditions that influence bacterial growth are moisture, adequate nutrients, temperature, light, and oxygen. Figure 5-9 summarizes these conditions and how they influence bacterial growth.

CONDITIONS THAT INFLUENCE BACTERIAL GROWTH

Moisture
- Ninety percent of a bacterial cell's volume is water.
- Bacteria are inactive in dry conditions.

Temperature
- Most bacteria grow best at a temperature range of 20° to 40° C.

Light
- Bacteria grow best in darkness.
- Sunlight kills many types of bacteria.

Oxygen
- Some bacteria grow best in the presence of oxygen; others grow best in the absence of oxygen.
- **Aerobic** (er ō′ bik) **bacteria** are those that require oxygen to live.
- Include bacteria that live in the body and many that cause disease.
- **Anaerobic** (an ər ō′ bik) **bacteria** are those that do not require oxygen to live.
- Include bacteria that live in soil, swamps, and estuaries.
- Cause deadly diseases, such as tetanus and botulism.

Fig. 5−9

Although cases of botulism are rare, they are often fatal. Improperly canned food is the most common cause of botulism.

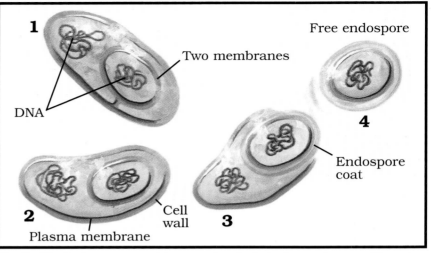

Fig. 5-10 Endospores enable some bacteria to live under conditions in which they normally could not survive.

Fig. 5-11 Harmful effects of bacteria include disease and food spoilage.

When conditions are not suitable for growth, many bacteria form endospores that are surrounded by a thick, protective coat (fig. 5-10). An endospore contains one chromosome and a small amount of cytoplasm. It forms inside the bacterial cell and is released when the cell breaks open. Because of its protective covering, the endospore can survive in harsh conditions, including freezing, drying, and boiling. When conditions are again suitable, the protective coat breaks open. The newly released endospore may germinate to produce a new cell.

Bacteria are an important part of life on Earth. They can be harmful or helpful. The can of food and the petri dish demonstrate the harmful effects of bacteria (fig. 5-11). The

BACTERIAL DISEASES	
Botulism	Salmonella
Cholera	Scarlet fever
Diphtheria	Strep throat
Dysentery	Tetanus
Gingivitis	Tooth decay
Impetigo	Toxic-shock syndrome
Leprosy	Tuberculosis
Meningitis	Typhoid fever
Pneumonia	Whooping cough

Fig. 5-12 Many diseases are caused by bacteria.

petri dish shows a culture of bacteria that causes sore throats. The bulging can illustrates food spoiled by bacteria.

Bacteria cause many diseases (fig. 5-12). Some are minor, such as pneumonia and strep throat. Others, such as staph infection and meningitis (men in jīt′ is), can be life threatening. Bacteria cause disease in two ways: by destroying cells and tissue of the host or by producing poisons, or **toxins**, which harm the host.

Another harmful effect of bacteria is spoiled food. Spoiling not only produces unpleasant smells and tastes, but it can also lead to serious illness when the spoiled food is eaten. Bacteria cause food poisoning in two ways. One type of food poisoning occurs when toxins produced by the bacteria are present in the food. **Botulism** (bäch′ ə liz əm) is an example of this type of food poisoning. (fig. 5-13). The second type of food poisoning occurs when food containing harmful bacteria is eaten. **Salmonella** (sal mə nel′ ə) bacteria are the most common cause of this type of food poisoning (fig. 5-14).

Figure 5-15 lists several ways food poisoning can be prevented.

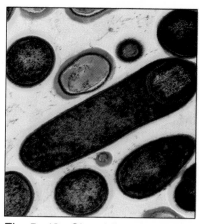

Fig. 5–13 *Clostridium botulinum* is the bacterium that causes botulism.

WAYS OF PREVENTING FOOD POISONING
• **Pasteurization** (pas tər i zā′ shən), heating milk to 72° F. for 15 minutes, then quickly cooling it, kills most harmful bacteria.
• Refrigeration helps slow bacterial growth and helps reduce the risk of food poisoning.
• Salt curing, smoking, or drying food retards bacterial growth.
• Chemical preservatives alter environmental conditions, making it difficult for bacteria to grow.

Fig. 5–15

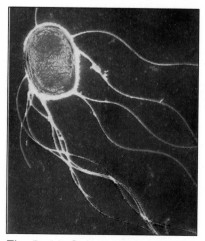

Fig. 5–14 Salmonella, a type of food poisoning, is often caused by the bacterium *Salmonella enteritidis*.

Although bacteria create many problems, they are also important to the environment and our own well-being (fig 5-16). Bacteria play an important role in recycling matter through the environment. Bacteria act as decomposers, breaking down matter that was once alive. In this decomposition process, the cells of dead organisms are broken down into compounds and elements. These materials are released into the soil and are then available to be used by other organisms.

Some bacteria get their energy from the hydrogen sulfide that comes from vents on the ocean floor. These bacteria form the base of a food chain that includes several different crustaceans and giant worms.

BENEFITS OF BACTERIA
• Break down dead organisms.
• Recycle elements and compounds.
• Produce nitrates in the soil.
• Aid digestion.
• Produce certain foods (yogurt, cheese).
• Used in scientific research.
• Used to synthetically produce certain proteins (insulin).

Fig. 5–16 Bacteria are beneficial in many ways.

Special nitrogen-fixing bacteria combine nitrogen in the air with other elements to produce compounds, primarily proteins, that are necessary to life. Some bacteria live in the soil, while others live in the roots of alfalfa, beans, and other members of the pea family. Structures on the roots of these plants house the nitrogen-fixing bacteria (fig. 5-17).

Bacteria play an important role in the digestion process of humans and other animals. Grazing animals, such as cattle and sheep, rely on bacteria to break down the cellulose of the plants they eat so it can be digested.

Bacteria are used to produce food. They break down the sugar in leaves of cabbage to make a weak acid and produce sauerkraut. A similar process is used to make cheese, yogurt, and buttermilk.

Scientists use bacteria for research because bacteria are simpler than other cells and reproduce more quickly. Research with bacteria has helped scientists gain a better understanding of DNA, RNA, cancer, viruses, and cell reproduction. In labs, bacteria are used to produce proteins such as insulin and interferon, which are both used in treating disease.

Fig. 5–17 Special structures on the roots of sweet peas and similar plants help add nitrogen to the soil.

REVIEW IT

1. What are the three main groups of bacteria based on shape?
2. What is fission?
3. What factors affect the growth rate of bacteria?
4. What are the harmful and beneficial effects of bacteria?

5-3 THE KINGDOM PROTISTA

OBJECTIVE

- Identify the characteristics of protists.

VOCABULARY
Protista

Do you see anything alive in the drop of water shown in figure 5-18? Probably not. Even if you looked at this drop with a magnifying lens, you still wouldn't see anything alive. But if you put this drop on a microscope slide and looked at it with a high-power microscope, you would discover a multitude of living things (fig. 5-19). Most of the living things would be examples of the **Protista** (prō tis′ tə) kingdom. Some protists, such as those in a drop of pond water, are

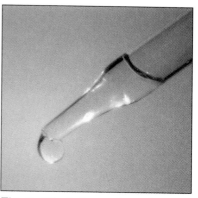

Fig. 5–18 A drop of pond water may contain a number of living organisms.

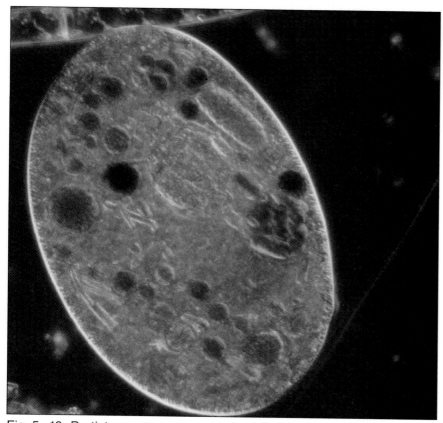

Fig. 5–19 Protists are common organisms that live in pond water.

DID YOU KNOW?
Of the more than 64,000 different species of protozoans identified, more than half are fossils.

Fig. 5–20 Seaweed are classified as protists.

microscopic. Other protists, such as seaweed, can be easily seen without a microscope (fig. 5-20).

Scientists have identified several characteristics common to protists. Study the chart in figure 5-21 to learn these features.

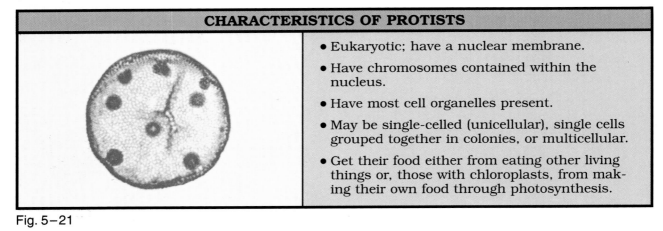

CHARACTERISTICS OF PROTISTS

- Eukaryotic; have a nuclear membrane.
- Have chromosomes contained within the nucleus.
- Have most cell organelles present.
- May be single-celled (unicellular), single cells grouped together in colonies, or multicellular.
- Get their food either from eating other living things or, those with chloroplasts, from making their own food through photosynthesis.

Fig. 5–21

REVIEW IT

1. What are the characteristics of protists?
2. Why are some protists able to photosynthesize and others are not?

126

5-4 PROTOZOANS AND ALGAE

OBJECTIVES

- Identify the characteristics of the major phyla of protozoans.
- Describe methods of movement in protozoans.
- Identify the characteristics of the major phyla of algae.

VOCABULARY
algae
algin
carrageen
cilia
cyst
diatom
dinoflagellate
flagella
protozoan
pseudopod

While all protists share the features described in figure 5-21, they also differ from each other. Scientists use these differences to group protists into two major groups: protozoans and algae.

The **protozoans** are single-celled organisms that must get their food from other organisms (fig. 5-22). Protozoans represent one group of protists. These tiny organisms are similar to animals: they do not have cell walls, they lack chlorophyll so cannot photosynthesize, and they are generally able to move about. Because of these similarities, biologists at one time considered protozoans to be single-celled animals. Today, however, biologists agree that protozoans are more like other protists than they are like animals. Characteristics of protozoans include the following:

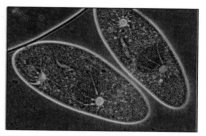

Fig. 5-22 Paramecium and similar protozoans must get their food from other animals.

CHARACTERISTICS OF PROTOZOANS
• Are unicellular.
• Have cell membranes but lack cell walls.
• Usually lack chlorophyll.
• Usually capable of movement.
• Usually obtain their food from other organisms.

You will remember that scientists classify living organisms into seven different levels: kingdom, phylum (division in plants and algae), class, order, family, genus, and species. These groups and subgroups help scientists organize living organisms so they are more easily studied. Review the levels of classification by examining figure 5-23.

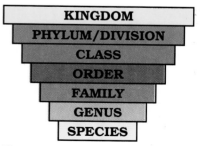

Fig. 5-23 Kingdom, phylum/division, class, order, family, genus, and species make up the seven major levels of classification.

Scientists classify protozoans into five main phyla: flagellates, ciliates, amoebas (ə mē′ bə), euglenas (yōō glē′ nə), and sporozoans (fig. 5-24).

Fig. 5–24

FLAGELLATES

- Use **flagella**, long whiplike structures, for movement.
- Most are internal parasites.
- Many cause disease.

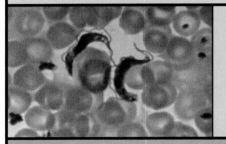

Example: *Trypanosoma*
- Parasitic.
- Lives in the blood of animals, including humans.
- Carried by the tsetse fly.
- Causes African sleeping sickness.

CILIATES

- Use **cilia**, short hairlike structures, for movement.
- Live in water.

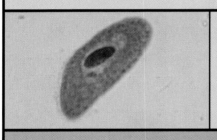

Example: *Paramecium*
- A slipper-shaped protozoan.
- Cilia beat in a rhythmic manner and allow protist to move and feed.
- Reproduces asexually by fission and sexually by exchanging nuclear material.

AMOEBAS

- Use **pseudopodia** (sōō dō pō′ de ə), fingerlike extensions of cytoplasm, to move and to capture food.
- Do not have a constant shape.
- Live in water, damp soil, and the intestines of animals.
- Cause amebic dysentery (ə mē′ bik dis′ ən ter ē).

Example: *Amoeba*
- Lives in ponds.
- Movement occurs as cytoplasm flows into an extended pseudopod of the cell.
- Forms a **cyst**, a thick-walled ball, to survive harsh conditions; when conditions become favorable, amoeba becomes active.

Fig. 5–24 continued

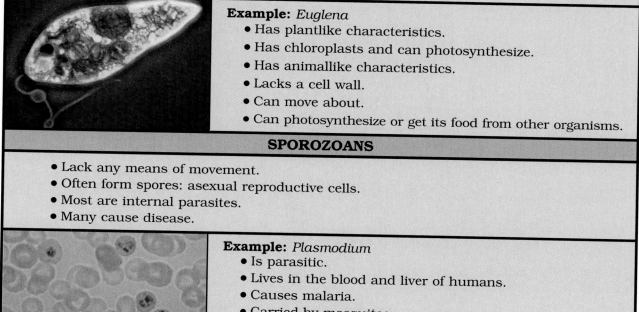

EUGLENAS

- Use flagellum for movement.
- Have characteristics of both plants and animals.
- Live in water and damp soils.

Example: *Euglena*
- Has plantlike characteristics.
- Has chloroplasts and can photosynthesize.
- Has animallike characteristics.
- Lacks a cell wall.
- Can move about.
- Can photosynthesize or get its food from other organisms.

SPOROZOANS

- Lack any means of movement.
- Often form spores: asexual reproductive cells.
- Most are internal parasites.
- Many cause disease.

Example: *Plasmodium*
- Is parasitic.
- Lives in the blood and liver of humans.
- Causes malaria.
- Carried by mosquitos.

You may have seen the green scum on the surface of a pond or the green film on the sides of an aquarium. If you have ever visited an ocean, you may also have seen seaweed washed up on the beach. Did you know the green scum and the seaweed are both algae (fig. 5-25)? **Algae** (al′ jē) represent the other major group of protists. Unlike protozoans, which are only unicellular, algae can be unicellular, form colonies, or be multicellular. They also use the process of photosynthesis to produce their own food because they all contain chlorophyll in their cells.

You will remember that biologists once classified protozoans as animals. In a similar way, they once thought algae were plants. In fact, some still classify algae as plants. But most scientists agree that algae have more characteristics in common with protists than with plants. Algae differ from plants in their early development and in their cell structure.

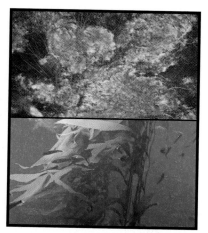

Fig. 5–25 The pond algae (top) and seaweed (bottom) are both protists.

Scientists classify algae into five main divisions: green algae, brown algae, red algae, diatoms, and dinoflagellates (dī nō flaj' ə lit) (fig. 5-26).

Fig. 5–26

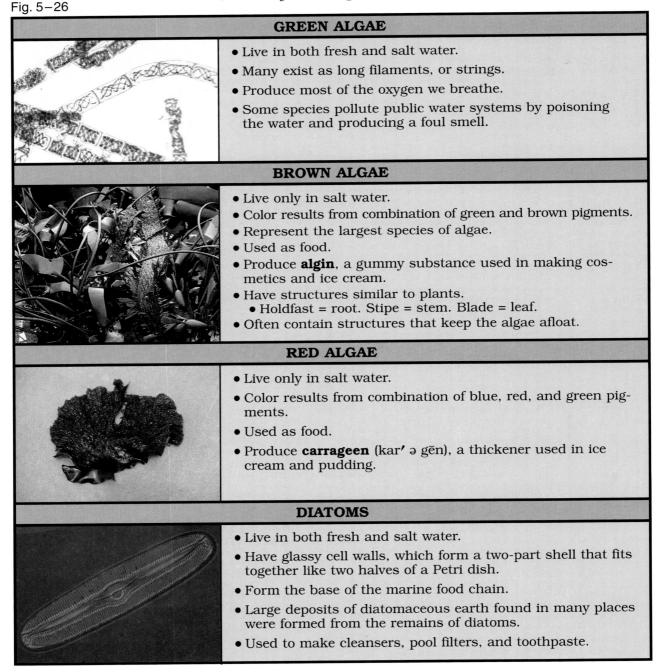

GREEN ALGAE

- Live in both fresh and salt water.
- Many exist as long filaments, or strings.
- Produce most of the oxygen we breathe.
- Some species pollute public water systems by poisoning the water and producing a foul smell.

BROWN ALGAE

- Live only in salt water.
- Color results from combination of green and brown pigments.
- Represent the largest species of algae.
- Used as food.
- Produce **algin**, a gummy substance used in making cosmetics and ice cream.
- Have structures similar to plants.
  - Holdfast = root. Stipe = stem. Blade = leaf.
- Often contain structures that keep the algae afloat.

RED ALGAE

- Live only in salt water.
- Color results from combination of blue, red, and green pigments.
- Used as food.
- Produce **carrageen** (kar' ə gēn), a thickener used in ice cream and pudding.

DIATOMS

- Live in both fresh and salt water.
- Have glassy cell walls, which form a two-part shell that fits together like two halves of a Petri dish.
- Form the base of the marine food chain.
- Large deposits of diatomaceous earth found in many places were formed from the remains of diatoms.
- Used to make cleansers, pool filters, and toothpaste.

DINOFLAGELLATES

- Live only in salt water.
- Have two flagella: one for locomotion and one for steering.
- Often appear red.
- Some release toxins into the water, causing a "red tide" that often kills large numbers of fish and other marine life.

TRY THIS 5-4: A Mini-Zoo

Materials:

baby-food jar
cover slips - 4
grass clippings (dry)
medicine dropper

microscope
microscope slides - 4
water (pond)

Procedure:

1. Write your name on the jar. Fill the jar about three-fourths full of pond water.
2. Add a small handful of dried grass clippings to the jar. Cover the jar loosely and place the jar where it will not be disturbed and where it is out of direct sunlight. Leave the jar for five days.
3. After five days, make several wet-mount slides. To make a wet-mount slide, add one drop of water on the slide and cover it with the cover slip. Use water collected from the following areas in the jar:
   a. just under the surface
   b. near the side
   c. in the middle of the grass
   d. from the bottom, including sediment
   - What microorganisms did you observe?
   - Where do you think it was best to sample the water? Why?
   - Were there different organisms present in different samples observed?
   - Where did these organisms come from?

REVIEW IT

1. What are the phyla of protozoans?
2. What different structures allow protozoans to move?
3. What are the divisions of algae?

5-5 THE KINGDOM FUNGI

OBJECTIVES

- Identify the characteristics of fungi.
- Explain how fungi get their food.
- Distinguish between the three main groups of fungi.

Many people like eating mushrooms (fig. 5-27). They enjoy them in salads, on pizza, and in spaghetti sauce. Gourmet cooks sauté mushrooms to serve in special dishes. Mushrooms are an example of a fungus. Yeast used in bread making and the mold that grows in shower stalls are also examples of fungi. These and similar organisms are in the Kingdom **Fungi** (fun′ jī). Scientists recognize several characteristics that all fungi have in common.

Fig. 5–27 Mushrooms are eaten raw in salads and cooked in pizza.

CHARACTERISTICS OF FUNGI
• Lack chlorophyll.
• Cannot photosynthesize and must get food from other organisms.
• Some have cell walls made of chitin; others have cell walls made of cellulose.
• Usually reproduce by spores.

Fungi grow best in areas where there is warmth and moisture. They are found living on and inside other organisms, on various surfaces, and in the soil. While some fungi are parasites, living off the bodies of their hosts, others are saprophytes. A **saprophyte** (sap′ rə fīt) is an organism that gets its nourishment from the remains of dead organisms. As a result, many fungi grow in areas where there are large amounts of organic debris.

Most fungi live on the things they use for food. Unlike animals—which take their food inside the body, where it is broken down by enzymes and digested—fungi secrete enzymes that digest the food outside the body of the fungus. Once the food is digested, it is then absorbed.

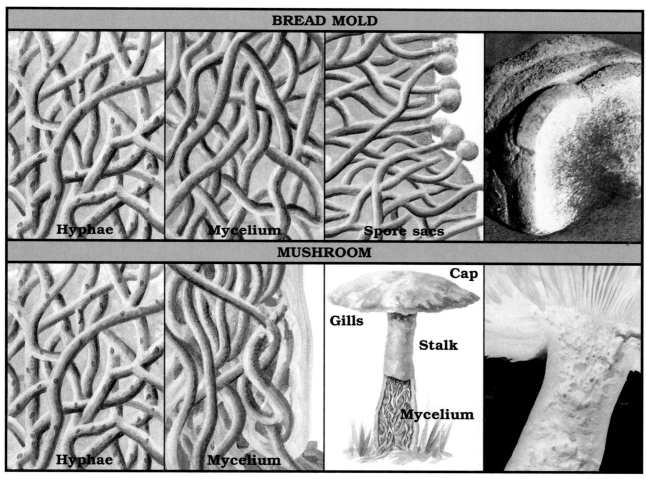

BREAD MOLD

Hyphae | Mycelium | Spore sacs

MUSHROOM

Hyphae | Mycelium

Cap
Gills
Stalk
Mycelium

Fig. 5—28

Fungi are different from other organisms (fig. 5-28). They are usually made of branching, threadlike structures called **hyphae** (hī′ fē). Some hyphae are divided into cells by cross walls; others have no dividing cell walls and look like long tubes. The hyphae grow together to form a **mycelium** (mī sē′ lē əm). The mycelium of some fungi, such as bread mold, grows into a thick twisted mass. In others, such as mushrooms and toadstools, the mycelium produces a stalk.

Fungi reproduce by **spores**, tiny reproductive cells that grow into new fungi. These spores can be formed sexually or asexually. One way scientists classify fungi is based on the type of spore-producing structures they have. Based on this characteristic, fungi can be divided into three groups: filamentous fungi, sac fungi, and club fungi (fig. 5-29).

TRY THIS 5-5: Mushrooms

Materials:
dissecting kit
magnifying lens

mushroom
paper towels

Procedure:
1. Examine your mushroom closely without dissecting it. Draw a labeled diagram of your mushroom.

   - Smell the mushroom. What does it smell like?

   - Where are the spores located?

   - What is the texture of the stalk?

   - How many gills does the mushroom have?

2. Remove the cap and use scissors or a scalpel to dissect one complete gill. Place the gill on a paper towel.

3. Use the magnifying lens to observe the surface of the gill. Draw a picture of what the gill looks like under magnification.

   - What structures can you see on the gill's surface?

FILAMENTOUS FUNGI

Characteristics

- Spore produced in ball-shaped structures at the ends of certain hyphae.

- Hyphae grow as filaments, or fine threads, that form puffy masses.

- Parasitic or saprophytic.

Importance

- Decomposers in soil.

- Cause disease.

- Spoil food.

Examples: Bread mold and downy mildew.

Fig. 5–29

Fig. 5—29 Continued

SAC FUNGI

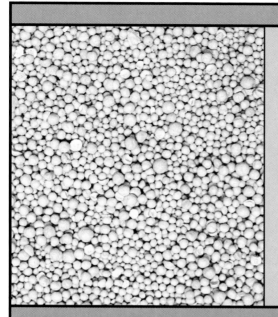

Characteristics
- Spores produced in sacs.
- Reproduce by **budding**, in which a new organism develops from an outgrowth of the parent (cell).
- Parasitic or saprophytic.

Importance
- Cause athlete's foot and ringworm.
- Cause Dutch elm disease
- The source of **penicillin**, an antibiotic used to kill disease-causing bacteria.
- Used to make bread and alcohol.

Examples: yeast, morel, and powdery mildew.

CLUB FUNGI

Characteristics
- Spores produced on a club-shaped structure.
- Hyphae form extensive underground growths; the hyphae above ground form the reproductive structure.
- Mushroom consists of three parts: stalk, cap, gills

Importance
- Parasitic on grain crops.
- Used for food.
- Used to produce drugs and medicines.
- Rot wood.

Examples: mushrooms and toadstools.

REVIEW IT

1. What are the characteristics of fungi?
2. How do fungi get their food?
3. Describe the three groups of fungi.

CHAPTER 5 WRAP-UP

THINKING SKILLS: Making Observations

Making observations is an important skill that scientists and many other people use every day. It is from careful observation that scientists make correct conclusions about various organisms. Look at the diagrams below and answer the following questions.

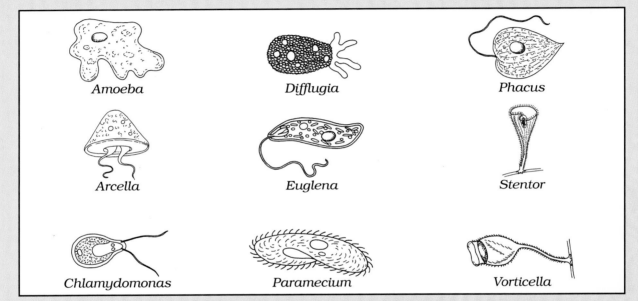

Amoeba   Difflugia   Phacus

Arcella   Euglena   Stentor

Chlamydomonas   Paramecium   Vorticella

1. Identify the method of locomotion for each protist. Use the key provided.

   C = cilia   F = flagella   P = pseudopodia

   ____ Amoeba   ____ Difflugia   ____ Phacus

   ____ Arcella   ____ Euglena   ____ Stentor

   ____ Chlamydomonas   ____ Paramecium   ____ Vorticella

2. What is similar about *Chamydomonas* and *Euglena*?
3. What is the major difference between *Paramecium* and *Stentor*?
4. Which protists would you expect to find swimming freely in the water of a pond? Explain.
5. Which protists would you expect to find moving about in the debris at the bottom of a pond? Explain.
6. Which protists would you expect to find as part of the "slime" that covers rocks in some rivers and streams? Explain.

QUESTIONS AND PROBLEMS

1. How do people contract malaria?
2. Using a two-kingdom system of classification (plants and animals), which protozoan may have been classified as a plant?
3. Why were new kingdoms added to the two already used in classification?
4. *Escherichia coli* is a bacteria that normally lives in the human intestine. What happens if many of these bacteria are destroyed?
5. What is a saprophyte?
6. How is the hyphae of fungus different from the root of a plant?
7. How are protists different from bacteria?
8. How are aerobic and anaerobic bacteria different?
9. Which group of fungi would most likely create problems for aquarium enthusiasts?
10. Explain how amoebas use pseudopodia to move about.
11. Which phyla of algae are used as food for people or produce substances used in processing food?
12. Why did biologists once classify most protists as animals?
13. Where are the chromosomes of bacteria located?
14. How is fission different from mitosis?

RESEARCH

1. Use library resources to find out about Lyme disease. Write a two-page report on your findings.
2. Make a flip book of an amoeba extending its pseudopods to hunt for food. Show how the pseudopods surround the food particle so it can be digested.
3. Talk with a restaurant owner or public-health worker to learn about the laws regarding the preparation and storage of food. Make a series of posters that summarize your findings.
4. Make a "mold" garden, using a variety of food samples. Try to grow as many different colored molds as possible. Use a magnifying glass or microscope to see the structure of your molds. Make drawings and organize your garden. Make a presentation of your work.
5. Write a script and cast a short play depicting the work of Pasteur, Fleming, or a microbiologist of your own choosing. Have your play performed before the class.

REVIEW

HIGHLIGHTS

1. Monerans share several characteristics, which are summarized in figure 5-3.
2. Cyanobacteria contain chlorophyll and are able to photosynthesize; other bacteria lack chlorophyll and are unable to photosynthesize.
3. Bacteria are classified into three major groups based on their shape. These groups are cocci, bacilli, and spirilla. Each of these groups is described in figure 5-7.

4. Bacteria reproduce by fission. During fission the chromosomes are first duplicated. Then the cell wall pinches together, trapping a set of chromosomes in each half of the cell. Finally, the cell pinches completely together and splits the cell in two.
5. Bacterial growth is affected by several factors, including moisture, temperature, light, and oxygen.
6. Harmful effects of bacteria include diseases and the decay and spoilage of food. The beneficial effects of bacteria include the decay of dead organisms, aiding digestion, food production, research.
7. Protists share several characteristics, which are summarized in figure 5-21 on page 126.
8. Protozoans are classified into five major phyla: flagellates, ciliates, amoebas, euglenas, and sporozoans. The characteristics of each of these groups are identified in figure 5-24.
9. Protozoans move by flagellum, cilia, or pseudopods.
10. Algae are classified into five major phyla: green algae, brown algae, red algae, diatoms, and dinoflagellates. Characteristics of each group are identified in figure 5-26.
11. Fungi share several characteristics, including the absence of chlorophyll, unable to photosynthesize, have cell walls, and usually reproduce by spores.
12. Fungi grow on their food, break it down with enzymes, and then absorb the digested material.
13. Fungi are divided into three groups: filamentous fungi, sac fungi, and club fungi. The characteristics of each group are described in figure 5-29.

VOCABULARY LIST

aerobic bacteria
Algae
algin
anaerobic bacteria
bacteria
botulism
budding
carrageen
cilia
cyanobacteria

cyst
diatom
dinoflagellate
fission
flagellum
Fungi
hypha
Monera
mycelium

pasteurization
penicillin
Protista
protozoan
pseudopod
salmonella
saprophyte
spore
toxin

PRACTICE

Multiple Choice. Choose the best answer.
1. Monerans lack
   a. coloration
   b. a nuclear membrane
   c. cytoplasm
   d. chromosomes

2. Cyanobacteria are different from bacteria because
   a. they make their food
   b. they live in water
   c. they are inedible
   d. none of these
3. Bacteria reproduce asexually by
   a. photosynthesis
   b. meiosis
   c. fission
   d. diffusion
4. Protists have a nucleus and are
   a. prokaryotic
   b. salmonellic
   c. capsular
   d. eukaryotic
5. Protozoans move by using
   a. cilia, euglena, flagella
   b. cilia, algin, euglena
   c. flagella, cilia, pseudopods
   d. pseudopods, algin, euglena
6. The main types of algae are red, green, brown, diatoms, and
   a. saprophytes
   b. prokaryotes
   c. mycelium
   d. dinoflagellates
7. Flagellates, amoebas, and euglenas are all
   a. fungi
   b. protists
   c. plants
   d. animals
8. Fungi lack
   a. a nucleus
   b. chromosomes
   c. chlorophyll
   d. oxygen
9. Fungi usually reproduce by
   a. seeds
   b. spores
   c. fission
   d. mitosis
10. Fungi get their food by
   a. absorbing digested food
   b. making pathogens
   c. small mouth pores
   d. spoilage

Matching. Match each word with its definition or description.
1. threadlike structure in fungi
2. hairlike structures used for movement
3. lack chlorophyll
4. a gummy substance
5. extension of cytoplasm in amoeba
6. causes food poisoning
7. a form of asexual reproduction that occurs in bacteria
8. long, whiplike structure used for movement
9. an organism that gets nourishment from dead organisms
10. formed by many hyphae growing together

a. algin
b. botulism
c. cilia
d. fission
e. flagellum
f. fungi
g. hyphae
h. mycelium
i. pseudopod
j. saprophyte

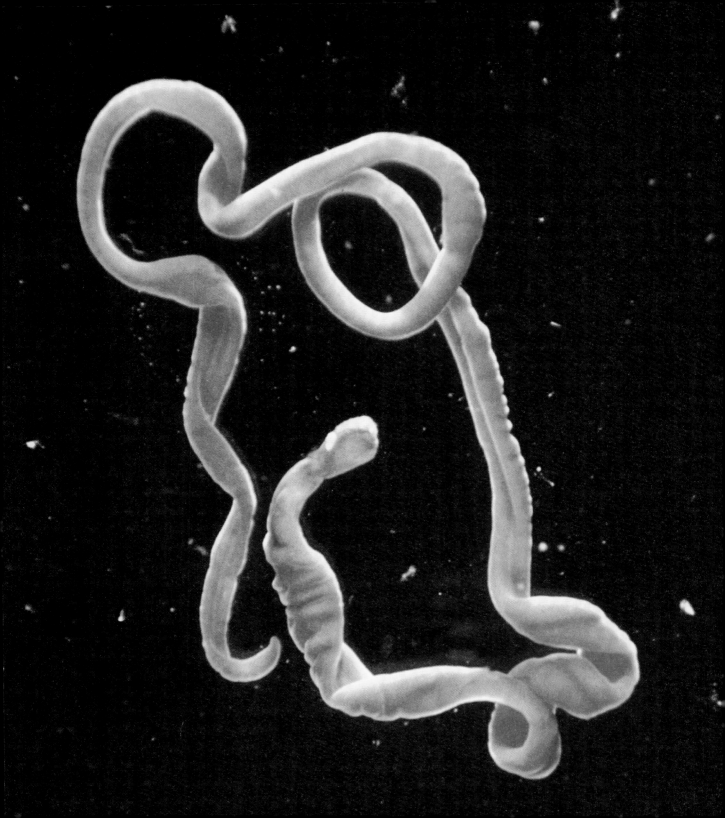

CHAPTER 6

SPONGES, CNIDARIANS, AND WORMS

INTRODUCTION

The bootlace worm pictured on page 140 is the longest worm on Earth. It commonly grows to more than 4.5 m (15 ft) long. Some species of this animal have grown to lengths of more than 30.5 m (100 ft). The longest bootlace worm ever found, washed up on the coast of Scotland, measured more than 55 m (180 ft)! The bootlace worm belongs to a group of worms called ribbon worms. In addition to their unusual length, these worms have been known to digest part of themselves when food was scarce. In one case, the specimen digested more than 95 percent of its body without suffering any ill effects. When food becomes available again the digested tissue grows back.

Ribbon worms are classed as invertebrates. In this chapter you will examine several groups of invertebrates and learn how they live.

SECTION TITLES

The bootlace worm is a type of ribbon worm that grows more than 4m long.

6-1 INVERTEBRATES

bilateral symmetry
invertebrate
radial symmetry
symmetry
vertebrate

OBJECTIVES

- Distinguish between vertebrates and invertebrates.
- Identify several phyla of invertebrates.
- Distinguish between bilateral and radial symmetry.

In chapters 4 and 5, you studied three kingdoms of living things: Monera, Protists, and Fungi (fig. 6-1). In this and the next two chapters, you will have an opportunity to study the animal kingdom.

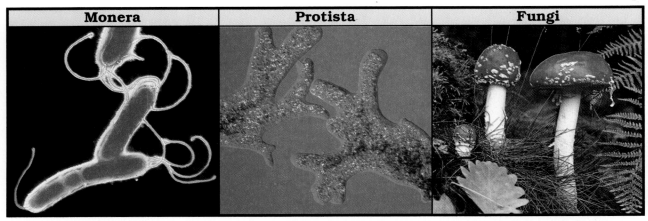

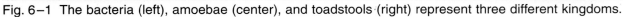

Fig. 6-1 The bacteria (left), amoebae (center), and toadstools (right) represent three different kingdoms.

Biologists have identified more than a million and a half species of animals. Yet, even with this many species identified, many more species remain unidentified (fig. 6-2).

Fig. 6-2 Many animals have not yet been classified by scientists.

142

Animals live all over the world in almost every available habitat. Animals are found in a wide variety of habitats: trout in mountain streams, penguins in Antarctica, tortoises in deserts, lobsters on the ocean floor, and moles underground. While they differ widely in size, appearance, and habits, they share common characteristics. You may remember the characteristics of the animal kingdom summarized in figure 6-3.

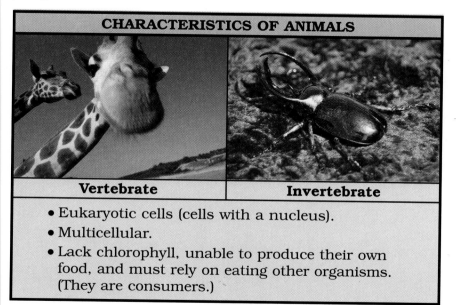

CHARACTERISTICS OF ANIMALS

Vertebrate	Invertebrate

- Eukaryotic cells (cells with a nucleus).
- Multicellular.
- Lack chlorophyll, unable to produce their own food, and must rely on eating other organisms. (They are consumers.)

Fig. 6—3 Animals share common characteristics.

Scientists divide animals into two major groups. One group, the **vertebrates**, have skeletons that include backbones inside the body. Sharks, toads, snakes, birds, and mammals are all vertebrates and make up one phylum of animals called the chordates. The second group of animals are the invertebrates. They make up about 30 phyla of the animal kingdom. The **invertebrates** are animals that lack backbones. They include sponges, jellyfish, earthworms, snails, and insects. While both groups of animals are fascinating to study, in this unit we will focus on the invertebrates. As you study this and the next two chapters, you will investigate the eight largest phyla of invertebrates: sponges, cnidarians (ni der′ ē ən), roundworms, flatworms, segmented worms, echinoderms (ē kī′ nō dɵrm), mollusks (mäl′ əsk), and arthropods (fig. 6-4).

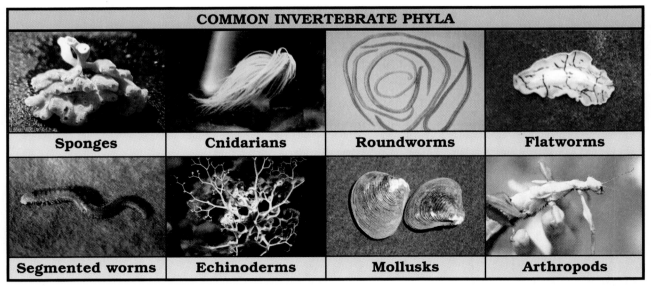

COMMON INVERTEBRATE PHYLA

Sponges	Cnidarians	Roundworms	Flatworms
Segmented worms	Echinoderms	Mollusks	Arthropods

Fig. 6–4

One characteristic scientists use when describing animals, particularly invertebrates, is body symmetry. **Symmetry** means a similarity, or likeness, in parts. Your two hands show symmetry (fig. 6-5). The structure of one hand is similar to the structure of the other. Scientists identify two main types of symmetry: bilateral and radial (fig 6-6).

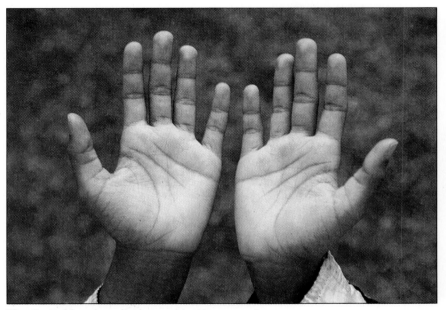

Fig. 6–5 Your hands demonstrate symmetry.

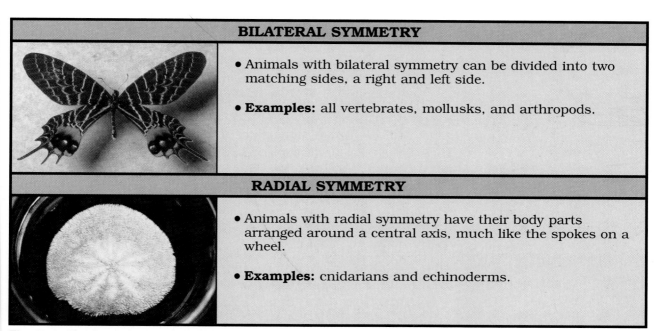

BILATERAL SYMMETRY	
	• Animals with bilateral symmetry can be divided into two matching sides, a right and left side. • **Examples:** all vertebrates, mollusks, and arthropods.

RADIAL SYMMETRY	
	• Animals with radial symmetry have their body parts arranged around a central axis, much like the spokes on a wheel. • **Examples:** cnidarians and echinoderms.

Fig. 6-6 The butterfly is an example of bilateral symmetry. The sand dollar demonstrates radial symmetry.

TRY THIS 6-1: What Kind of Arrangement Is This?

Materials:
   Special Master R137

Procedure:
   1. Obtain a copy of the Special Master.
   2. On the Special Master you will notice drawings of several animals and a four-column chart with these headings: Animal, Bilateral Symmetry, Radial Symmetry, and No Symmetry. In the column labeled "Animal," name each animal pictured in the drawings.
   3. For each animal listed, determine whether it shows bilateral symmetry, radial symmetry, or no symmetry. Mark the appropriate column for each animal.
      • Which animals show bilateral symmetry?
      • Which animals show radial symmetry?
      • Which animals show no symmetry?
      • Is body symmetry a phylum characteristic?

REVIEW IT

   1. How are invertebrates different from vertebrates?
   2. List the eight common invertebrate phyla.
   3. What is the difference between bilateral and radial symmetry?

6-2 SPONGES

VOCABULARY
collar cell
pore
regeneration
spicule
Sponge
spongin

OBJECTIVES

- Identify the characteristics of sponges.
- Describe the structure of sponges.
- Explain how sponges get their food.
- Explain regeneration.

Look at the two sponges in figure 6-7. What difference do you see? The sponge on the top is a synthetically produced sponge; the sponge on the bottom is a natural sponge, commercially harvested from the sea. This sponge was once a living animal! Until the mid-1800s people thought sponges were plants, because they do not move about as most animals do. But **Sponges** are pore-bearing animals that live in both fresh water and salt water. Unlike most other invertebrates, sponges lack any type of body symmetry. Although sponges differ considerably in size and appearance, they share several common characteristics. These are summarized in figure 6-8.

Although sponges lack skeletons, they are designed with material or structures that provide support. **Spongin** is a flexible substance that forms a network between the cells and provides support for the bodies of some sponges. Other sponges have **spicules** (spik′ yōol), hard, spikelike structures that form a framework of support. Some spicules are made of silica, the mineral used to make glass. Others are composed of calcium carbonate, the material that makes up the shells of snails and clams.

Fig. 6-7 Artificial sponge (top) and natural sponge (bottom).

CHARACTERISTICS OF SPONGES
• A hollow body.
• Cells are not specialized into tissues.
• Water and materials move into the body through numerous openings called **pores**.
• Waste moves out of the body through a large opening at the top of the sponge.

Fig. 6-8

STRUCTURE OF A SPONGE

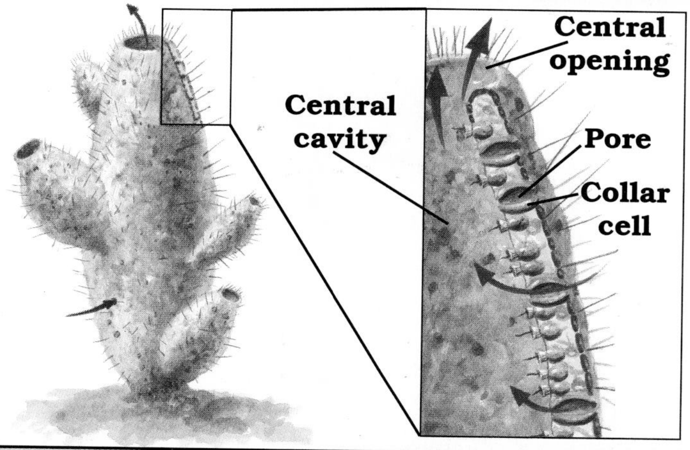

Central cavity—	the large space in the body of a sponge.
Central opening—	an opening at the top of a sponge through which wastes pass out of the body.
Pores—	many small openings through which water, food, and oxygen enter the sponge.
Collar cells—	cells that make up the inner layer. Each collar cell has a flagellum that moves back and forth to create a current of water.

Fig. 6–9

DID YOU KNOW?
The sponge Leuconia stands about 10 cm (4 in) tall and 1 cm (.4 in) in diameter and has about 2 million collar cells.

While many scientists consider sponges to be "simple" invertebrates, they are designed in a fascinating way. The intricate arrangement of spicules and spongin, and the organization of the cells provide strong evidence of a Creator. Study figure 6-9 to learn the structure of a sponge.

When water is drawn in by the beating of the collar cells, it brings in food and oxygen. Collar cells trap and digest some of the food. Other particles move into the jellylike material lying between the cells, where they are digested and transported to other cells. Since a sponge is only two layers thick, oxygen and food are near all of the cells. Wastes from the cells are carried away by water currents and out the central opening.

Fig. 6-10 Regeneration allows sponges to regrow body parts.

Fig. 6-11 Commercial sponge farmers harvest living sponges from the beds they cultivate.

Sponges, like many invertebrates, are capable of regeneration. **Regeneration** involves the ability to regrow lost or damaged body parts (fig. 6-10). In some cases a complete new sponge can be grown from just a few cells. If a sponge is cut up into many small pieces, each piece can grow into a new sponge. Commercial sponge farmers grow new sponges by cutting up existing sponges (fig. 6-11).

REVIEW IT

1. What are the main characteristics of sponges?
2. Describe the structure of sponges.
3. How do sponges feed?
4. What is regeneration?

6-3 CNIDARIANS

- Identify the characteristics of cnidarians.
- Compare the two body forms of cnidarians.
- Explain how cnidarians get their food.
- Explain how coral is different from other cnidarians.

Hundreds of Portuguese men-of-war sometimes blow into shore along the eastern coast of the United States (fig. 6-12). When this occurs, swimmers may receive painful stings from these jellyfishlike animals. The Portuguese man-of-war, jellyfish, hydras, sea anemones, and corals all belong to the phylum **Cnidaria** (fig. 6-13). Animals in this phylum are distinguished by a hollow body and a mouth surrounded by tentacles. These animals share the characteristics outlined in figure 6-14.

VOCABULARY
Cnidaria
medusa
polyp
stinging cell
tentacle

Fig. 6–12 Persistent winds often blow weak-swimming jellyfish into coastal areas, where they are washed up on beaches.

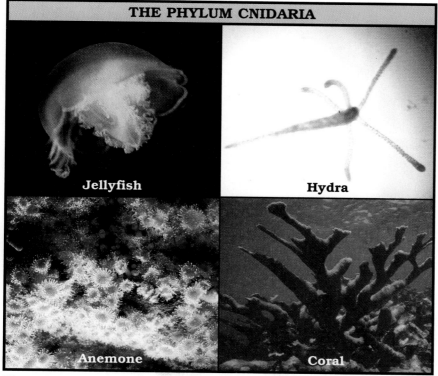

THE PHYLUM CNIDARIA

Jellyfish

Hydra

Anemone

Coral

Fig. 6–13

RESEARCH IT
Find out what hydra eat.

DID YOU KNOW?
The water pressure inside stinging cells can reach 400 times atmospheric pressure.

CHARACTERISTICS OF CNIDARIANS

- Hollow sac-like body that occurs in two forms:
  - a vase-shaped body called a polyp, or
  - a bell-shaped body called a medusa.
- Cells are specialized into tissues.
- Only one opening into the body.
- Tentacles with stinging cells.

Fig. 6—14

DID YOU KNOW?
Sea anemones and corals are both placed in the class of Cnidaria called *Anthozoa*, meaning "flower animals."

DID YOU KNOW?
The largest jellyfish measured 2.3 m (7.5 ft) across, and its tentacles stretched out more than 37 m (120 ft).

RESEARCH IT
What are the main predators of the jellyfish?

Cnidarians have one of two body forms (fig. 6-15). One form, called the **medusa** (mə dōo′ sə), is shaped like an umbrella or bell and is designed for swimming. Adult jellyfish have this body form. In a medusa the mouth is pointed down and is surrounded by hanging tentacles. In the second body form, called a **polyp** (päl′ ip), the body is shaped like a vase and is designed to be attached to something. In polyps the mouth is pointed up and is surrounded by tentacles that pull food into the upward-pointing mouth. Sea anemones and corals are examples of polyps. Although many cnidarians show either one body form or the other, a few develop both polyp and medusa stages.

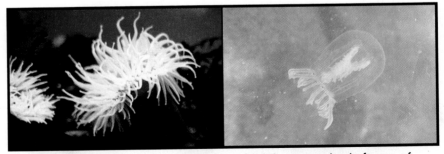

Fig. 6—15 The polyp (left) and medusa (right) are two body forms of Cnidarians.

Unlike sponges, which lack specialized tissues, the cells of the cnidarians are clearly organized into tissues. Study the diagram of *Hydra*, a freshwater cnidarian, in figure 6-16 to learn its structure.

STRUCTURE OF *HYDRA*

Mouth

Tentacle

Sperm/Testes

Stinging cells on tentacles

Egg/ovary

Digestive cavity

Mouth—	opening at the top, through which water, oxygen, food, and waste pass.
Digestive cavity—	large space in the body where digestion takes place.
Tentacles—	armlike extensions used to capture and bring food into the digestive cavity.
Stinging cells—	specialized harpoonlike cells that shoot poison into the prey and help hold it.

Fig. 6–16

Most cnidarians capture their prey by using the stinging cells on their tentacles. Each stinging cell looks like a miniature harpoon, complete with a barbed point at one end and an attached thread at the other (fig. 6-17). The other end of

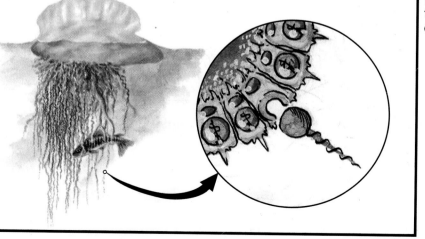

Fig. 6–17 The stinging cells on the tentacles of Cnidarians help capture and hold prey.

RESEARCH IT
Study nematocysts to find how they work.

RESEARCH IT
How are clown fish protected from the stinging cells of the tentacles they swim around?

the thread stays attached to the tentacle. When the tentacle comes in contact with potential prey, these specialized cells are shot into the prey's body and release a paralyzing poison. The threads help to hold the prey until it is subdued. Once the prey is captured, the tentacles push it through the mouth and into the digestive cavity.

Fig. 6–18 The Great Barrier Reef is considered by some to be the largest living thing on Earth.

Some people consider the Great Barrier Reef, located off the coast of Australia, to be the largest living thing on Earth (fig. 6-18). This massive structure stretches 2027 km (1260 mi) long and covers an area of 200 000 sq km (80 000 sq mi). The Great Barrier Reef and similar reefs are made up of billions of tiny coral polyps.

Unlike other cnidarians, most corals live in colonies and form reefs by cementing their calcium skeletons to skeletons of adjacent polyps. When the polyps die, their hardened skeletons remain, serving as a foundation for new polyps. The reefs, formed by corals, provide food and shelter for a host of animals.

REVIEW IT

1. What are the characteristics of Cnidaria?
2. What are the two body forms of cnidarians?
3. How do cnidarians capture food?
4. How are corals different from other cnidarians?

6-4 WORMS

- Distinguish between the major phyla of worms.
- Describe representative examples of worms.

Annelida
Nematoda
Platyhelminthes

The earthworm is probably one of the most familiar worms. These animals improve the soil by loosening and aerating it. Tapeworms, which may grow to lengths of 20 m (66 ft.), live as parasites in the intestines of many animals including humans

The ice worm of Alaska has a body temperature of 10°C.

Fig. 6-19 Many animals, including humans, have tapeworms that live in their intestines.

(fig. 6-19). Like sponges and cnidarians, earthworms, tapeworms, and all other kind of worms are invertebrates. While all worms are similar, scientists classify worms into three distinct phyla: flatworms, roundworms, and segmented worms (fig. 6-20).

Fig. 6-20

CHARACTERISTICS OF FLATWORMS

- Belong to the phylum **Platyhelminthes** (plat i hel′ minth ēz).
- Flattened body, distinct head and tail.
- May be free-living or live as internal parasites.
- Free-living: *Planaria* (plə ner′ ē ə)
  - Light-sensitive eyespots.
  - Tubelike mouth.
- Internal parasites: tapeworm.
  - Head with sucking mouthparts surrounded by many hooks.
  - Parasites in many animals, including humans.
Examples: *Planaria* and tapeworm.

153

Fig. 6—20 Continued

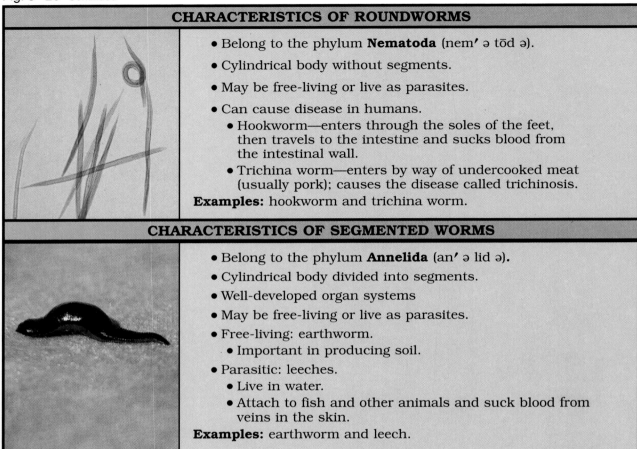

CHARACTERISTICS OF ROUNDWORMS

- Belong to the phylum **Nematoda** (nem′ ə tōd ə).
- Cylindrical body without segments.
- May be free-living or live as parasites.
- Can cause disease in humans.
  - Hookworm—enters through the soles of the feet, then travels to the intestine and sucks blood from the intestinal wall.
  - Trichina worm—enters by way of undercooked meat (usually pork); causes the disease called trichinosis.

Examples: hookworm and trichina worm.

CHARACTERISTICS OF SEGMENTED WORMS

- Belong to the phylum **Annelida** (an′ ə lid ə).
- Cylindrical body divided into segments.
- Well-developed organ systems
- May be free-living or live as parasites.
- Free-living: earthworm.
  - Important in producing soil.
- Parasitic: leeches.
  - Live in water.
  - Attach to fish and other animals and suck blood from veins in the skin.

Examples: earthworm and leech.

RESEARCH IT

According to the Bible, what meats are considered unclean? Which of these might contain parasitic worms?

REVIEW IT

1. How do the three phyla of worms differ?
2. For each description listed, name the worm and the phylum to which it belongs.
   a. enters humans through the soles of the feet
   b. external parasite on fish
   c. has light-sensitive eyespots
   d. comes from undercooked pork

CLASS ACTIVITY 6-4: Earthworm

Question: What are the external and internal structures of an earthworm?

Materials:

balance
dissecting kit and pan
earthworm (living)
earthworm (preserved)
magnifying lens

metric ruler
paper towels - 5
petri dish
Special Master R143
water

Procedure:

1. Get a Special Master and a living and preserved earthworm. Tear a paper towel in half and wet one half thoroughly. Fold the wet towel and place it in the bottom half of the petri dish. Place the living worm on the wet towel and place the cover on the petri dish.
2. Place the preserved worm on a paper towel and cover it to keep it from drying.
3. Observe the living worm inside the petri dish. Find the external structures identified on the Special Master.
4. Take the worm out of the petri dish. Weigh and measure it. Record.
5. Make a labeled drawing of your living worm.
6. Weigh and measure the preserved worm. Record.
7. Make a labeled drawing of your preserved worm.
8. Follow the directions on the Special Master and dissect the preserved worm. Identify all structures listed.

Data:

Living Worm	Preserved Worm
Weight _____ Length _____ Number of Segments _____	Weight _____ Length _____ Number of Segments _____

Questions:

1. How can you distinguish between the top and bottom side of an earthworm?
2. How can you distinguish between the front and back of an earthworm?
3. How does an earthworm move?
4. What is the function of the crop and gizzard?
5. To what phylum does the earthworm belong?

Conclusion: Write 3-5 sentences about what you learned from this activity.

CHAPTER 6 WRAP-UP

THINKING SKILLS: Interpreting Evidence

Much of what we know about the living organisms, their life processes, and their interrelationships has been discovered by observing them in the field. These observations have provided data and evidence that scientists use to explain what they observe.

Answer the questions below after reading the following paragraphs.

The Aswan High Dam was dedicated in 1971. This dam, which stretches across the upper Nile River in Egypt, was designed to control flooding, provide irrigation water, and provide electrical power. Although the dam has accomplished these goals, it has also made a negative impact on the environment. The river no longer carries the nutrient-rich silt into the farmland. This has made heavy use of chemical fertilizers necessary. The dam has created additional problems by clogging the river, resulting in an accumulation of human, animal, and industrial waste.

A serious health problem has also developed. In the past few years there has been a dramatic increase in the incidence of a parasitic fluke, a type of flatworm. This parasite causes serious intestinal and urinary-tract infections. People infected with the fluke suffer continual fatigue and, if untreated, often die from the infection. The fluke breeds in the bodies of aquatic snails living in the water behind the Aswan High Dam. Simply stepping into the water can lead to infection. Health officials have discovered that the rate of people infected by the fluke has increased from 1 percent to 80 percent since the completion of the dam.

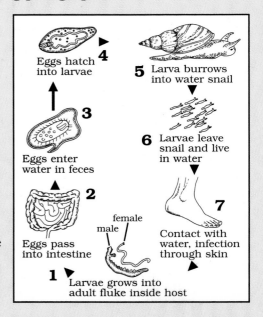

1. Why did the dam cause a dramatic increase in the rate of fluke infection in the population?
2. Explain why each of the following would favor or oppose plans to build the dam.
    a. a farmer
    b. a doctor
    c. the owner of a fertilizer company
3. What age group of the population do you think is probably most prone to infection? Why?
4. Study the diagram and decide at which stage each of the following would be most effective.

____injections or pills   ____aquatic pesticides

____staying out of the water   ____snail-eating fish

____aquatic herbicide   ____improved restroom and sewage-treatment facilities

QUESTIONS AND PROBLEMS

1. Why did God command the Israelites not to eat pork?
2. How are animals different from protists?
3. Do jellyfish pursue their prey? Explain.
4. How are earthworms helpful to human beings?
5. How do the stinging cells of cnidarians help the animals capture food?
6. How are sea anemones and jellyfish similar?
7. What simple practice can prevent infection by hookworms?
8. How are natural sponges harvested?
9. Why are vertebrates generally larger than invertebrates?
10. How are leeches different from flukes?
11. Why is it necessary for a sponge to have pores?
12. Why were sponges once considered plants?
13. In a natural sponge used for cleaning, what material makes up the sponge?

RESEARCH

1. Visit a tropical-fish store and find out what invertebrates it sells. List each species, where it comes from, its natural habitat, and why it is sold (is it for display or as a food for something else). Write a report on your findings.
2. Design an experiment that can be used to find out whether synthetic sponge or natural sponge is more absorbent. Make a display that identifies the materials used, the procedure followed, the data recorded, and the conclusion reached.
3. Use library resources to discover how leeches were used in medicine from the Middle Ages to the nineteenth century. Present an oral report on the subject.
4. Create a bulletin board that illustrates the life cycle of the common jellyfish.
5. Use library resources to find out about parasitic worms. Write a report that discusses how they infect their hosts, the symptoms of infection, and treatment. Include a drawing of each worm with your report.

REVIEW

HIGHLIGHTS

1. Vertebrates are animals with backbones; invertebrates are animals without backbones.
2. Major phyla of invertebrates include sponges, cnidarians, roundworms, flatworms, segmented worms, echinoderms, mollusks, and arthropods.
3. Animals with bilateral symmetry can be divided into two matching sides, a right and left side. Animals with radial symmetry have body parts that are arranged around a central axis, much like the spokes on a wheel.
4. Sponges share several characteristics: they lack skeletons; they have hollow bodies; their cells are not specialized into tissue; materials move in and out of their bodies through pores.
5. The structure of a sponge is illustrated in figure 6-9.

6. Sponges use collar cells to move water through their pores, where they filter the water to capture food.

7. Regeneration occurs when lost or damaged body parts are regrown.

8. Cnidarians have several common characteristics: they lack skeletons; they have hollow saclike bodies; their cells are specialized into tissue; they have tentacles with stinging cells.

9. The structure of a cnidarian is illustrated in figure 6-16.

10. Cnidarians use their tentacles to capture their prey. Once the prey is captured, the tentacles push it through the mouth and into the digestive cavity.

11. Cnidarians have two body shapes. One is tube-shaped with a mouth at the top. The other is umbrella-shaped with the mouth underneath. Both have mouths surrounded by tentacles.

12. The three main phyla of worms are flatworms, roundworms, and segmented worms.

13. Flatworms have flattened bodies; roundworms have smooth, cylindrical bodies; and segmented worms have cylindrical bodies and many segments.

14. Examples of worms representing each phyla are identified and described in figure 6-20.

VOCABULARY LIST

Annelida	Platyhelminthes	Sponge
bilateral symmetry	polyp	spongin
Cnidaria	pore	stinging cell
collar cell	radial symmetry	symmetry
invertebrate	regeneration	tentacle
medusa	spicule	vertebrate
Nematoda		

PRACTICE

Multiple Choice. Choose the best answer.

1. Which is not true of all animals?
   a. they are eukaryotic
   b. they are vertebrates
   c. they reproduce
   d. they are made of cells

2. All animals can be divided into either
   a. amphibians or reptiles
   b. prokaryotes or eukaryotes
   c. vertebrates or invertebrates
   d. protists or fungi

3. Which is true about all invertebrates?
   a. they lack backbones
   b. they are poisonous
   c. they live only in the sea
   d. all of these

4. Sponges are basically
   a. solid with pores
   b. plantlike animals
   c. parasites
   d. hollow with pores

5. Sponges trap food by filtering water through their
    a. mouths
    b. pores
    c. spores
    d. spongin
6. When a lost or damaged body part is regrown, it is called
    a. spontaneous generation
    b. regeneration
    c. invertebrate genesis
    d. star trek the next generation
7. Which phyllum of animals has tentacles used for capturing food?
    a. Platyhelminthes
    b. Cnidaria
    c. Annelida
    d. Nematoda
8. Cnidarians acquire food by
    a. parasitic feelers
    b. collar cells and spongin cells
    c. absorbing dissolved food
    d. using stinging cells to capture prey
9. Which invertebrate is ingested by eating undercooked pork?
    a. leeches
    b. trichina worms
    c. flukes
    d. hookworms
10. Roundworms are different from segmented worms because
    a. they lack antennae
    b. they lack segments
    c. they only live in water
    d. all of these

Matching. Match each word with its definition or description.
1. regrowing of body parts
2. hydras and jellyfish
3. structure used in capturing food
4. shoots poison into the body of prey
5. hard, spikelike structure
6. has a backbone
7. jellyfish, sea anemones, and worms
8. contains the flagella in sponges
9. where food and water enter sponges
10. helps support a sponge's body

a. Cnidaria
b. collar cells
c. invertebrate
d. pore
e. regeneration
f. spicule
g. spongin
h. stinging cell
i. tentacle
j. vertebrate

159

CHAPTER 7

MOLLUSKS AND ECHINODERMS

INTRODUCTION

Imagine having 20 or more eyes. That is how many eyes the scallop has. In addition to its eyes, this clamlike animal also has sensory tentacles. It uses its eyes and tentacles to search for food and to watch for danger. When it spots danger, the scallop escapes by clapping its two shells together to swim quickly away. The scallop is a mollusk, a large phylum of invertebrates that includes snails, clams, and octopuses.

In this chapter you will learn about the mollusks and the echinoderms, another phylum of invertebrates.

SECTION TITLES

The scallop uses its eyes and tentacles to search for food and to watch for danger.

EGWs–11

7-1 CHARACTERISTICS OF MOLLUSKS

Fig. 7–1 The common garden snail is a mollusk.

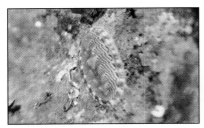

Fig. 7–2 Chitons are another type of mollusk.

Fig. 7–3 The giant squid is the largest invertebrate.

OBJECTIVES

- Identify the characteristics of mollusks.
- Explain how mollusks get food.

Mollusks are soft-bodied animals often covered by hard shells. This group of invertebrates includes a variety of animals; snails, clams, and octopus are the most common (fig. 7-1). Less familiar examples include nudibranchs, chitons, and nautiluses (fig. 7-2). Biologists have identified nearly 85,000 species of mollusks and believe that many more exist that have not been identified.

Mollusks may or may not have a shell. Snails have one shell, clams have two shells, squid have internal shells, and octopus lack shells altogether. Members of this phylum range in size from the tiny snail that lives off the British coast, less than 0.5 mm (1/16th in) in diameter, to the giant squid of the Atlantic Ocean, which reaches more than 15 m (50 ft) in length (fig. 7-3). Some mollusks, such as slugs and snails, move extremely slowly, while octopus and squid are some of the fastest invertebrates (fig. 7-4).

Fig. 7–4 An octopus can swim rapidly by using a type of jet propulsion.

Mollusks are found in a wide variety of habitats, from the bottom of the ocean to altitudes in excess of 7000 m (22,000 ft). They inhabit ponds, rain forests, gardens, tidepools, and deserts.

Although mollusks vary in appearance and habits, they have several common characteristics, which are summarized in figure 7-5.

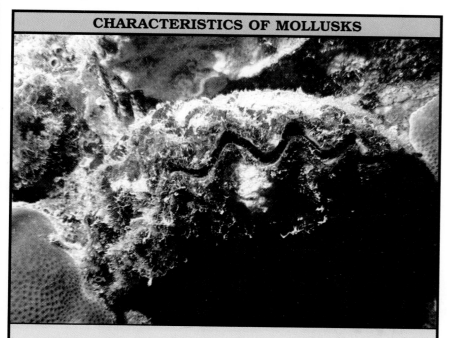

CHARACTERISTICS OF MOLLUSKS

- Lack skeletons.

- Have soft bodies.

- Some are covered by hard shells; others are not.

- Bodies are divided into three parts: head, foot, and mantle.

  - **Head:** structure that contains the mouth and sense organs.

  - **Foot:** muscular structure that extends from the body and is used for movement.

  - **Mantle:** fleshy tissue that covers and protects the internal organs and also secretes the shell.

Fig. 7-5

RESEARCH IT
The heart of an oyster may beat only six times per minute.

DID YOU KNOW?
The largest animal eye, reaching a diamter of 39 cm (15 in), belongs to the giant squid.

DID YOU KNOW?
The radula of some snails may have as many as 250,000 sharp teeth.

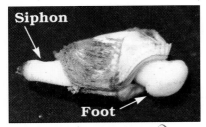

Fig. 7–6 Most clams feed by using the siphon to bring plankton-rich water into the stomach.

The Creator designed a number of different ways for mollusks to get their food. Some obtain their food by filtering plankton or other small particles of food from the water (fig. 7-6). To do this, special tubes pump water in and out. Some clams have special rod-shaped structures that secrete enzymes, which help digest their food. Other mollusks, such as snails and slugs, use rasplike tongues, called **radulas** (raj′ oo ləs), to scrape off the microscopic plankton film that covers many rocks and seaweeds, or to munch on vegetation in or out of the water (fig. 7-7). Some predatory snails use their radulas to kill other mollusks by boring holes in their shells and injecting poison to kill the prey. Squid and octopus actively hunt for their food by stalking or chasing it and use their tentacles to capture it.

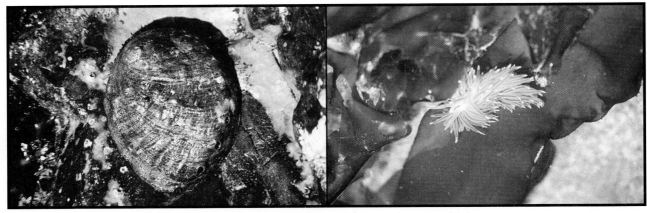

Fig. 7–7 Abalone and similar snails feed by grazing on algae or plant material.

REVIEW IT

1. What are the main characteristics of mollusks?
2. How do mollusks feed?

CLASS ACTIVITY 7-1: Structure of a Clam

Question: What is the external and internal structure of a clam?

Materials:

balance
clam (preserved)
dissecting kit/pan

kite string
metric ruler
Special Master R173

Procedure:
1. Obtain a clam and a Special Master.
2. Look over the clam. In the chart describe its color and shape. Make a sketch of it on the Special Master. Label the external features. (Refer to the Special Master.)
3. Measure the length, width, girth (distance around), and mass of your clam. (Use the string to help measure the girth.) Record.
4. Open your clam and identify these structures: (Refer to the Special Master.)

adductor muscle
digestive gland
excurrent siphon
foot
gills
heart

incurrent siphon
intestine
mantle
reproductive organ
stomach

Data:

Feature	Description		
Color			
Shape			

Feature	Measurement	Class Average
Mass (0.1 g)		
Length (1.0 mm)		
Width (1.0 mm)		
Girth (1.0 mm)		

Questions:
1. What characteristics help classify the clam as a mollusk?
2. Explain the purpose of these structures:

   A. adductor muscle
   B. excurrent siphon
   C. foot

   D. incurrent siphon
   E. mantle
   F. shell

3. Explain how this clam gets its food.
4. Why might it be unhealthful to eat clams and similar animals?

Conclusion: Write 3–5 sentences about what you learned from this activity.

7-2 TYPES OF MOLLUSKS

OBJECTIVES

- Explain how mollusks are classified.
- Identify the major classes of mollusks.
- Describe characteristics and examples of each mollusk class.

Look at the mollusks in figure 7-8. How would you organize these animals into groups? You might group them according to whether they have a shell or perhaps by the habitat they live in. Scientists classify mollusks into four

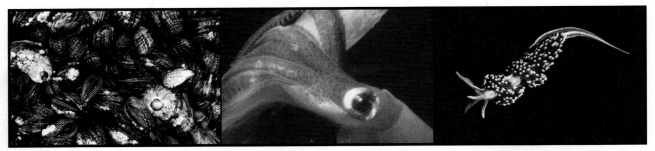

Fig. 7-8 The mussel (left), squid (center), and nudibranch (right) represent three classes used to classify mollusks.

main classes based on the shape of the muscular foot: the hatchet-footed mollusks, the stomach-footed mollusks, the head-footed mollusks, and the chitons (kī′ tins). Figure 7-9 shows characteristics and examples of each group.

Fig. 7-9

CHARACTERISTICS OF HATCHET-FOOTED MOLLUSKS

- Also called **bivalves**, or pelecypods (pə les′ i päd).
- Have shells hinged together.
- Lack the head region of other mollusks.
- Usually filter food from water using a special tube, called a siphon, that brings water into digestive organs.

Examples: Clams, oysters, and scallops.

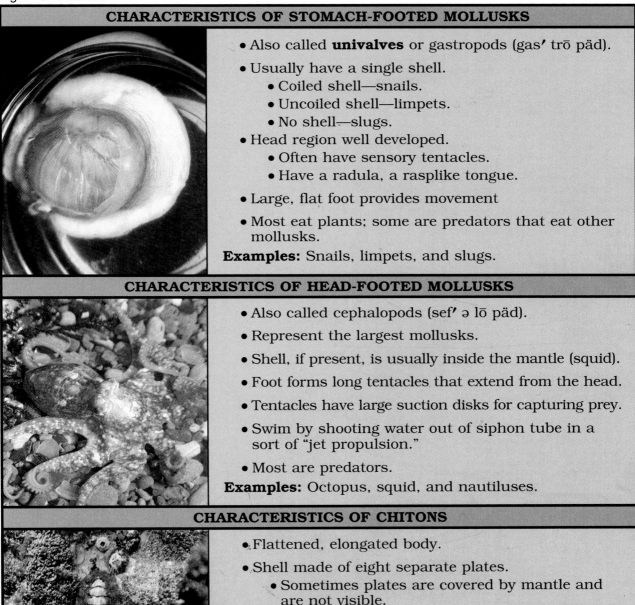

CHARACTERISTICS OF STOMACH-FOOTED MOLLUSKS

- Also called **univalves** or gastropods (gas′ trō päd).
- Usually have a single shell.
  - Coiled shell—snails.
  - Uncoiled shell—limpets.
  - No shell—slugs.
- Head region well developed.
  - Often have sensory tentacles.
  - Have a radula, a rasplike tongue.
- Large, flat foot provides movement
- Most eat plants; some are predators that eat other mollusks.

Examples: Snails, limpets, and slugs.

CHARACTERISTICS OF HEAD-FOOTED MOLLUSKS

- Also called cephalopods (sef′ ə lō päd).
- Represent the largest mollusks.
- Shell, if present, is usually inside the mantle (squid).
- Foot forms long tentacles that extend from the head.
- Tentacles have large suction disks for capturing prey.
- Swim by shooting water out of siphon tube in a sort of "jet propulsion."
- Most are predators.

Examples: Octopus, squid, and nautiluses.

CHARACTERISTICS OF CHITONS

- Flattened, elongated body.
- Shell made of eight separate plates.
  - Sometimes plates are covered by mantle and are not visible.
- Head region is small.
  - Radula present.
- Most are plant eaters.

Example: Chitons.

TRY THIS 7-2: Garden Snails

Materials:

garden snail
glass square 10 cm x 10 cm

razor blade (single-edged)
sandpaper

Procedure:

1. Obtain a garden snail.
2. Place the snail on the glass square. Allow the snail to begin to move about on the glass. Observe.
   - How many pairs of tentacles does the snail have?
   - How does the snail move?
   - Can the snail crawl uphill? downhill? upside down?
   - To what class of mollusks does the snail belong? How do you know?
3. Place the snail on the sandpaper. Observe.
   - Is there any difference between the way the snail moves on the sandpaper and the way it moved on the glass? Explain.
4. Carefully place the snail on the edge of the razor blade. Observe.
   - How can the snail move on the edge of the razor blade without being cut?
   - Do garden snails prefer a moist or dry environment? Why?
   - Why do garden snails usually feed at night?

REVIEW IT

1. How do scientists classify mollusks?
2. What are four classes of mollusks? Name an example of each.
3. Which class of mollusks exhibits the following:
   a. a coiled shell
   b. two shells hinged together
   c. shell made of eight separate plates
   d. shell completely inside mantle

7-3 CHARACTERISTICS OF ECHINODERMS

OBJECTIVES

- Identify the characteristics of Echinoderms.
- Explain how tube feet work.

VOCABULARY
Echinoderm
endoskeleton
tube foot

Fig. 7–10 Sea urchins live in the ocean.

Have you ever seen living sea urchins? They look like pin cushions (fig. 7-10). It is hard to imagine eating one of these spiny creatures, but that is exactly what the sunflower star does. It does this by swallowing the urchin whole. Inside the star's stomach, strong digestive juices quickly dissolve the tissue that holds the urchin's spines in place, and they are pushed aside while the rest of the meal is digested. When feeding is completed, the sunflower star spits out the "shell" of the sea urchin and the other undigested material. People often find these empty sea urchins and use them to make decorative lamps or wall hangings (fig. 7-11).

Both the sea urchin and the sunflower star are **Echinoderms**, spiny-skinned animals. Echinoderms, which also include sand dollars and sea cucumbers, live only in the ocean and share several characteristics (fig. 7-12).

Fig. 7–11 The skeletons of sea urchins are used to make decorative lamps.

CHARACTERISTICS OF ECHINODERMS

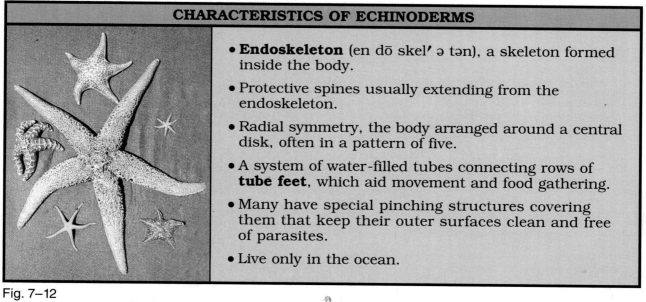

- **Endoskeleton** (en dō skel' ə tən), a skeleton formed inside the body.
- Protective spines usually extending from the endoskeleton.
- Radial symmetry, the body arranged around a central disk, often in a pattern of five.
- A system of water-filled tubes connecting rows of **tube feet**, which aid movement and food gathering.
- Many have special pinching structures covering them that keep their outer surfaces clean and free of parasites.
- Live only in the ocean.

Fig. 7–12

Fig. 7–13 Tube feet enable sea stars and other Echinoderms to move from place to place.

Fig. 7–15 Sea stars are able to regenerate lost body parts.

Tube feet are unique to Echinoderms (fig. 7-13). These unusual structures, which end in suction cups, allow Echinoderms to move about and to grasp food. By regulating water pressure inside each foot, the Echinoderm can create suction and shorten the foot or break suction and elongate the foot. When filled with water, the tube foot is elongated, and the suction is released. When the water is removed, suction is created, and the foot is shortened. By increasing and decreasing the pressure of the tube feet, Echinoderms are able to move about and hold firmly onto rocks or food (fig. 7-14). If a sea star or other Echinoderm is held in the air, the water leaks out of the tube feet, leaving the animal unable to move. Sea stars cast up on shore during storms or heavy seas may die because they are unable to crawl back to the sea.

Fig. 7–14 Sea stars use their tube feet to hold firmly onto rocks that are pounded by the surf.

Like the sponges studied in chapter 6, Echinoderms are also able to regenerate lost or damaged body parts. Sea stars that lose legs are able to grow new ones (fig. 7-15). When sea stars are cut up, they can regenerate entire bodies. Fishermen who have tried to kill sea stars by cutting them up have discovered this phenomena. Instead of destroying the sea stars, thousands of new sea stars have developed from the many cut-up pieces.

REVIEW IT

1. What are the main characteristics of Echinoderms?
2. How do tube feet work?

7-4 TYPES OF ECHINODERMS

OBJECTIVE

• Describe the major classes of Echinoderms.

Biologists have identified about 6000 species of echinoderms living in the world's oceans. They organize these species into four distinct classes: sea lilies and feather stars, sea stars and brittle stars, sea urchins and sand dollars, and sea cucumbers. Study figure 7-16 to learn about the classes of echinoderms.

CHARACTERISTICS OF SEA LILIES AND FEATHER STARS	
	• Also called crinoids (krī′ noids). • Spines absent. • Young attached by "stems" to bottom; adults usually detach from "stem." • Have long arms that stretch upward. • Arms have long, tentaclelike tube feet used to capture food.
CHARACTERISTICS OF SEA STARS AND BRITTLE STARS	
	• Also called stellaroids. • Spines present. • Body is a central disk, with arms that extend radially. • Tube feet used for movement in some species (sea stars), but not in others (brittle stars). • Brittle stars pursue prey, using their legs rather than tube feet.

Fig. 7–16

Fig. 7–16 Continued

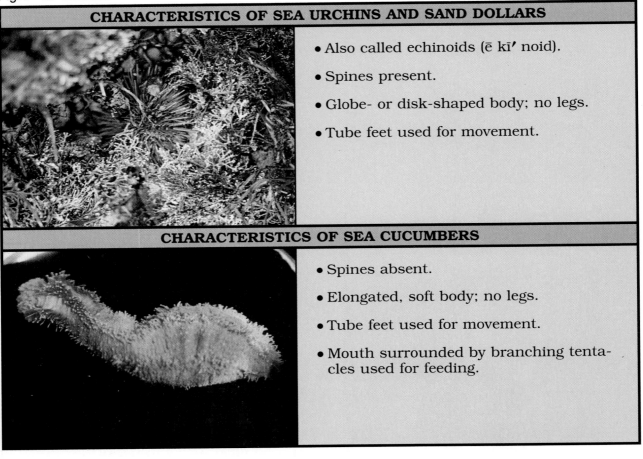

CHARACTERISTICS OF SEA URCHINS AND SAND DOLLARS

- Also called echinoids (ē kī′ noid).
- Spines present.
- Globe- or disk-shaped body; no legs.
- Tube feet used for movement.

CHARACTERISTICS OF SEA CUCUMBERS

- Spines absent.
- Elongated, soft body; no legs.
- Tube feet used for movement.
- Mouth surrounded by branching tentacles used for feeding.

REVIEW IT

1. Describe the major classes of Echinoderms.

These floating rafts don't look much like a farming operation, and the surrounding water certainly doesn't look like farmland. But to Thomas Ebert of U.S. Abalone, and to other "sea farmers," this is prime "land." Ebert's company and similar companies are tapping into a resource that has been around as long as the sea itself.

Aquaculture, the true name for "sea farming," is an agricultural activity that was first developed more than 2000 years ago. Archeological evidence indicates that China, Rome, and Egypt all practiced aquaculture. Early efforts in aquaculture involved stocking wild fingerlings in ponds and allowing them to grow to maturity. Mollusk farming was developed by the French and Japanese nearly 700 years ago, when they discovered that juvenile mussels and oysters would settle on upright posts set in intertidal areas or driven into the sea floor.

Besides the obvious differences, other differences exist between terrestrial farming (land farming) and aquaculture. For example, terrestrial farming primarily produces starchy staple crops, while aquaculture primarily produces protein crops. In land farming animals' waste can be removed from the area where the animals are being grown. The waste produced in aquaculture accumulates in the same place where the crop grows. As a result, sea farmers have to

take precautions to protect their "crop" from toxicity and poor water quality that could interfere with production and make the product unsafe to eat.

Aquaculturists utilize a variety of methods to grow their crops. The methods used depend on the desired product. Fish and many crustaceans are grown in ponds equipped with inlets and outlets that enable the farmer to regulate water flow. Other methods of aquaculture involve using cages in lakes and raceways with continuous flowing water. Mollusk farmers raise their crops by spreading the juvenile organisms over a prepared area of the ocean floor or by attaching juveniles to ropes suspended from floating rafts or by placing them in rafts made of open barrels in which the juvenile mollusks are allowed to grow to maturity.

In 1992, aquaculturists produced more than 19 million metric tons of product. This yield represented nearly $33 billion. This production was composed of 49 percent fish, 28 percent algae and aquatic plants, 18 percent mollusks, and 5 percent crustaceans. Aqua-culture production has grown steadily and is expected to grow about 5 percent annually through the coming years. Sea farmers and many scientists believe that aquaculture will be relied on more and more to provide food for the world's increasing population.

Questions:
1. Who first developed aquaculture?
2. How do the products of terrestrial farming and sea farming compare?
3. Describe several methods aquaculturists use to grow their crops.
4. Do you agree that aquaculture will be relied on more and more to produce food for the world's population? Why or why not?

CHAPTER 7 WRAP-UP

THINKING SKILLS: Outlining

Information is always easier to understand if it is organized. In science classes, as well as English and history classes, outlining is particularly valuable and practical as an organizing tool. In an outline information is organized according to topics, subtopics, and supporting details.

Look over the list of words or phrases and organize them by putting them into the skeletal outline. Put the letter of the word or phrase on the blank provided. Some have been done for you.

Mollusks (p)
A. Characteristics (b)
    1. No skeleton (t)
    2. Soft body (z)
    3. Body in three parts (a)
        a. _____
        b. head (k)
        c. _____
B. _____
    1. Hatchet-footed (j)
        a. Characteristics (b)
            (1) _____
            (2) _____
        b. Examples (f)
            (1) _____
            (2) _____
    2. _____
        a. _____
            (1) Sensory tentacles (w)
            (2) _____
        b. Examples (f)
            (1) _____
            (2) _____
    3. _____
        a. _____
            (1) Tentacles (cc)
            (2) _____
         b. _____
            (1) Octopus (u)
            (2) _____
    4. _____
        a. _____
            (1) _____
            (2) _____
        b. _____
            (1) Lined Chiton (n)
            (2) _____

a. body in three parts
b. characteristics
c. chitons
d. clams
e. classes of mollusks
f. examples
g. flattened, elongated body
h. foot
i. garden snail
j. hatchet-footed
k. head
l. head-footed
m. limpet
n. lined chiton
o. mantle
p. mollusks
q. mossy chiton
r. move by jet propulsion
s. no head region
t. no skeleton
u. octopus
v. oysters
w. sensory tentacles
x. shell of eight plates
y. single shell (usually)
z. soft body
aa. squid
bb. stomach-footed
cc. tentacles
dd. two hinged shells

QUESTIONS AND PROBLEMS

1. How are snails and slugs similar? Different?
2. How are the tentacles of an octopus different from the tentacles of a sea anemone?
3. Which class of Echinoderms lacks spines?
4. What are nudibranches?
5. Why don't oysters and clams need eyes?
6. Why are brittle stars called "brittle"? *break easy*
7. Based on the feeding method of clams and oysters, why is it *not* advisable to eat them? *Pollution and poisons*
8. Which Echinoderm has a soft body?
9. What is radial symmetry?
10. Which classes of mollusks are exclusively marine?
11. If you try to kill a sea star by cutting it up, what might happen? Why?
12. Which group of mollusks has a shell made of eight separate plates?
13. How are crinoids unlike other echinoderms?
14. What is the main food of the giant squid?

RESEARCH

1. Use library resources to find out how commercial pearl farms operate. Make a bulletin board displaying the process of culturing and harvesting commercial pearls.
2. Draw a picture of a squid, nautilus, snail, and clam. Label the head, foot, and mantle on each. Display your drawings.
3. Make a shell collection and identify each shell by its common name. Organize and display your shells. Present and explain your collection to your class.
4. Visit a public aquarium and make a list of mollusks and echinoderms displayed. Write a brief report summarizing your visit.
5. Use library resources to find out about the natural history of sand dollars. Make a series of color posters that describe what you learned.

REVIEW

HIGHLIGHTS

1. Characteristics of mollusks include the absence of a skeleton and a soft body divided into three parts: head, foot, and mantle.
2. Mollusks get their food in a number of ways. Many filter their food from the water; some scrape it off rocks and seaweed. Still other mollusks hunt for and capture their food.
4. Mollusk classification is based on the shape of the muscular foot.
5. The major classes of mollusks are the hatchet-footed mollusks, stomach-footed mollusks, head-footed mollusks, and chitons.
6. Characteristics and examples of each mollusk class are identified in figure 7-9.

7. Characteristics of echinoderms include an endoskeleton, radial symmetry, protective spines, and tube feet for movement and food gathering.

8. Tube feet work by suction. The suction is created by changing water pressure inside each individual tube foot. When filled with water, suction is released; when water is pumped out of a tube foot, suction is created. By increasing and decreasing the pressure of the tube feet, echinoderms are able to move.

9. Sea lilies and feather stars lack spines and have long arms that stretch upward. Sea stars and brittle stars have spines and central disks around which arms extend radially. Sea urchins and sand dollars have spines and globe- or disk-shaped bodies with no arms. Sea cucumbers lack spines and have elongated, soft bodies; the mouths are surrounded by branched tentacles.

VOCABULARY LIST

bivalve	head	radula
Echinoderm	mantle	tube foot
endoskeleton	Mollusk	univalve
foot		

PRACTICE

Multiple Choice. Choose the best answer.

1. What are the three main body parts of mollusks?
   a. head, foot, mantle
   b. head, foot, thorax
   c. head, thorax, abdomen
   d. none of these

2. Which mollusk would most likely filter its food out of the water?
   a. a clam
   b. a squid
   c. a snail
   d. a chiton

3. Which class of mollusks includes the bivalves?
   a. the chitons
   b. the head-footed mollusks
   c. the hatchet-footed mollusks
   d. the stomach-footed mollusks

4. Mollusks are classified by the
   a. shape of their shell
   b. shape of their foot
   c. type of their mantle
   d. size of their shell

5. Mollusks are hatchet-footed, stomach-footed, head-footed, or
   a. chitons
   b. bivalves
   c. shell-footed
   d. none of these

6. The octopus, squid, and nautilus are members of which class?
   a. round-bodied mollusks
   b. head-footed mollusks
   c. hatchet-footed mollusks
   d. stomach-footed mollusks

7. Which two are characteristics of echinoderms?
   a. endoskeleton, exoskeleton
   b. radula, univalve
   c. radial symmetry, endoskeleton
   d. tube feet, radula

8. Tube feet aid in
   a. swimming
   b. radial symmetry and moving
   c. movement and food gathering
   d. none of these
9. Which Echinoderms use their legs to "run" after prey?
   a. sea stars
   b. sand dollars
   c. brittle stars
   d. sea cucumber
10. How are sea stars and sea urchins similar?
   a. use tube feet for movement
   b. two shells
   c. long arms, long legs
   d. all of these

Matching. Match each word with its definition or description.
 1. used to classify mollusks
 2. body arranged around a central disk
 3. two hinged shells
 4. internal skeleton
 5. tissue that secretes the shell
 6. single shell
 7. contains mouth and sense organs
 8. used to move and gather food
 9. rough, scraping tongue
10. spiny-skinned sea animals

a. bivalve
b. echinoderm
c. endoskeleton
d. foot
e. head
f. mantle
g. radial symmetry
h. radula
i. tube feet
j. univalve

CHAPTER 8

ARTHROPODS

INTRODUCTION

How many animals in this picture do you recognize? Some may be familiar to you. Others you probably have never seen before. Although these animals may look quite different, they are all related. They are all invertebrates, belonging to the most extensive phylum in the animal kingdom. These animals are all arthropods. Arthropods (är′ thrō päd) include crustaceans (krus tā′ shən), spiders, centipedes, insects, and many others.

What is an arthropod? How do arthropods differ from each other? How do they live? You will explore answers to these and other questions as you study this chapter.

SECTION TITLES

All of these animals are arthropods.

8-1 CHARACTERISTICS OF ARTHROPODS

VOCABULARY
abdomen
antennae
book lung
compound eye
exoskeleton
facet
head
molt
simple eye
spiracle
thorax

OBJECTIVES

- Identify the characteristics of the arthropods.
- Describe the function of an exoskeleton.
- Explain the process of molting.
- Identify the major classes of arthropods.

Arthropods are invertebrates that have an exoskeleton and jointed legs. Members of this phylum are found almost everywhere on Earth. They live in rain forests, in deserts, in the soil, at the bottom of the ocean, in your home, and even on your body (fig. 8-1)! Scientists have identified nearly 900,000 different species of arthropods. The arthropod phylum contains more species than all the other animal phyla combined (fig. 8-2).

Fig. 8-1 The body mite lives on your skin.

RESEARCH IT
What is hemolymph?

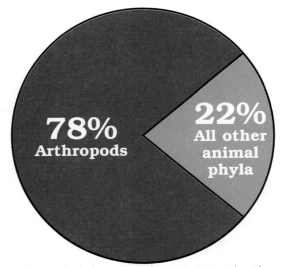

78% Arthropods

22% All other animal phyla

Fig. 8-2 The arthropod phylum contains more species than all the other animal phyla combined.

Arthropods range in size from the microscopic water flea to the huge spider crab that grows more than 3 m (12 ft) in diameter (fig. 8-3). They come in many shapes and colors. Some are easily visible; others are camouflaged so well it is hard to find them.

Fig. 8-3 The spider crab is the largest arthropod.

- A segmented body.
- An exoskeleton.
- Pairs of jointed legs.
- Most have eyes and one or more pairs of antennae.

Fig. 8–4 Arthropods share several common characteristics.

Although tremendous variation is evident in arthropods, they share several common features (fig. 8-4).

The segmented bodies of arthropods are often divided into three parts: the head, thorax, and abdomen. Look closely at the beetle in figure 8-5 and find these three parts. The segments that make up the **head** contain the sensory organs and the mouth. The segments that make up the **thorax** (thôr′ aks) connect the head to the abdomen and are where the legs and wings, if any, are attached. The **abdomen** is made up of the third set of segments and contains the digestive, respiratory, and reproductive structures.

Fig. 8–5 The beetle's body is made of a head, thorax, and abdomen.

If you have ever stepped on a bug or squashed a spider, you may have heard a crunch. This is the sound of the animal's outer covering cracking and breaking. This outer covering is called an **exoskeleton** (eks ō skel′ ə tən). Like a suit of armor, the exoskeleton protects against enemies and weather, prevents the animal from drying out, provides support for body organs and a place for muscles to attach, and allows for movement (fig. 8-6).

Although the exoskeleton is part of the animal, it is nonliving and does not grow as the animal grows. This makes the exoskeleton get too tight and makes it necessary for arthropods to **molt**, or shed, the old "skin" and replace it with a new one. This process occurs when the animal wiggles out of the old exoskeleton and emerges with a new, soft exoskeleton

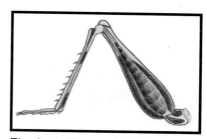

Fig. 8–6 The exoskeleton makes up the outer covering of arthropods.

that has been growing underneath (fig. 8-7). Once the old exoskeleton is discarded, the arthropod quickly makes itself as large as possible, stretching its new skeleton before it hardens. Once stretched, the new "skin" dries, and the arthropod is once again protected by a hard outer covering.

Fig. 8–7 When arthropods molt, they climb out of the old exoskeleton and emerge with a soft, new exoskeleton that quickly hardens.

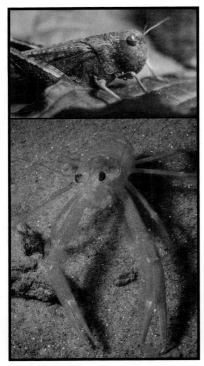

Fig. 8–8 All arthropods have legs and antennae.

Look at the animals in figure 8-8. What structures do they all have? If you said legs and antennae, you are right. All arthropods have one or more pairs of jointed legs. The joints allow the legs to bend and move. An arthropod's legs may be designed for walking, running, hopping, or swimming. Scientists use the number of legs to help classify arthropods.

Like many mollusks (snails and chitons), the primary sense organs of arthropods are **antennae** (fig. 8-9). These structures are extremely sensitive to chemical stimuli. They detect food, enemies, and potential mates. Antennae come in many sizes and shapes. Some arthropods have two pairs of antennae, while others only have one pair. The antennae serve as the main link between arthropods and their environment.

Fig. 8–9 Moths, crabs, and praying mantis, like all arthropods, use antennae to explore their surroundings.

In addition to antennae, most arthropods have eyes (fig. 8-10). The eyes of arthropods are of two types: simple eyes and compound eyes. **Simple eyes** have one lens and are sensitive to changes in light. **Compound eyes** are made up of hundreds of simple eyes called **facets**. These simple eyes work together to create a mosaiclike image (fig. 8-10). Compound eyes detect motion and color.

Like all animals, arthropods must breathe. Those in water breathe by gills. Land-dwelling arthropods breathe by special openings in the abdomen called **spiracles** (spir′ ə kəl). These openings lead to a system of air tubes, which branch into smaller and smaller tubes. When air enters through the spiracles, it travels through this system of tubes. In the smallest of the tubes, oxygen passes from the tubes into the cells, and carbon dioxide passes into the tubes and is carried outside the body. Some spiders also have **book lungs**, small air-filled sacs that look similar to pages in a book (fig. 8-11). These structures work along with the spiracles and allow for breathing.

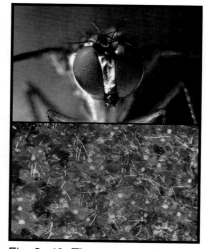
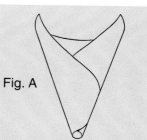

Fig. 8–10 The compound eyes of anthropods give a mosaic view of their surroundings.

TRY THIS 8-1: Pill Bug Race

Materials:

chalk
kite string - 50 cm
pill bugs (living) - 3

plastic cup
white paper (8.5 x 11)

Fig. A

Procedure:

1. Get three pill bugs and put them into the plastic cup. Observe.
   - What characteristics of the pill bug identify it as belonging to the arthropod phylum?
   - How many legs does a pill bug have?
2. Make a starting cone by folding and taping a sheet of paper as shown in figure A.
3. Find an area of sidewalk. Tie the chalk to one end of the string and draw a circle about 1 m in diameter.
4. Drop each pill bug into the cone. Once the pill bugs are in the cone, lift it and begin the race. Record the result.
5. Repeat step 4 two more times.
   - Was one of the three pill bugs consistently faster than the other two?
6. Pick your fastest pill bug and challenge other classmates to race their best pill bug against yours. Record the results of each race.
   - Was one pill bug clearly the winner in every race?
   - What advantage does speed have for a pill bug?
   - What are the main predators of the pill bug?

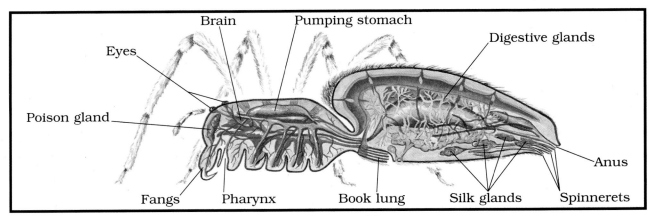

Fig. 8–11 Book lungs are one of several organs unique to spiders.

Although arthropods share a number of common characteristics, they are divided into several smaller groups, or classes. Classes of arthropods include crustaceans, arachnids, millipedes, centipedes, and insects (fig. 8-12).

CLASSES OF ARTHROPODS

Crustacean

Arachnid

Insect

Millipede

Centipede

Fig. 8–12

REVIEW IT

1. What are the main characteristics of arthropods?
2. What is the function of the exoskeleton?
3. Explain what occurs when an animal molts.
4. What are the main classes of arthropods?

8-2 CRUSTACEANS

OBJECTIVES

- Describe the characteristics of crustaceans.
- Identify examples of crustaceans.

The barnacle is one of nature's oddities (fig. 8-13). When it is young, the barnacle is shaped somewhat like a tadpole and swims about freely. After several weeks, dramatic changes take place. The young barnacle settles on a solid surface and positions itself so that it rests on its upper back and head (fig. 8-14). Then it secretes a powerful glue and cements itself permanently to the surface and begins to produce a hard, shell-like covering.

VOCABULARY
cephalothorax
crustacean

Fig. 8–13 Barnacles are often abundant on rocks and pilings.

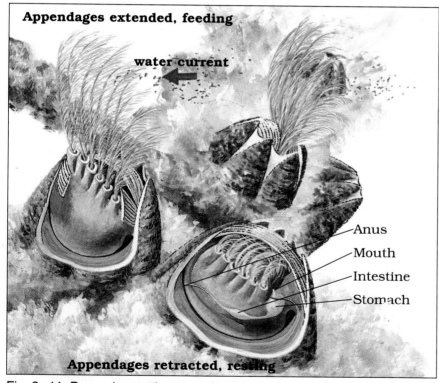

Appendages extended, feeding

water current

Anus

Mouth

Intestine

Stomach

Appendages retracted, resting

Fig. 8–14 Barnacles settle onto a hard surface, glue themselves to it, then secrete a hard, shell-like protective covering.

DID YOU KNOW?
One type of South Pacific crab climbs coconut trees, snips off the coconut and climbs down to eat it.

RESEARCH IT
What are statocysts?

Barnacles, crabs, crayfish, shrimp, and similar animals make up one class of arthropods called **crustaceans**.

Crustaceans are found both on land and in water (fig. 8-15). Although they may appear quite different from each other, crustaceans share several common characteristics summarized in figure 8-16.

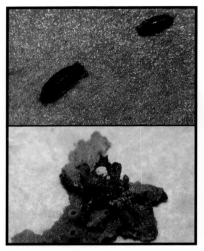

Fig. 8–15 The isopod (top) and the masking crab (bottom) are both crustaceans

CHARACTERISTICS OF CRUSTACEANS

- Body with two main segments.
  - **Cephalothorax** (sef ə lō thor′ aks), the fused head and thorax.
  - Abdomen.
- Five pairs of legs.
  - First pair has large claws used for defense and food gathering.
  - Other pairs of legs are used for movement.
- Two pairs of antennae.
  - Short pair used for touch, taste, and smell.
  - Long pair used for touch, taste, and balance.
- Breathe through gills.
- Compound eyes on movable stalks.

Examples: Crabs, shrimp, crayfish, and lobsters.

Fig. 8–16

Crustaceans are an important part of the food chain. Billions of microscopic crustaceans are found in the ocean, in rivers and streams, and in lakes and ponds. These tiny animals, as well as larger crustaceans, are a major food source for fish and other aquatic or marine animals. Some crustaceans—such as lobsters, crabs, and shrimp—are a staple of the human diet.

REVIEW IT

1. What are the main characteristics of crustaceans?
2. Name three examples of crustaceans.

CLASS ACTIVITY 8-2: Structure of a Crayfish

Question: What is the structure of a crayfish?

Materials:

balance	medicine dropper
crayfish (living)	metric ruler
dissecting pan	Special Master R201
food coloring	water
magnifying lens	

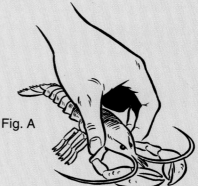

Fig. A

Procedure:
1. Obtain a crayfish and a Special Master.
2. Place the crayfish in the pan and cover it with water.
3. Pick the crayfish up by grasping it behind the pincers as shown in figure A. Find the structures labeled in the diagrams on the Special Master.
4. Continue examining the crayfish and record your observations.
5. Put the crayfish back into the pan of water. Draw a detailed diagram of your crayfish. Label the parts listed:

abdomen	cephalothorax	maxilliped	telson
antennae	cheliped	mouth	uropod
antennule	compound eye	rostrum	walking legs
anus	mandible	swimmerets	

6. Move your hand toward the crayfish. Observe what happens. Record.
7. Use the medicine dropper to place several drops of food color in the water over the middle of the cephalothorax. Observe what happens. Record.

Data:

Number of segments	
Number of legs/segment	
Total number of legs	
Mass	

	Antennae	Antennules	Chelipeds	Leg (avg.)	Abdomen
length (mm)					

Questions:
1. What characteristics help identify the crayfish as a crustacean?
2. When in the pan of water, in what direction does the crayfish move when you move your hand toward it? Explain.
3. What happens to the food coloring when placed above the cephalothorax? Why?
4. Why must water circulate around the body of the crayfish?
5. What is the function of the swimmerets?

Conclusion: Write 3–5 lines about what you learned from this activity.

8-3 ARACHNIDS, MILLIPEDES, AND CENTIPEDES

OBJECTIVES

- Describe the characteristics of arachnids.
- Explain how spiders are different from other arachnids.
- Distinguish between millipedes and centipedes.

Spiders, scorpions, mites, and ticks make up another class of arthropods called the **arachnids** (ə rak′ nid). Arachnids have exoskeletons, segmented bodies, and jointed legs like all other arthropods. But they also have several characteristics that differ from other arthropods, as summarized in figure 8-17.

Fig. 8–17

CHARACTERISTICS OF ARACHNIDS

- Body has two main segments.
  - Cephalothorax, the fused head and thorax.
  - Abdomen.
- Four pairs of legs.
- No antennae.
- Breathe through spiracles.
- Simple eyes.
- Strong sucking mouth parts.

Examples: Spiders, scorpions, ticks, and mites.

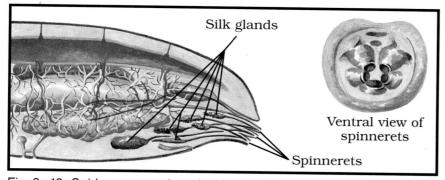

Fig. 8–18 Spiders are equipped with several kinds of silk glands. Each produces a different kind of silk.

DID YOU KNOW?
The sun spider can run 16 km/hr (10 mi/hr). This spider eats lizards.

Spiders represent the largest group of arachnids. Spiders are able to produce silk from special glands in their abdomens (fig. 8-18). As these glands produce silk, the hind legs pull the silk through special structures called **spinnerets** (spin ə ret'), which spin the silk into thin fibers used for building webs (fig. 8-19). Spiders have fangs near the mouth for injecting poison when they bite their prey. While the bites of black widows and brown recluses are poisonous to humans, most spider bites are harmless.

Mites and ticks make up the second-largest group of arachnids (fig. 8-20). Mites are the smallest arachnids. Some of these tiny creatures are parasites; others are predators on even smaller organisms. The bite of one species of mite, the chigger, causes extreme itching. Ticks are parasites that suck blood and fluids from their hosts (fig. 8-21). They may carry diseases such as Rocky Mountain spotted fever and Lyme disease. Humans who are bitten by infected ticks risk contracting disease.

Fig. 8–19 Spinnerets allow a spider to spin its web.

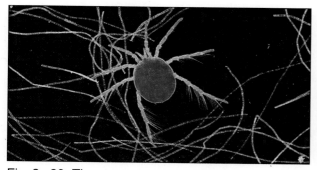

Fig. 8–20 The common water mite is an arachnid.

Fig. 8–21 Ticks carry Rocky Mountain spotted fever and Lyme disease.

Scorpions are another type of arachnid. These arthropods are easily recognized by the large stinger extending from the end of the abdomen (fig 8-22. The stinger contains a poison used to subdue prey. While the sting of a scorpion may be painful, most scorpions do not pose a serious problem to humans.

Fig. 8–22 The stinger of a scorpion is used to capture food and to protect against enemies.

Look at the two animals in figure 8-23. What difference do you see? The most obvious difference is the number of legs each animal has. The animal on the left is a millipede; the one on the right is a centipede. Millipedes and centipedes represent two more classes of arthropods. These arthropods have long bodies that are separated into many segments. While they look similar, millipedes and centipedes have distinct characteristics summarized in figure 8-24.

Fig. 8–23 The millipede (left) and the centipede (right) represent two classes of arthropods.

Fig. 8–24

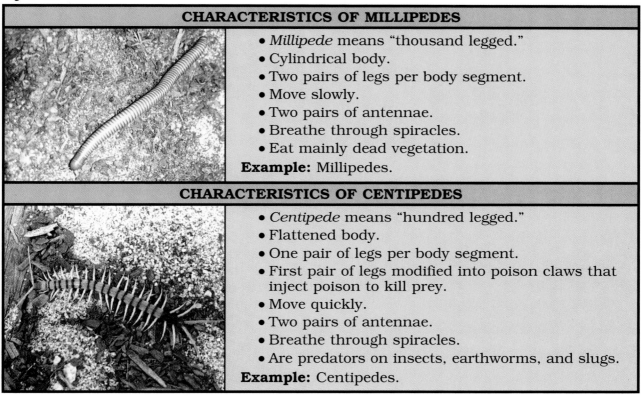

CHARACTERISTICS OF MILLIPEDES	
	• *Millipede* means "thousand legged." • Cylindrical body. • Two pairs of legs per body segment. • Move slowly. • Two pairs of antennae. • Breathe through spiracles. • Eat mainly dead vegetation. **Example:** Millipedes.
CHARACTERISTICS OF CENTIPEDES	
	• *Centipede* means "hundred legged." • Flattened body. • One pair of legs per body segment. • First pair of legs modified into poison claws that inject poison to kill prey. • Move quickly. • Two pairs of antennae. • Breathe through spiracles. • Are predators on insects, earthworms, and slugs. **Example:** Centipedes.

REVIEW IT

1. What are the main characteristics of arachnids?
2. How are spiders different from other arthropods?
3. How do centipedes and millipedes differ?

8-4 INSECTS

insect
larva
metamorphosis
nymph
pupa

OBJECTIVES

- Identify the characteristics of insects.
- Distinguish between incomplete and complete metamorphosis.
- Identify common insect orders and examples.
- Explain how insects are helpful and harmful.

A cockroach scurries up a wall, a honeybee searches for nectar in a wildflower, while a grasshopper munches on a blade of grass, and a dragonfly patrols the bank of a small creek (fig 8-25). What do all these animals have in common? They are all insects.

Scientists have identified more than 800,000 different kinds of insects, making them the largest class of arthropods (fig. 8-26). There are so many different kinds of insects that scientists estimate that two out of every three animals on Earth are insects.

Fig. 8-25 Dragonflies are often found near water.

RESEARCH IT
Find out what ecdysis is.

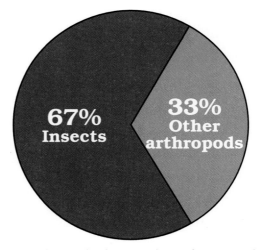

Fig. 8-26 Insects make up the largest class of arthropods.

DID YOU KNOW?
Scientists estimate that an acre of pasture land may contain as many as 360 million insects.

What is an insect? Some people believe that any small, quickly moving critter is a "bug" or insect. But many creatures thought to be insects are not. **Insects** represent a class of arthropods that have three body parts, six legs, usually one or two pairs of wings, as well as other characteristics (fig. 8-27).

CHARACTERISTICS OF INSECTS

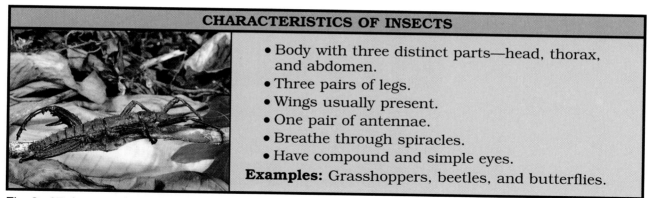

- Body with three distinct parts—head, thorax, and abdomen.
- Three pairs of legs.
- Wings usually present.
- One pair of antennae.
- Breathe through spiracles.
- Have compound and simple eyes.

Examples: Grasshoppers, beetles, and butterflies.

Fig. 8–27 Insects share common characteristics.

Insects range in size from species that are barely visible to giant 30 cm (12 in) walking sticks that live in tropical forests. Some are easily identified by their shape; others have such strange shapes they are difficult to recognize. Regardless of size and shape, all insects share the same basic body structure, as represented by the grasshopper in figure 8-28. Look at this diagram and learn about the parts of an insect.

Fig. 8–28

PARTS OF AN INSECT

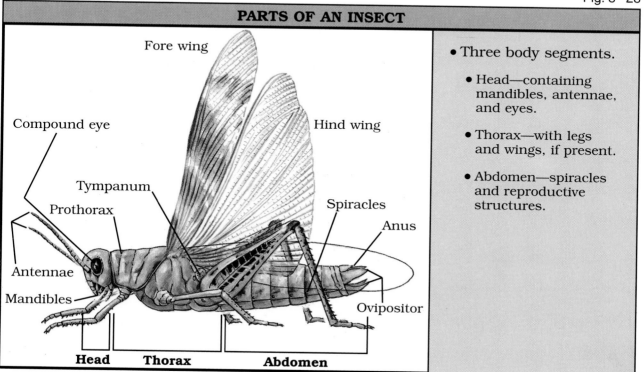

Fore wing, Compound eye, Hind wing, Tympanum, Prothorax, Spiracles, Anus, Antennae, Mandibles, Ovipositor

Head   Thorax   Abdomen

- Three body segments.
  - Head—containing mandibles, antennae, and eyes.
  - Thorax—with legs and wings, if present.
  - Abdomen—spiracles and reproductive structures.

Insects reproduce sexually when the male deposits sperm in a special sac in the body of the female. The eggs and sperm do not combine until the female is ready to deposit her eggs. She lays hundreds, sometimes thousands, of eggs. Even though a large number of eggs never develop into adults, the massive number of eggs laid guarantees many offspring.

Once a fertilized egg is laid, development begins. There are two patterns of development, or **metamorphosis** (met ə mor′ fə sis), in which insects mature from egg to adult: incomplete and complete. Incomplete metamorphosis involves three stages: the egg, nymph (nimf), and adult. Complete metamorphosis includes four stages: the egg, larva, pupa, and adult. Study figure 8-29 to learn what takes place in each of these forms of insect development.

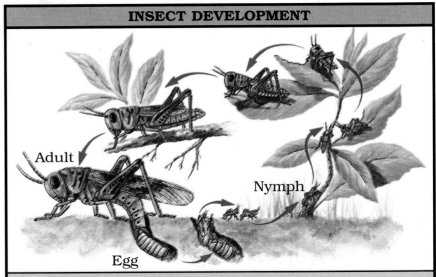

INSECT DEVELOPMENT

Adult

Nymph

Egg

Incomplete Metamorphosis

- The egg is laid.

- The egg hatches into a **nymph**, a young insect that looks like an adult but lacks wings.

- The growing nymph molts many times.

- After each molt the nymph has larger wings and looks more like an adult insect.

- The nymph eventually changes into an adult.

Fig. 8–29

Fig. 8–29 Continued

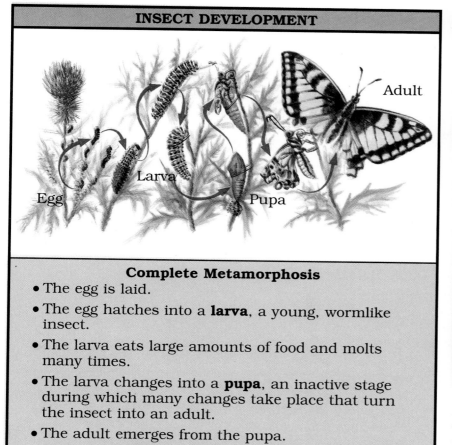

INSECT DEVELOPMENT

Egg

Larva

Pupa

Adult

Complete Metamorphosis

- The egg is laid.
- The egg hatches into a **larva**, a young, wormlike insect.
- The larva eats large amounts of food and molts many times.
- The larva changes into a **pupa**, an inactive stage during which many changes take place that turn the insect into an adult.
- The adult emerges from the pupa.

A

B

Fig. 8–30 Adaptations can be seen in the way insects are designed (a), in their coloration (b), and in the way they get food (c).

Insects are perhaps the most adaptable of all creatures. This adaptation is demonstrated by body structure, by shape and coloration, and by feeding habits (fig. 8- 30). The mouths of insects show particularly well their special design. The long, tubelike mouth of the butterfly is designed to suck nectar. The jaws of the grasshopper are designed to eat grass and other vegetation. The biting mouth parts of the giant water bug are just right for eating aquatic insects and small fish. And the spongelike mouthparts of the housefly are perfect for soaking up food left on desktops and kitchen counters.

Scientists classify insects into several different orders, including grasshoppers, termites, bugs, beetles, butterflies, flies, bees and wasps, and several others. Study figure 8-31 to learn names of these orders and examples.

Fig. 8–31

COMMON INSECT ORDERS		
	Order	**Example**
	Orthoptera (ôr thäp′ tər ə)	grasshoppers, crickets, cockroaches, praying mantis
	Isoptera (ī säp′ tə rə)	termites
	Odonata (ōd ə näd′ ə)	damselflies, dragonflies
	Hemiptera (hē mip′ tər ə)	true bugs
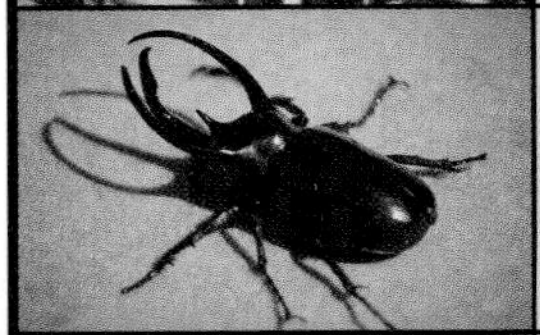	Coleoptera (kō lē äp′ tər ə)	beetles
	Lepidoptera (lep ə däp′ tər ə)	butterflies, moths
	Diptera (dip′ tər ə)	flies
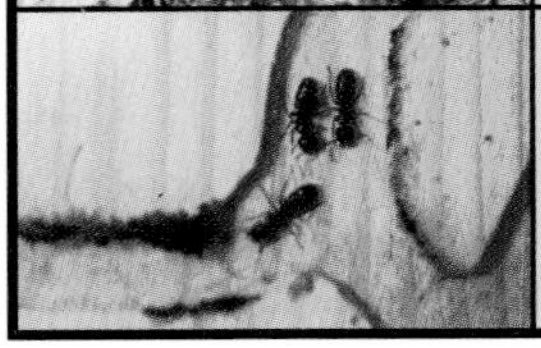	Hymenoptera (hī mə näp′ tər ə)	bees, wasps, ants

Many of these insects are important to humans. Some, like honeybees, are helpful because they pollinate valuable crops. Others, such as the lacewing and praying mantis, are important because they destroy harmful pests that destroy crops and carry disease (fig. 8-32).

Although many insects are beneficial, others create problems. The boll weevil and similar insects destroy billions of dollars worth of crops. Insects such as the mosquito spread malaria and yellow fever. Every year billions of dollars are spent trying to control the damaging effects of these insects (fig. 8-33).

Fig. 8-32 A parasitic wasp has laid its eggs on this harmful sphinx moth caterpillar. When the wasp larva hatch, they will feed on the caterpillar, preventing it from harming tomato crops.

Fig. 8-33 Insecticides are sprayed over large areas in an effort to kill harmful insects.

REVIEW IT

1. What are the characteristics of insects?
2. How do complete and incomplete metamorphosis differ?
3. List the order to which each insect belongs:
   a. praying mantis   d. damselfly
   b. housefly   e. termite
   c. ant   f. beetle
4. How are insects helpful? How are they harmful?

CHAPTER 8 WRAP-UP

THINKING SKILLS: Making a Table

A table is used to place a large amount of information in a relatively small space. Having information in a table makes it easier to see the information at a glance and makes it easier to pick out specific points and ignore those not needed. The paragraphs that follow discuss several common orders of insects. Read the information and organize it into the table on the Special Master R211.

Scientists organize the insect class into 27 different orders, based partly on wing structure and metamorphosis. Twelve of the most common insect orders are described in the following paragraphs.

The order Odonata includes dragonflies and damselflies. The order is named for the characteristic "teeth" these insects have. The "toothed" insects have two pairs of wings and undergo incomplete metamorphosis.

Orthoptera are the "straight-winged" insects. Grasshoppers, crickets, and cockroaches belong to this order. These insects have two pairs of wings and often have the third pair of legs larger than the other two pairs for jumping. Grasshoppers undergo incomplete metamorphosis.

Earwigs may not appear to have wings, but they do. The outer pair is quite small and skinlike. It covers the larger second pair. This characteristics identifies the order to which they belong, Dermaptera, meaning "skin-winged." Earwigs undergo incomplete metamorphosis.

Isoptera is the order termites belong to. The order name means "equal-winged" and is descriptive of the two pairs of wings that appear the same size and shape. Termites undergo complete metamorphosis.

One of the few orders of wingless insects is the order Anoplura. This order includes the sucking lice, which undergo complete metamorphosis.

Hemiptera means "half-winged." It is the order that includes the true bugs. Many of these insects are aquatic and undergo incomplete metamorphosis. Examples include backswimmers, waterstriders, and giant water bugs.

The cicadas belong to the order Homoptera, meaning "same-winged." These insects are characterized by one pair of wings that are the same. Cicadas undergo complete metamorphosis. In some species the pupa stage lasts for 21 years.

The lacewings, snake-flies, and dobsonflies have two pairs of wings that appear to have a network of tiny nerves that run through the wing. This characteristic gives their order the name Neuroptera, meaning "nerve-winged." Members of Neuroptera undergo complete metamorphosis.

Butterflies and moths are some of the most beautiful and showy of all insects. Lepidoptera, "scale-winged," is the order for these insects. If you have ever touched one of the four wings of a moth or butterfly, you may have noticed the "powdery scales" that rubbed off the wing. Members of Lepidoptera undergo complete metamorphosis.

One of the most common orders of insects is the flies. Flies have two wings and are assigned to the order Diptera, meaning "two-winged." These insects undergo complete metamorphosis.

Beetles belong to the largest order of insects, Coleoptera. The name means "sheath-winged." In beetles the thick outer wings protect the more membranous second pair. Beetles undergo complete metamorphosis.

Bees, wasps, hornets, and most of the stinging insects belong to the order Hymenoptera, meaning "membrane-winged." Members of Hymenoptera undergo complete metamorphosis and have two pairs of wings.

QUESTIONS AND PROBLEMS

1. A millipede having 87 body segments would have how many feet?
2. What would be the easiest way to tell if a specimen is an insect or a crustacean?
3. Since female insects lay hundreds of thousands of eggs at a time, why aren't there more insects in our environment?
4. Why do you think there are so many more arthropods than other animals?
5. Why don't arthropods get as large as reptiles or mammals?
6. What is the advantage of incomplete metamorphosis over complete metamorphosis?
7. What are book lungs? How are they similar to your lungs?
8. How do spiders that do not spin webs capture their food?
9. Why do animals that have just molted often seek a hiding place?
10. For what are antennae used?
11. In what ways do insects and arachnids differ?
12. Why does spreading a film of oil on stagnant water prevent mosquitoes from developing?

RESEARCH

1. Create a set of color posters that shows the life cycle of the monarch butterfly.
2. Many pesticides are harmful to the environment. Talk with a nursery employee or someone from the local department of agriculture to find out about biological control of pests. Develop an oral presentation that includes visual aids.
3. Do research on the two most common poisonous spiders in North America, the black widow and the brown recluse. On a map, mark the regions they occupy. Find their scientific names and place them on your map. Display in class.
4. Make a bulletin board illustrating the major classes of arthropods.
5. Use library resources to find out how to collect insects. Use the information you learn to make your own collection of local insects.

REVIEW

HIGHLIGHTS

1. Characteristics of arthropods include a segmented body, an exoskeleton, pairs of jointed legs, and one or more pairs of antennae.
2. The exoskeleton protects against enemies and weather, prevents the animal from drying out, provides support for body organs and a place for muscles to attach, and allows for movement.
3. Molting involves the shedding of the old exoskeleton and its replacement by a new one.
4. The major classes of arthropods include crustaceans, arachnids, millipedes, centipedes, and insects.
5. Crustaceans have two main body parts, five pairs of legs, two pairs of antennae, and compound eyes on movable stalks. They breathe with gills.
6. Examples of crustaceans include crabs, shrimp, and crayfish.

7. Arachnids have two main body parts, four pairs of legs, no antennae, simple eyes, and strong sucking mouth parts.

8. Arachnids include spiders, scorpions, ticks, and mites.

9. Unlike other arachnids, spiders produce silk and have poison fangs.

10. Millipedes have cylindrical bodies and two pairs of legs per body segment, eat vegetation, and move slowly. Centipedes have flattened bodies, one pair of legs per body segment, and a poison claw; are predators; and move quickly.

11. Insects have a body made up of a head, thorax, and abdomen; have three pairs of legs and one pair of antennae; breathe with spiracles; have compound and simple eyes; and usually have wings.

12. Incomplete metamorphosis has three stages: egg, nymph, and adult. Complete metamorphosis has four stages: egg, larva, pupa, and adult.

13. Insects have been able to adapt to many environments because of their different types of mouths, wings, legs, and coloration.

14. Some insects help people by pollinating flowers and crops, but other insects devour crops and carry disease.

VOCABULARY LIST

abdomen	exoskeleton	nymph
antennae	facet	pupa
arachnid	head	simple eye
book lung	insect	spinneret
cephalothorax	larva	spiracle
compound eye	metamorphosis	thorax
crustacean	molt	

PRACTICE

Multiple Choice. Choose the best answer.

1. What are three main characteristics of arthropods?
   a. molting, antenna, skeleton
   b. segments, wings, antennae
   c. jointed legs, head, thorax
   d. segments, exoskeleton, antennae

2. What are the three body parts of most arthropods?
   a. head, antenna, body
   b. exoskeleton, antenna, eyes
   c. head, abdomen, spiracles
   d. head, thorax, abdomen

3. The exoskeleton is replaced in a process known as
   a. molting
   b. metamorphosis
   c. regeneration
   d. none of these

4. Crustaceans have only two body parts, the
   a. cephalothorax and legs
   b. cephalothorax and antenna
   c. cephalothorax and abdomen
   d. head and abdomen

5. Which is true about arachnids?
    a. eight legs and no antennae
    b. six legs and two antennae
    c. four legs, two pinchers, two antennae
    d. none of these
6. How are spiders different from other arachnids?
    a. compound eyes, spiracles
    b. spiracles, antennae
    c. spinnerets, poison fangs
    d. cephalothorax, abdomen
7. Millipedes are unlike centipedes because they have
    a. more legs and move quickly
    b. round bodies and more legs
    c. strong mouth parts
    d. eat insects and worms
8. What is the basic body plan for insects?
    a. head, thorax, wings
    b. head, antennae, legs
    c. head, cephalothorax, abdomen
    d. head, thorax, abdomen
9. What are the stages of complete metamorphosis?
    a. egg-pupa-adult
    b. egg-larva-pupa-adult
    c. egg-nymph-adult
    d. none of these
10. How are insects helpful?
    a. they reproduce slowly
    b. they carry disease
    c. they hibernate during winter
    d. they pollinate crops

Matching. Match each word with its definition or description.
    1. contains the reproductive system
    2. air-filled sac
    3. provides support for body organs
    4. discarding of the exoskeleton
    5. fused head and thorax
    6. special openings for breathing
    7. spiders, ticks, and mites
    8. used to spin silk in making webs
    9. inactive stage of insect
    10. wormlike stage of insect

    a. abdomen
    b. arachnids
    c. book lungs
    d. cephalothorax
    e. exoskeleton
    f. larva
    g. molting
    h. pupa
    i. spinneret
    j. spiracle

CAREERS

Zoologist

Description of Work
Zoologists are life scientists who study animals. They observe animals both in their natural habitats and in the laboratory in order to learn as much as possible about animal life. Most zoologists are employed by colleges and universities, where they teach and do research.

Personal Qualifications
Zoologists must be interested in animals and like working with them. They must be able to cooperate with and communicate their ideas to other people. They need to use careful, precise methods in their work.

Requirements
A high-school diploma and four to eight years of college.

Career Information
American Institute of
  Biological Sciences
730 Eleventh Street, NW
Washington, DC 20001

Entomologist

Description of Work
Entomologists are life scientists who study insects and their relation to plant and animal life. Entomologists identify and classify species of insects. They aid in the control and elimination of insects that are hazards to farmland and buildings by developing improved pesticides.

Personal Qualifications
Entomologists must be willing to spend many hours outdoors and in remote areas studying rare species. They must also be able to tolerate unpleasant working conditions at times. They must be proficient in science and communication.

Requirements
A high-school diploma and four to eight years of college.

Career Information
American Entomological
  Society
1900 Race Street
Philadelphia, PA 19103

Microbiologist

Description of Work
Microbiologists are life scientists who study organisms that are so small that they must be viewed under a microscope. They study growth, structure, development, and general characteristics of bacteria and other microorganisms. These scientists study the distribution of microorganisms in nature as well as the ways in which they interact with other living things.

Personal Qualifications
Microbiologists must be able to work carefully and take precautions. They should be good at scientific experimentation and mathematics. Microbiologists must be able to work either independently or as part of a team.

Requirements
A high-school diploma and four to eight years of college.

Career Information
American Society for
  Microbiology
1325 Massachusetts Avenue,
  NW
Washington, DC 20005

Apiculturist

Description of Work
Apiculturists study bee culture and breeding. They conduct experiments regarding causes and controls of bee diseases. They also study the factors that affect the production of nectar and pollen in the plants visited by the bees. Apiculturists improve the successive generations of bees by selective breeding.

Personal Qualifications
Apiculturists must enjoy working outdoors and have an interest in bees.

Requirements
A high-school diploma and two years of college.

Career Information
American Beekeeping
  Federation
P.O. Box 998
Gessup, GA 31545

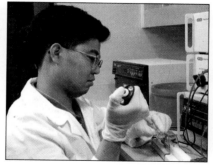

Genetic Engineering Research Assistant

Description of Work
A genetic engineering research assistant works with research scientists in developing and testing of genetically engineered products. Genetic engineering often involves isolating and altering genetic material from one organism and transplanting it into another. Research assistants are employed by chemical or pharmaceutical companies or may work in medical research facilities.

Personal Qualifications
Research assistants must be able to follow instructions precisely. They should enjoy doing extremely meticulous work and maintaining accurate, detailed records.

Requirements
A high-school diploma and two to four years of college. Most hiring companies provide on-the-job training.

Career Information
Alliance for Engineering in
  Medicine and Biology
1101 Connecticut Avenue, NW
Washington, DC 20036-4303

Cytogenetic Technologist

Description of Work
A cytogenetic technologist prepares, examines, and analyzes chromosomes found in biological specimens to aid in diagnosis and treatment of genetic diseases. Their long-term research focuses on finding the cause and cure of genetic diseases. They then report the results to physicians.

Personal Qualifications
Cytogenetic technologists must enjoy doing meticulous work. They must be very careful in experimentation. They also must have good communication skills.

Requirements
A high-school diploma and two to four years of college.

Career Information
National Genetics Foundation
180 West 58th Street
New York, NY 10019

UNIT II

THE GREAT SABOTAGE

INTRODUCTION

"Look out! Here it comes!" someone yells as the raft heads for the waterfall. Seconds later, WHOOSH! The raft is flooded by gallons of water, and all on board are soaked to the skin. At the end of the ride through the rapids, the group of friends step from their raft laughing and shouting, ready to go again.

God designed us to be able to enjoy all of life's exciting events. He planned that our lives would be an unending series of adventures and discoveries. He wanted us to be happy while we behaved responsibly. But Satan changed all that. He took many of the greatest experiences God planned for us and destroyed their beauty, making them a source of conflict and unhappiness.

In this unit you will take a look at God's original plan, how Satan sabotaged it, and the results of his sabotage.

CHAPTER TITLES

White-water rafting with friends is great fun!

CHAPTER 9

WHAT HAPPENED TO THE PLAN?

INTRODUCTION

"In the beginning God created. . . ." Everyone knows the story of creation. Everyone can name the first human beings—Adam and Eve. They are the parents of the human race. But what does that story have to do with you today? One reason the story is relevant to you at this stage of your life is that it lays out God's plan for human sexuality.

SECTION TITLES

Young parents enjoying their new baby is part of God's plan.

9–1 SEXUAL FEELINGS

OBJECTIVES

- Explain what sexual feelings are.
- Describe what happens at puberty.
- Explain why sexual feelings begin at puberty.

SCENE ONE

"Give this to Jerry, but don't let him know I gave it to you," Sherrie whispered.

"Oh, I'd never tell," Pam said as she slipped the note inside her book.

Pam waited until lunchtime to deliver the note, then watched Jerry as he read it (fig. 9-1). She knew Sherrie would want to know how Jerry reacted to what the note said.

Fig. 9–1 Pam watches Jerry's reaction to Sherrie's note.

Fig. 9–2 The bookbag was hidden behind the trash container.

SCENE TWO

Ron had done it again! He had managed to take Alice's bookbag when she wasn't looking (fig. 9-2). He was sure he had hidden it where she would never find it, unless someone told on him. What would she say this time? Last time she threatened never to talk to him again, but he didn't think she meant it.

When class ended, Alice started to pack up her books. Where was her bookbag? She asked several friends, then looked at Ron. He was gazing out the window, although he was acutely aware of Alice's search.

"Ron, have you seen my bookbag?" Alice asked.

"Want me to help you look for it?" Ron answered. She spoke to him! Now he could spend time with her while he "helped" her look. He would make sure that it was a long search!

SCENE THREE

The volleyball game was full of action. The teams were fairly balanced, and the score was close. But most exciting of all to Linda was that she was playing next to Larry, the best athlete in school.

"Spike it," several team members shouted as Larry jumped for the ball (fig. 9-3).

Larry slammed the ball over the net. As he came back down, his arm landed on Linda's shoulder.

"Sorry about that," Larry said.

"No problem," Linda said. "That was a great play."

Which of these three scenes shows students expressing sexual feelings? The answer is, "All three." Feelings of attraction between male and female, boys and girls, are **sexual feelings**, and they can be expressed in many ways. The desire to be noticed by another person, to be touched by someone you like, and to tell someone you think he or she is special are ways of expressing sexual feelings.

Fig. 9–4 Most students become aware of sexual feelings during junior-high school.

Boys and girls usually become aware of sexual feeling when they reach puberty (fig. 9-4). **Puberty** is the time when a child grows into a teenager and becomes sexually mature. It occurs when hormones cause the reproductive glands to develop. This usually happens between the ages of 10 to 14

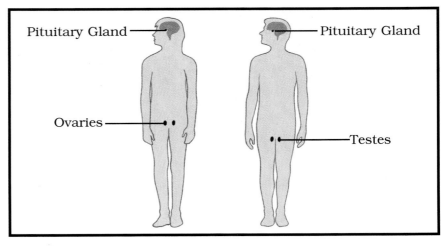

Fig. 9–5 The pituitary gland in the brain secretes a hormone that stimulates the testes and ovaries to begin producing male or female hormones.

for girls and 11 to 16 for boys. You may remember that puberty begins when the **pituitary** (pi tōō′ ə tər ē) **gland**, a small pea-sized gland at the base of the brain, begins to secrete the growth hormone (fig. 9-5). This stimulates the sex glands, **testes** in boys and **ovaries** in girls, to secrete male and female hormones. The male hormone, **testosterone** (tes täs′ tər ōn), causes the development of male characteristics in boys. In girls, **estrogen** (es′ trə jən), the female hormone, causes the development of female characteristics.

The same hormones that cause the physical changes of puberty also set the stage for emotional changes. Because puberty often occurs in girls at an earlier age than in boys, girls usually experience these changes sooner than boys.

Finding wholesome ways to express these natural human emotions will take patience on your part and guidance from parents and teachers (fig. 9-6).

Fig. 9−6 Eating together is a good way of getting to know people.

REVIEW IT

1. What are sexual feelings?
2. What causes these feelings to occur during puberty?

9-2 GOD'S PLAN

OBJECTIVES

• Describe God's plan for sexual relationships.
• Identify reasons why God made humans sexual beings.

Fig. 9-7 Young children enjoy playing make-believe with their toys.

Most seventh and eighth graders have sexual thoughts and feelings. It's a normal part of growing up. Understanding these thoughts and feelings—and acting on them wisely—are necessary for your future happiness. You are past the age of playing make-believe with dolls or trucks (fig. 9-7). You have reached the age when you are beginning to think seriously about what you want from life when you become an adult.

In a survey, some young people about your age, and a little older, were asked what they wanted most from adult life. A frequent response was that they wanted to love and marry one person and to stay with that person always. These young people recognized that to be happy, they need to be secure with the one they love—and to be secure, they need to entrust their lives to one person. They understood that you never forget the first person with whom you share sexual intimacy, and that you never get over the loss if it is not a lasting relationship. More and more young people are pledging publicly that they want to be sexually abstinent until marriage. They want the first person they have sex with to be their husband or wife. They are pledging to wait until marriage to have sex (fig. 9-8).

Fig. 9-8 Many adolescents are making public pledges to be sexually abstinent.

Over the years, many people have shared these same feelings. Why do they feel this way? Why do words in love songs talk about "always" and "forever"? Even children's fairy tales end with the prince and princess getting married and living "happily ever after." And if you've listened carefully at the weddings you've attended, you know the vows include the words "till death do us part," or a modern wording of the same idea.

Why? Because we know from instinct and experience that separation brings loneliness and hurt. The closer we are to someone, the greater can be the hurt if we are separated. We need to be close, but we need to know that we will not be betrayed or abandoned. The promise made to one another at the marriage ceremony gives the best opportunity for this security (fig. 9-9). God understood this need even before He created people. At the beginning of this world, when God created man and woman, He also created sex. "Therefore shall a man leave his father and his mother, and shall cleave unto his wife: and they shall be one flesh" (Genesis 2:24). Sexuality is a gift God has given us.

God made us sexual beings for two important reasons. One is so that we can reproduce, or have children. Adam and Eve had a whole planet all to themselves. God could have created other humans to live here, but, instead, He gave us the joy of sharing in the creative process by having our own children (fig. 9-10). The love that results in the birth of the children is the foundation of a home and helps ensure that mothers and fathers will love and care for their children.

Fig. 9-9 God designed marriage as the best setting for sexual relations.

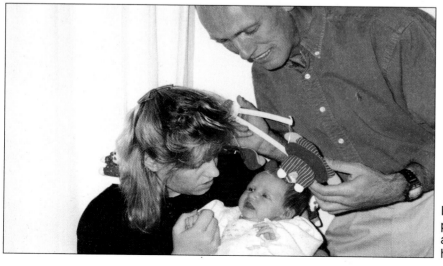

Fig. 9-10 In God's plan, the love parents have for each other is also expressed in the love they have for their children.

Fig. 9–11 The intimacy of a husband and wife is not to be shared with anyone else.

The other reason God gave us the gift of sexuality is so that a husband and wife can be close and intimate in a way that they share with no other person (fig. 9-11). This relationship strengthens the ties of love and binds husband and wife together. Within marriage, sexual love brings joy and satisfaction—happiness and contentment. A marriage broken by death leaves the remaining spouse feeling that part of him or her has died. A marriage broken by divorce leaves one or both persons feeling as if they have lost part of themselves—and so they have.

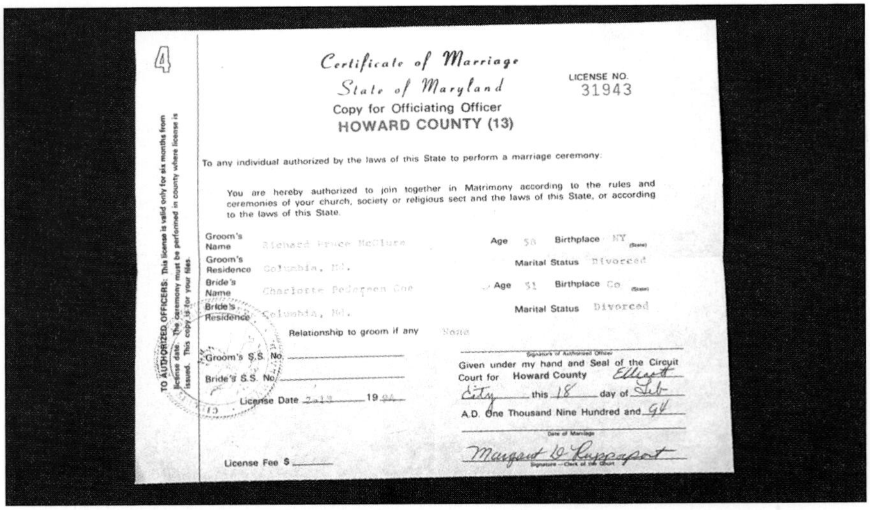

Fig. 9–12 A marriage certificate is a symbol of lifelong commitment.

This closeness, and the pledge in marriage always to be there for each other, is the basis for building a home (fig. 9-12). In the home husband and wife can enjoy each other's company and share the fun and the work of life together. Together they can bring up the children their love created. This security and constant sharing is what makes the sexual relationship fulfilling. Some people think that sexual intimacy is a way to get to know someone. Not true. Sexual intimacy is most fulfilling with the person who shares all parts of your life, the one to whom you have pledged yourself in marriage. This is God's plan!

REVIEW IT

1. What was God's original plan for sexual relationships?
2. Why did God make humans sexual beings?

9-3 GOD'S PLAN SABOTAGED

OBJECTIVES

- Explain how Satan sabotaged God's plan for sexual relationships.
- Compare God's plan for sex with Satan's sabotage.

God is interested in our happiness, pleasure, and well-being. Satan is not! Things that would bring as much happiness and goodness to people as marriage, homes, and sexual love came under early attack by Satan. As with all the Creator's work, Satan set about to sabotage (sab′ ə täzh) this plan in several different ways:

Satan's Sabotage of God's Plan

1. He tried to destroy the concept of faithfulness in marriage.

2. He tried to destroy the ideal of sexual abstinence until marriage.

3. He tried to destroy the reproductive system through disease.

4. He tried to destroy our values by enticing us with cheap substitutes for the real thing.

5. He tried to suggest ways of experiencing sexuality that differ from God's plan.

From the time sin first entered this world, people have practiced immoral sexual relations. We find many examples of Satan's sabotage in Bible times (fig. 9-13). People divorced and remarried; some sold their bodies for money; others

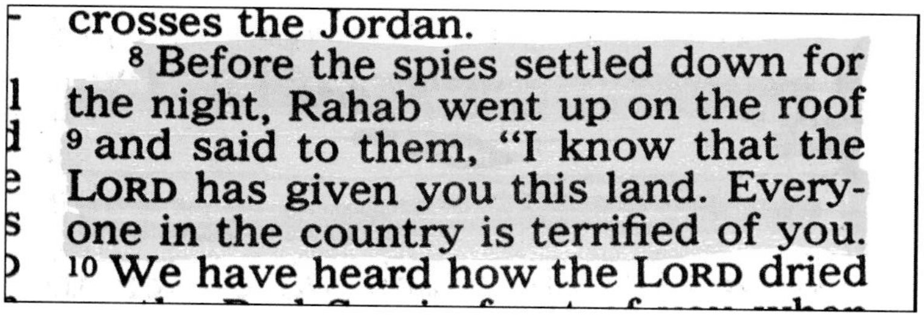

crosses the Jordan.
⁸ Before the spies settled down for the night, Rahab went up on the roof ⁹ and said to them, "I know that the LORD has given you this land. Everyone in the country is terrified of you. ¹⁰ We have heard how the LORD dried

Fig. 9–13 Although Rahab worked as a prostitute in Jericho, God used her to rescue the two Israelite spies.

practiced sexual activity with persons of the same sex or had sexual relations outside of marriage; and many—even some of the patriarchs—married more than one wife. Throughout human history Satan has brought misery from something God intended to bring happiness.

Satan is still working today. The practices of Bible times are still in existence. Anyone watching television can be led to believe that sex outside of marriage is good, that divorce and remarriage are normal, and that any kind of sex is everyone's right. Figure 9-14 outlines some of the differences between God's plan for us and Satan's substitute.

God's Plan	Satan's Substitute
• Heterosexual relationships.	• Homosexual relationships.
• Sexual intimacy with one's marriage partner.	• Sex with any willing partner.
• Tender care of the newborn.	• Destruction of the unborn.
• Respect for others' sexuality.	• Disrespect for others' sexuality.
• Loving acts of oneness.	• Forced acts of violence.

Fig. 9–14

The young people mentioned in the survey on page 212 are making not only the right decision, but also a wise one. They will avoid the hurt of a broken trust and the damage to future relationships. They will also escape the feelings of guilt and unworthiness that often go along with sex before marriage. Most important, they will be following God's plan for happiness.

REVIEW IT

1. List several ways Satan sabotaged God's plan for sexual expression.
2. What are the effects of Satan's sabotage?

CLASS ACTIVITY 9-3: The Media and Satan's Sabotage

Question: How much of Satan's sabotage is featured in our most common forms of media?

Materials:
Special Master R239

Procedure:
1. Discuss with your parents what you have been studying about Satan's sabotage of God's plan for sexuality. Decide with your parents which of the following options would be best for you to research.
2. Choose one of the following media:
    a. Review one issue of a news magazine (*Time, Newsweek,* or *US News and World Report*) and look for examples of Satan's sabotage (include advertising).
    b. Review one issue of an entertainment/variety magazine (*People, US,* or *Life*) and look for examples of Satan's sabotage (include advertising).
    c. View one hour of prime-time television (beginning at 8:00 p.m.) on one of the major networks (ABC, CBS, NBC, or CBC) and look for examples of Satan's sabotage.
3. Briefly describe each example and identify the area of sabotage each example illustrates, using the Sabotage Codes at the bottom of the chart.
4. Record the number of pages/minutes containing each example.
5. Record the percentage of pages/minutes devoted to the sabotage.

Data:

Example Description	Sabotage Code	Negative Pages/Min
Total number of pages/min of sabotage = _____		
Total percent of magazine/TV program involving sabotage = _____		

Sabotage Code: 1 = family   3 = premarital sex   5 = child abuse
                        2 = marriage   4 = homosexuality   6 = sexual violence

Questions:
1. What was the most common type of sabotage?
2. Was the sabotage more common in the advertising, content, or both?
3. What influence do these negative examples of Satan's sabotage have on the reader/viewer?
4. How much effect does this have on the reader's/viewer's values?

Conclusion: Write 3–5 sentences about what you learned from this activity.

9-4 SEXUAL ISSUES

abortion
date rape
gay
heterosexual
   orientation
homosexual
   orientation
incest
lesbian
prostitution
rape
sexual abuse
sexual harassment

OBJECTIVES

- Identify sexual issues in today's society.
- Analyze these issues in light of God's original plan.

Because God's plan for sexual behavior is so widely ignored, people have a variety of ideas about what is right and wrong (fig. 9-15). These differences of opinion about sexual behavior in society become sexual issues. None of today's sexual issues are new. Most have been debated since ancient times, although people's ideas about them have changed from one generation to another. As you consider these issues, consider how each is a sabotage of God's original plan and what a Christian's position should be.

DID YOU KNOW?

God condemns many sexual practices that are issues today. In First Corinthians, He says, "Do not be deceived: Neither the sexually immoral nor idolaters nor adulterers nor male prostitutes nor homosexual offenders nor theives nor the greedy nor drunkards nor slanderers nor swindlers will inherit the kingdom of God" (1 Corinthians 6:9, 10, NIV).

Fig. 9–15 Many magazines, TV shows, and movies promote inappropriate sexual behavior.

HOMOSEXUALITY

God created men and women to be attracted to each other. This is **heterosexual orientation** (ôr ē en tā′ shən), which leads ideally to marriage, homes, and children. Men who are attracted to other men and women to other women have a **homosexual orientation**. A homosexual woman is sometimes called a **lesbian** (lez′ bē ən). A homosexual man may be called **gay**. Scientists are not in agreement as to why some people have a homosexual orientation. Christians believe that this is part of Satan's effort to sabotage God's plan for men and women. A person with a homosexual orientation, however, need not practice homosexual behavior. Homosexual behaviors were not part of God's plan.

Most young people about your age have close friends of the same sex. This does not mean that they are homosexual. These friendships provide an opportunity to practice unselfishness, thoughtfulness, and putting someone else first—qualities they will need when they begin to have close friendships with someone of the opposite sex.

PROSTITUTION

Selling one's body for sexual activity is called **prostitution**. Prostitutes appear in several Bible stories, and the practice is still common today. Prostitution is promoted by poverty and the use of drugs. People who see no other way to earn a living may become prostitutes. Sadly, runaway teenagers sometimes become prostitutes when they think they have no place to live and no money for food or drugs, or when they have been sexually abused. But there are always ways for young people to get help. Prostitution is not the answer.

In most places prostitution is illegal, and both prostitutes and the persons buying their services can be arrested. But arrest is not the worst outcome. Loss of self-respect, high risk of sexually transmitted diseases, suffering, and sometimes murder are common dangers for both the prostitute and the customer. Prostitution and its accompanying dangers are certainly not part of God's plan.

ABORTION

Abortion is the premature termination of a pregnancy, and it is one of the most controversial issues today (fig. 9-16). A woman may want to end a pregnancy for a variety of reasons. The pregnancy may pose a serious threat to her health or life. The doctor may have diagnosed the unborn child with a serious defect. The pregnancy may have been caused by rape or incest. Sometimes, however, the mother may just not want a baby, or not want a baby at the time. This is often the case with teenagers who are not married,

Fig. 9-16 Abortion is a controversial issue in our society.

who do not want anyone to know they are pregnant, who have have not finished school, or who have no way to take care of a baby. Whatever the reason, the decision to have an abortion is a serious one. It presents the father, as well as the mother, with a moral dilemma. Whatever the reason, is it important enough to end a potential human life? Once an abortion is performed, nothing can undo the decision.

The decision to have an abortion is also a health issue. The abortion may cause immediate or future physical problems. Sometimes women who have abortions are unable to have children in the future. Even when it doesn't cause physical problems, having an abortion always leaves emotional scars on those involved. Although the abortion is performed on the woman, the father, grandparents, and others may be affected as well.

At one time abortions were illegal in the United States, Canada, and Bermuda. Today, in most places, this is a decision that is usually made by the woman and her doctor. Making this decision is traumatic and should be made only after appropriate counseling and much prayer. Unmarried teenagers need the help of parents and other caring adults if they are pregnant. They need to know that abortion is not the only answer to the problem. Personal decisions about abortion always should be made according to a study of the Scriptures and the laws of God regarding life and death. Abortion is not part of God's original plan!

RAPE

Forcing sexual acts on individuals without their permission is called **rape**. Rape is an act of violence, as well as an act of sex. The rates of rape are now so high in North America that one in three females will be raped in her lifetime. **Date rape**, or rape that occurs between two people who are friends or acquaintances, is more common than rape by a stranger. As many as 75 percent of all rapes are committed by acquaintances. Figure 9-17 lists warning signs of potential sexual violence and protective steps against sexual violence. Forcing sexual acts on someone is not God's plan!

WARNING SIGNS OF POTENTIAL SEXUAL VIOLENCE
• Emotional or verbal abuse.
• Taking control, such as demanding you stop seeing certain friends.
• Excessive jealousy, suspicion, or mistrust.
• Heavy drinking or drug use.
• A history of childhood violence; having been abused by parents.
• Inability to handle frustrations.
• Cruelty to animals.

PROTECTIVE STEPS AGAINST SEXUAL VIOLENCE
• Avoid being alone with anyone who makes unwanted sexual advances.
• Do not make friends with those who use alcohol or drugs.
• Avoid dangerous areas.
• Be home at a reasonable time.
• Contact your local social services if you are the target of sexual abuse or harassment.
• Pray for God's protection.

Fig. 9–17

SEXUAL ABUSE

In **sexual abuse**, an adult forces another adult or a child into sexual acts. Often the abuser is a family member or friend living with the family. It can even be a parent, teacher, or pastor. When the abuser is a family member, the sexual abuse is called **incest**. Usually the abuser wants to keep the sexual activity a secret and threatens to punish or even to kill the victim if he or she tells. When the abuser is someone the child loves or trusts, the threat to withhold love may be enough to secure silence. This causes fear, hurt, and even despair to the abused. Often the abused is made to feel guilty, **even though it is never the victim's fault**. The abuser is the one who is guilty.

All types of sexual abuse are illegal and should be reported to a trusted adult (fig. 9-18). Only in this way can the one abused be protected and save others from being abused also. How do you think God feels about sexual abuse?

Fig. 9–18 Any instances of abuse should be reported to a trusted adult.

SEXUAL HARASSMENT

Unwanted teasing, badgering, or heckling because of gender is **sexual harassment** (hə ras′ mənt). Sexual harassment by a person of the opposite sex or the same sex can take many forms. Comments, jokes, looks, or physical contact that has sexual overtones are types of sexual harassment. Although you may not think sexual harassment can occur in the classroom, it sometimes does, and should be reported to a teacher, principal, or parent.

In most places, laws protect people from sexual harassment when they have told the offender to stop (fig. 9-19). Laws also provide procedures to punish those who choose to continue this negative behavior.

Current thinking on each of these issues changes from time to time in society, but God's plan for us does not change. Following His plan cannot protect you from all the evil in society, but it can protect you from much heartache and grief for yourself and others.

As you know, not every person in the world has chosen to obey God and to reject Satan. People who live on this planet at the end of time will see Satan try to sabotage every plan God has made. Only Christ's coming will bring an end to evil. You, however, can make the choice today to live your life according to God's plan.

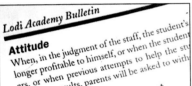

Fig. 9–19 All schools have policies to protect students from sexual harassment.

REVIEW IT

1. What are some sexual issues in our society?
2. How would following God's original plan for sexual expression prevent problems relating to sexual issues?

9-5 PRINCIPLES TO LIVE BY

OBJECTIVES

- Identify guidelines for sexual behavior that help a person fulfill God's plan.
- Identify appropriate ways of expressing sexual feelings as a teenager.

Good relationships are built on respect—respect for yourself and for other people. Though intense at times, sexual feelings are temporary; today you may be very fond of a person, but six months from now the feelings may be gone.

Respect and friendship, on the other hand, build over time (fig. 9-20). People who really care for you respect your values and decisions. They care when you do well and share your feelings when things don't go well. People who respect you will not use you to satisfy their own desires. They will not encourage you to do something that is morally wrong. They will not ask you to break any of God's laws.

Fig. 9-20 Loving relationships are built over many years.

Materials:
   Special Master R233

Procedure:
1. Obtain a Special Master and follow the directions.
2. Discuss your responses with your classmates.

MINIBIOGRAPHYMINIBIOGRAPHYMINIBIOGRAPHYMINIBIOGRAPHYMINIBIOGRAPHY

Eunice Diaz

Eunice Diaz, a Latino health educator, was born in Puerto Rico. She completed degrees at Loma Linda University, first in physical therapy, then both a master of science and a master of public health degree in health education. She served as a health educator for the Los Angeles County Health Department for 10 years, becoming a household name because she so often appeared on radio and television, speaking about public-health issues. Later, she used her knowledge of the county and the health problems of its people to administer programs in the University of Southern California School of Medicine and the White Memorial Hospital.

She is best known, however, for her work with AIDS. She was involved with the first reported cases of this new disease in 1981 and has made it her life-work. The Hispanic community asked her to be their spokesperson and to advocate for assistance to their members who were living, and dying, with AIDS. In 1988, President George Bush recognized the quality of her work by naming her as a member of the National Commission on AIDS, a position she held for five years. She developed educational materials and videos for students, for families, and for health-care workers. She has worked with the AIDS epidemic in Puerto Rico, the Dominican Republic, and Argentina. She has made it her special work to help ministers and church members alike to know how best to work with persons living with AIDS. The National Council of La Raza awarded her their highest honor for the significant contribution she has made to the health of Latinos.

MINIBIOGRAPHYMINIBIOGRAPHYMINIBIOGRAPHYMINIBIOGRAPHYMINIBIOGRAPHY

TRY THIS 9-5B: Assertiveness Inventory

Materials:
Special Master R235

Procedure:
1. Obtain a Special Master and follow the directions.
   - What is your average score?
2. Give your sheet to a friend and have him or her rate your assertiveness.
   - How does your friend's rating of you compare to your own rating? Explain.
   - How assertive are you? Very, somewhat, a little, not very.
   - What advantage is there in being assertive?
   - What disadvantage is there in being assertive?

Guidelines for sexual behavior include choosing to follow God's plan and to make friends among those who share your moral values and goals in life. A Christian school and church are places where you can make such friendships. Teenagers can safely express their sexual feelings by choosing activities that demonstrate caring, yet set specific limits. Look at the suggested list in figure 9-21. Add others to the list as you discuss them in class or with your parents. Chapter 10 presents suggested limits for sexual behavior, as well as reasons for those limits.

APPROPRIATE WAYS OF EXPRESSING SEXUAL FEELINGS
• Join in group activities.
• Enjoy sports activities together.
• Join musical groups together.
• Study together in groups.
• Show additional courtesy.
• Go on a church mission project together.
• Give small gifts to each other.

Fig. 9–21 Adolescents have many healthy and appropriate ways to express sexual feelings.

REVIEW IT

1. On what are good relationships built?
2. List several appropriate ways of expressing sexuality.

CHAPTER 9 WRAP-UP

THINKING SKILLS: Identifying the Main Idea

Scientists find it necessary to identify the main idea of paragraphs or articles so they can organize the information or ideas expressed. Organizing main ideas of an article allows scientists to better understand and use what they read.

In this activity you are to match supporting ideas with the main ideas they correspond to. Put the letter of the main idea on the blank provided for each supporting idea.

Actions That Support Abstinence
A. Develop a high self-esteem.
B. Have clear goals.
C. Use decision-making skills in advance.
D. Be involved with your family.
E. Choose responsible friends.
F. Avoid tempting situations.
G. Avoid alcohol and other drugs.
H. Choose entertainment that promotes a healthy sexuality.

1. _____ Go out in groups, not alone in couples.
2. _____ Become involved in school activities.
3. _____ Work hard to get the best grades you can get.
4. _____ Avoid music and magazines or books that condone premarital/extramarital sex.
5. _____ Decide what you will say if someone pressures you to have sexual relations.
6. _____ Develop self-discipline.
7. _____ Participate in family outings.
8. _____ Avoid drugs that interfere with reason and judgment.
9. _____ Think about what you want in the future.
10. _____ Choose friends who engage in healthful behaviors.
11. _____ Spend time at home with a boyfriend/girlfriend when your parents are present.
12. _____ Eat dinner with your family at least once a week.
13. _____ Leave a party if alcohol or drugs are being used.
14. _____ Avoid watching movies that encourage casual sex.
15. _____ Choose friends who have chosen to be abstinent.

QUESTIONS AND PROBLEMS

1. What needs did God create in humans?
2. What is date rape?
3. What prostitute in the Old Testament was promised protection because of her kindness to men of Israel?
4. Why are group activities among teenagers better than couple dating?
5. Why is Satan so interested in sabotaging God's gift of sexuality?
6. How is sexual harassment different from the teasing that takes place between teenage boys and girls?
7. How does security, love, and companionship in a family help a teenager in that family?
8. How should prostitutes and homosexuals be treated?
9. Why should sexual intimacy be saved for marriage?
10. How is alcohol a factor in today's violence?
11. What do you think is the greatest damage caused by Satan's sabotage of God's plan for sex?
12. What health risks are associated with prostitution?

RESEARCH

1. Use library resources to find several cultures in the world that allow polygamy. Prepare an oral presentation on your findings.
2. Make a bulletin-board display that teaches how to reduce the risk of sexual violence.
3. Interview an unwed teenage mother to find out what difficulties she has experienced. Write a report on your findings.
4. Find out what the policy of your school is regarding sexual harassment and the related disciplinary actions. Make a color poster that displays your findings.
5. Research to find the number of marriages and divorces of the past five years in the United States and Canada. Draw a graph that illustrates your findings.
6. Use library resources to describe the positions of Pro-Choice and Pro-Life supporters. Write a report that compares positive and negative aspects of these two positions. Include a discussion of your view and an explanation.

REVIEW

HIGHLIGHTS

1. Sexual feelings are feelings of attraction between males and females, boys and girls.
2. At puberty the pituitary gland begins to secrete growth hormone. This hormone stimulates the sex glands (testes in boys, ovaries in girls) to secrete sex hormones. The male sex hormone, testosterone, causes the development of male characteristics in boys. The female hormone, estrogen, causes the development of female characteristics in girls.

3. Sexual feelings between boys and girls result from hormones that begin to be produced during puberty. These hormones not only cause physical changes to occur, but they also cause emotional changes as well.

4. God planned that sex would not only allow humans to share in the creative process by having children, but also that a husband and wife could be close and intimate in a way that they would share with no other person. This relationship was to strengthen the ties of love and to bring joy, satisfaction, and contentment to the relationship.

5. Satan sabotaged God's plan by (1) destroying the concept of faithfulness in marriage, (2) destroying the ideal of abstinence until marriage, (3) destroying the reproductive system through disease, (4) destroying our values by enticing us with cheap substitutes for the real thing, and (5) suggesting ways of experiencing sexuality that differ from the way God designed sexual expression to occur.

6. God's plan for sexuality includes heterosexual relationships, sexual intimacy within marriage, care of children, respect for others' sexuality, and loving acts. Satan's sabotage of God's plan includes homosexual relationships, sex with any willing partner, abortion and child abuse, disrespect for others' sexuality, and forced acts of violence.

7. Sexual issues today include homosexuality, prostitution, abortion, rape, sexual abuse, and sexual harassment.

8. Current thinking on today's issues may change in society, but God's original plan did not include them.

9. Guidelines for sexual behavior include choosing to follow God's plan and making friends with those who share your moral values.

10. Appropriate ways for teenagers to express their sexuality are identified in figure 9-21.

VOCABULARY LIST

abortion	incest	rape
date rape	lesbian	sexual abuse
estrogen	ovary	sexual feelings
gay	pituitary gland	sexual harassment
heterosexual orientation	prostitution	testes
homosexual orientation	puberty	testosterone

PRACTICE

Multiple Choice. Choose the best answer.

1. Teenagers feel many different emotions because of
   a. love
   b. age
   c. hormones
   d. Satan

2. Being sexually attracted to a teenager of the opposite sex is
   a. abstinence
   b. normal
   c. abnormal
   d. morally wrong

3. Boys and girls learn how to relate to their future marriage partners by
   - a. watching their peers
   - b. watching television
   - c. growing in a family
   - d. getting a job
4. What was to precede sexual intimacy in God's original plan?
   - a. children then marriage
   - b. courtship then children
   - c. marriage then children
   - d. courtship then marriage
5. Which of Satan's attempts to sabatoge God's plan are described in the Bible?
   - a. prostitution
   - b. adultery
   - c. homosexuality
   - d. all of these
6. Which of the following is a sign of potential sexual violence?
   - a. abortion
   - b. poverty
   - c. cruelty to animals
   - d. time in jail
7. God designed His plan so that people would be
   - a. heterosexual
   - b. homosexual
   - c. gay
   - d. none of these
8. Which of the following increases as prostitution increases?
   - a. poverty
   - b. STDs
   - c. runaway teenagers
   - d. homosexuality
9. Good relationships with other people are built on
   - a. fear
   - b. respect
   - c. a long acquaintance
   - d. religion
10. Which of the following would not be an acceptable way for a Christian teenager to express sexual feelings?
    - a. partying with alcohol
    - b. playing Ping-Pong together
    - c. going on a youth outing
    - d. giving a small gift

Matching. Match each word with its definition or description.
1. sexually attracted to the same sex
2. sexually attracted to the opposite sex
3. termination of pregnancy
4. begins puberty by secreting hormones
5. forced sexual act
6. a homosexual woman
7. heckling because of gender
8. selling sexual services
9. rape between people who are friends or acquaintances
10. sexual abuse by family member

- a. abortion
- b. date rape
- c. heterosexual orientation
- d. homosexual orientation
- e. incest
- f. lesbian
- g. pituitary gland
- h. prostitution
- i. rape
- j. sexual harassment

CHAPTER 10

WHY WAIT?

INTRODUCTION

We all make choices every day. They may be small ones: What will I wear today? What shall I eat for breakfast? What shall I say about the project I didn't finish? Or they may be major ones: Which school shall I attend? What profession or occupation should I choose? What does God mean in my life?

Some choices take little time or thought, while others take a great deal of planning and consideration. The big choices will probably need talking over with parents, friends, and counselors. How to handle your sexual feelings and what to do about sexual behavior is a major choice. This chapter presents ideas you need to consider in making that choice.

SECTION TITLES

Trying to decide what to wear is sometimes a difficult decision.

10–1 RESPONSIBLE SEXUAL BEHAVIOR

sexual abstinence
virgin

OBJECTIVES

- Define the term **sexual abstinence**.
- Identify the benefits of sexual abstinence.
- Describe ways to support a decision for sexual abstinence.

God created the sexual urge as one of the most powerful of the human body. Created to bring happiness, sexual activity can also bring misery and grief (fig. 10-1). Young teenagers are learning to live with many changes in their lives, including new emotions and feelings that come with puberty. The swift change of moods, the intense interest in one member of the opposite sex, and the shift of interest to a different person in a few months can be very confusing. Longer arms and legs, pimples, and other body changes can erode self-confidence (fig. 10-2). Yet learning to cope with these changes, as well as with new sexual feelings, is your particular developmental task.

Fig. 10–1 Unwanted pregnancies often result in unwanted children who become victims of abuse.

Fig. 10–2 Pimples and other blemishes can erode self-confidence.

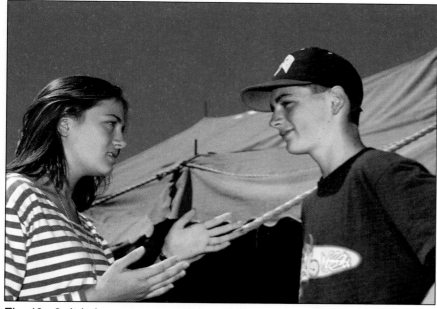

Fig. 10–3 It is important to make decisions about drug use and sexual activity before situations arise.

DID YOU KNOW?
Alcohol is a common feature of unwanted sex. Studies show that 40 percent of unwanted sex among teenagers occurs when one or both of the partners were using alcohol.

The teenage years can be troublesome, but they can also be exciting. It is a time of new friendships and new experiences. It is a time of making decisions, both good and bad, that will shape your adult life (fig. 10-3). A firm decision for **sexual abstinence** (ab′ stə nəns) now, choosing not to have sexual intercourse, can give you the freedom to enjoy this new phase of your life without fear and uncertainty. Choosing to remain a **virgin** and not to have sexual intercourse until marriage has many rewards: self-respect, true friendship, and increased happiness with a committed partner. In addition, such a choice protects you against pregnancy before marriage and against sexually-transmitted diseases. Holding firmly to that choice until you marry safeguards you from many emotional and physical dangers.

There are certain skills you can learn and certain precautions you can take to help you avoid becoming sexually involved. These are listed in figure 10-4, on page 234.

If you want to uphold your decision to be abstinent, you need to be aware of the stages of sexual activity and of the strength of the urge to go from one type of activity to the next.

233

Fig. 10-4

Satan is very clever in trapping us into sin. Eve had no intention of disobeying God when she wandered near the tree of the knowledge of good and evil. Adam sinned because of his love for Eve and his lack of trust that God could work things out. God forgave them freely and willingly, even sending His Son to die for them. But God could not change the consequences of their sin. He grieved because He knew that their sin caused pain and suffering that could not be avoided.

It's the same for young people who fall into Satan's plans for sexual behavior. God freely forgives them. He loves them no less than before, but there are consequences that cannot be changed. In John 8:1-11 we read the story of the woman who was caught in adultery and dragged to Jesus. His words to her were, "Neither do I condemn thee: go, and sin no more."

Some young people feel, however, that they are missing something. That there is no fun for them now. Not true. Each stage in life has its own pleasures. You are at the age for friends and fun and developing recreation skills. You can enjoy the company of many young people, both boys and girls, in a way you can't when you are concentrating on one individual. Now is the time to observe different personality traits and decide which are most important in a potential husband or wife. It is also a time to develop physical and social skills. Learning to ski, to skate, to play tennis, to share your faith, or to cook can be fun when you are with friends.

You are also at the age of firsts: the first banquet, the first long dress, the first driver's license, the first time to invite a girl or boy to the school picnic, the first time to plan a party for your parents, the first time to go away to school. Savor each experience. Don't be in a hurry to rush through this period of your life.

REVIEW IT

1. What is sexual abstinence?
2. What are the benefits of sexual abstinence?
3. What are some ways to reinforce your decision to be sexually abstinent?

10–2 TEEN PREGNANCY— A STORY

OBJECTIVES

- Describe the effects of a teenage pregnancy on the girl who becomes pregnant.
- Describe the effects on the boy who gets a girl pregnant.
- Analyze the potential problems of a child born to teenage parents.

Fig. 10–5 Working at a summer camp can be a great experience.

Summer camp had been great fun (fig. 10-5). The greatest thing that happened, Karen thought, was meeting Kevin. Swimming, boating, water skiing, roasting marshmallows at the campfire—they had done so many things together. What memories!

Karen was less pleased about something else they had done together. She had found herself going too far with Kevin. They hadn't really meant it to happen that way. Her conscience bothered her, and she wondered if she could forget that night after campfire when they went off alone.

Fig. 10–6 Karen was shocked to find that she was pregnant.

Six weeks later, Karen found out she would never forget that night (fig. 10-6). What was she going to tell her parents? The school nurse had told Karen she was pregnant! It just couldn't be true. After all, she had only done it once. You couldn't get pregnant from one time of sexual intercourse, could you? The nurse informed her the answer was Yes.

Karen was devastated. Questions crowded her mind (fig. 10-7). How could she finish school? What would she tell her friends? What would her parents say? What would she do with a baby? Wouldn't it be terribly painful to have a baby? She just wouldn't think about it anymore. Maybe the nurse wasn't right. Maybe the whole thing was a nightmare, and she would wake up and find it wasn't so.

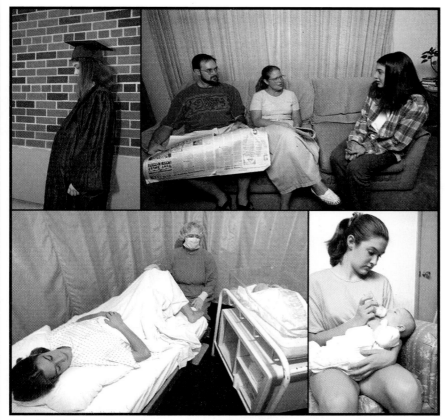

Fig. 10—7 Many questions crowded Karen's thoughts.

As the weeks went by, however, she realized that somehow, someway, she was going to have to tell her parents. It was the hardest thing she had ever done. The look of disappointment on her mother's face said it all. Her parents didn't criticize her, but their tears were almost more than she could stand. They asked many of the same questions she had asked. Her mother added one, however: Have you told Kevin?

"No," Karen said. "Do I have to?"

"Well, no you don't," her mother said. "But it is going to be his baby, too."

Karen decided not to tell him.

When it came time for Karen's baby to be born, she endured 14 hours of labor. But that pain was less than the pain she suffered in giving her baby up for adoption (fig. 10-8). She and her parents had decided it would be best for the baby and for Karen to find good adoptive parents. Karen longed to hold her baby just once, to see him—if only for an hour. But she knew she didn't dare. If she once held him, she knew she could never give him up!

Fig. 10−8 Karen's decision to give her baby up for adoption was very painful.

Kevin didn't find out he was a father until a friend told him that Karen had had a baby. When he heard this, Kevin began thinking. He counted up the months since he and Karen had been together at camp.

"It's my baby," he thought. "Why didn't she tell me?"

Several phone calls confirmed that the baby boy had been given up for adoption (fig. 10-9). He had never even gotten to see it! Hurt and angry, he tried to talk to Karen, to her parents, to the social worker. The social worker asked him if he thought he could keep the baby.

Fig. 10−9 Phone calls confirmed what Kevin had heard.

"Sure. I can manage," he replied. Then he thought of all the things he would have to give up if he had a baby to care for—after-school games, a job at the grocery store, evenings and weekends with his friends. He was headed for college after graduation. Selfishly, he wished Karen would have kept the baby; that way, he could have gotten to see him once in a while.

Kevin and Karen now realized that teenage pregnancies cause difficulties for everyone concerned: the teenage father, the girl who is pregnant, their families, and the baby when it is born. Teenage mothers who keep their babies find it very difficult to finish their schooling and care for a baby at the same time. A baby gets in the way of the mother's social life, leading to all kinds of frustration (fig. 10-10). Teenage mothers rarely are able to earn the money they need. Because of this stress, mothers often abuse their babies.

Fig. 10–10 Teenagers find it difficult to deal with the stress of being a parent.

Teenagers who become pregnant are left with lifelong regrets and emotional scars from the guilt they feel as a result of choosing to have an abortion or putting the baby up for adoption. Teenage fathers, in most states or provinces, have few rights concerning their babies. Pregnant girls do not need to consult them about an abortion or adoption. Proposing marriage as a solution rarely yields a marriage that lasts.

Fig. 10–11 The teenage years are a time to enjoy friends and fun.

Teenagers are supposed to be free to have fun, to grow and mature before they take on the responsibilities of parenthood (fig. 10-11). They are not ready to cope with the tasks of raising children.

God's ideal calls for families who will protect and care for babies as they grow. Parenting means providing for the emotional, physical, and spiritual needs of children. Teenagers still face the task of meeting their own needs without the added burden of caring for babies and young children. Parenting is never an easy task, but it is doubly hard if you are a teenager.

What could Karen and Kevin have done to prevent pregnancy? The best answer is: Decide in advance not to have sex. Because they waited to make that decision until they were alone meant they had no time to think about their values and future goals.

In spite of all the dangers, some teenagers do become sexually active. They may use some method of birth control such as condoms, shields, foams, or birth-control pills to prevent unwanted pregnancy. By having sexual intercourse at all, however, they are lowering their own moral standards.

No amount of birth control can undo the emotional damage caused by going against God's moral law.

As Karen faced her wedding day five years later, two thoughts haunted her: "I wish I had my virginity back!" and "Where is my little boy now?"

REVIEW IT

1. What are the effects of pregnancy on a teenage girl?
2. What are the effects of pregnancy on a teenage boy?
3. What problems face a child of teenage parents?

10-3 TIME FOR EMOTIONS TO MATURE

OBJECTIVES

- Identify normal emotional changes that occur during adolescence.
- Describe ways to build friendships that last.

Adolescence (ad'l es′ ′ns) is a time when people change from children to adults. Puberty occurs during this time and results in sexual maturity. But in addition to these physical changes, important emotional changes are happening as well. Many of you have already experienced the physical changes in your own bodies. You may also have noticed the emotional changes taking place. These changes include dramatic mood swings, difficulty in handling emotions, insecurity about physical appearance, sensitivity to peer pressure, and increased interest in the opposite sex (fig. 10-12).

NORMAL EMOTIONAL CHANGES DURING ADOLESCENCE

- Dramatic mood swings.
- Difficulty handling emotions.
- Insecurity about physical appearance.
- Sensitivity to peer pressure.
- Increased interest in the opposite sex.

Fig. 10-12 Many emotional changes take place during adolescence.

These emotional changes affect your attitudes and interests. Your changing interests may make you do some things that only a year ago you thought were foolish (fig. 10-13). The desire to be popular, one of the things you most want, may drive you to do things you wish you hadn't. The words "everybody's doing it" seem to have an irresistible power over you. You end up doing things you really don't want to do at all, just to show you are part of the group. **(Please Note: Very rarely is *everyone* doing it.)**

Fig. 10-13 Many teens choose to attend banquets with a "date," something they wouldn't have considered a few years earlier.

You may become totally obsessed by someone of the opposite sex. You toss around the word *love*, for you are sure you can't live without this person. You want to spend all your time with each other (fig. 10-14). And you just know that this relationship is going to last "forever." Six months later the idea of "forever" is forgotten.

If you have felt this way, you are normal. Remember, hormones trigger these changes and feelings. If you ask your parents, they probably can remember having the same feelings. Even your teachers will know what you are talking about—if you can bring yourself to discuss things with them. Adults have all been teenagers and may be able to relate to the problems you have.

One of the biggest jobs teenagers have is handling their emotions. Another is learning how to relate to others, especially those of the opposite sex.

Relating to others is a skill, and, as with any other skill, it needs to be practiced. School, church, and family activities all provide a place in which you can practice making friends and getting along with others (fig. 10-15). Such activities should be planned so that no individuals are left out, even if they have no special partners. Caring for each other's feelings is a mark of emotional maturity.

Fig. 10-14 Many teen couples want to be together all the time.

Fig. 10-15 Youth group outings are a good setting in which to learn social skills.

As a teenager, you may make friendships that last for years. You will do this, however, only if you go out of your way to be a friend. What characteristics do you want to demonstrate as a friend? Figure 10-16 lists some ways of building friendships that last.

WAYS OF BUILDING FRIENDSHIPS
• Be mutually supportive. • Never ask anyone to go against their values. • Show respect and appreciation for each other's families. • Be unselfish and caring. • Don't take advantage of each other. • Don't be jealous of each other. • Don't put each other down. • Share good times and bad. • Want the best for each other. • Stand up for each other.

Fig. 10–16

You can build friendships by planning activities that others enjoy, by learning to listen and learning to share. Search for ways to be thoughtful. Remember special occasions—even if you have to create them. Be available in the rough times as well as the fun times.

Explore values and goals together; discuss things you dream of doing when you're 21. Explore together what you think God wants you to do with your lives.

REVIEW IT

1. What emotional changes take place during the teenage years?
2. What are several ways of building lasting friendships?

CLASS ACTIVITY 10-3: Dumb Reasons

Question: What reasons do teenagers give for having sexual relations?

Materials:
Special Master R267

Procedure:
1. Form groups of two or three and read the reasons teenagers give for having sexual relations. As a group, rank these reasons in order of what you think is the most common reason cited to the least common reason given. Record your ranking in the data table.
2. With your group decide on a statement that provides a good argument against each of the eight reasons listed.
3. Compare your responses with those of the rest of the class.

Data: (See Special Master)

Questions:
1. According to your group, what is the most common reason given by teenagers for having sexual relations? What is the least common reason?
2. How do the responses of other groups compare to the responses of your group?
3. Which, if any, of the reasons do you feel are valid?
4. What is the strongest argument you can give for waiting until marriage for sexual relations?
5. How can you make a decision of "no sex before marriage" work?

Conclusion: Write 3–5 sentences about what you learned from this activity.

10–4 ANOTHER CHANCE? ANOTHER CHOICE?

OBJECTIVE

• Describe the steps in making decisions.

Fig. 10–17 Toddlers often desire to be independent and to do things for themselves.

"I'll do it all by myself," toddler Jeff said. Determined to be independent, he struggled with his boots (fig. 10-17). Somehow, the boots kept ending up on the wrong feet. He looked at the toes pointing in the wrong direction. He was so frustrated that tears trickled down his cheeks.

Teenagers, while far from being two-year-olds, also struggle to be independent. They want to make their own decisions.

While they may not use the words, "I'll do it all by myself," the same intent is there. And parents struggle too. It is often no easier for them to watch teenagers wrestle with their own decisions than it was for them to allow their two-year-olds to struggle with difficult tasks.

Decision making is a learned skill that takes practice to do well. There will be some mistakes during the practice. Usually mistakes can be corrected, but as you have seen in the story of Kevin and Karen, the results of some mistakes cannot. That is why learning to make the right decision is so important. Figure 10-18 identifies steps you can follow to improve your decision-making skills.

The six steps described in figure 10-18 do not need to be taken in the order listed, but each step is important to the

---

STEPS IN DECISION MAKING

1. Choose from among alternatives.
2. Choose after considering the consequences.
3. Choose after considering what God says.
4. Consider what is most important to you.
5. Affirm your decision by speaking to others about it, when appropriate.
6. Act on your decision.

Fig. 10–18 There are several steps in decision making.

process. Gathering information before you make a decision will alert you to the consequences of different alternatives. Often, you may need to talk with someone with more experience—one of your parents, teachers, or a youth leader—to try out your ideas (fig. 10-19). Explore the consequences by talking about them before you act. Others may have ideas or information you had not thought of.

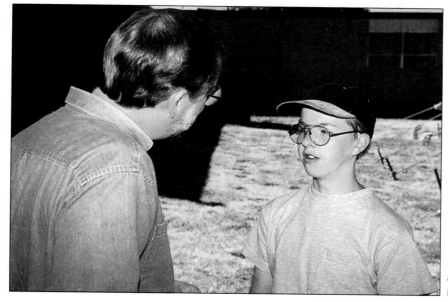

Fig. 10–19 Talking to trusted adults can be beneficial when making decisions.

For example, Michelle has an older sister whose friends frequently come home with her. Michelle has a lot of fun when they are around, their music is great, and they always bring the best pizza. Sometimes they even take her along when they are going out: they always find something exciting to do.

Lately, however, one of her sister's friends has been coming over to see her after school. At first, it was pretty neat; Tom was a good-looking guy. He would bring the latest CD or her favorite food. When Michelle told some of her friends at school, they agreed that it was really something that she could attract a guy like Tom.

Then she noticed that Tom always left the house before her older sister or her parents came home. Didn't he want them to know? She realized she had not told them, either. It was their secret. About this time, a discussion in class at school caught her attention. To prevent getting into unwanted sex, the group decided, you had to avoid couples being alone at home. Was that where this relationship with Tom was leading?

Michelle's best friend was her older sister. Even though they were four years apart in age, they could talk about almost anything. Together, they explored the possible consequences of Tom's visits. They asked questions: "Why is Tom coming only when you're alone? What would happen if . . . they went beyond hugging and kissing?" What would happen if . . . it led to sexual intercourse?"

Michelle knew the words, but didn't know much more than that, so her sister explained.

"But I want to have fun," Michelle protested.

"You can still have a good time," her sister said. "But you have to think about the consequences. If Tom really likes you, he'll wait." Michelle decided her sister was right; she didn't want to risk it. But what would she tell Tom? Together, she and her sister planned what she could say to him.

Fig. 10–20 In school, Michelle learned the importance of making decisions in advance.

Fortunately for Michelle, the class discussion at school made her aware that she needed to be making decisions before there was a problem (Fig 10-20). Her sister acted wisely in using the steps in decision making to help Michelle think things through. Michelle thanked God for giving her a sister who was so helpful and caring.

You cannot always wait for something to happen in class, however. Most of the time you need to hunt for the information you need. Books, health professionals, counselors, parents, pastors, or teachers—any one of them may be able to provide the needed information, if you will ask for it.

Seeking to learn God's will in your life is the most important step. God has already spoken through His written word (fig. 10-21). You have to study it, however, to know what He has said. He continues to speak, through His Holy Spirit, in answer to prayer (fig. 10-22). If He chooses to speak to you through other people or books, He will never contradict what He has said in the Bible. God indeed can be the best friend you will ever have, because He cares for you more than anyone else does. He will help you make right choices for a full and happy life.

Fig. 10–21 The Bible gives God's plan for us.

Fig. 10–22 Through prayer, the Holy Spirit can speak to us.

REVIEW IT

1. What are the steps of decision making?
2. Where can you get information that will help you to make good decisions about sexual activity?

CHAPTER 10 WRAP-UP

THINKING SKILLS: Using Numbers

Much of the data collected by scientists is in the form of numbers. These numbers must be studied and analyzed in order for scientists to make any sense out of them. The analysis of numbers involves math. Mathematics allows scientists to identify trends and to draw conclusions about what they study.

Preventing teenage pregnancy is a major concern of society. Health professionals are always trying to develop materials and programs that will help to stop this problem. A study conducted in 1990 may have identified one of the reasons these programs may not always be successful. The raw data of this study is given in the table. Calculate the percents and see if you can identify the clues this study provides for lack of success in such programs.

Father's Age in Births Among Girls Age 11-15		
Father's age	Number of births	Percent
Less than 15	378	
16-18	2,171	
19-24	2,339	
More than 25	306	
Total	5,194	
Father's Age in Births Among Girls Age 16-18		
Father's age	Number of births	Percent
Less than 15	300	
16-18	9,124	
19-24	25,052	
More than 25	5,492	
Total	39,968	

1. For girls age 11-15, what percentage of the fathers are the same age as the girls? What percentage are older?
2. For girls age 16-18, what percentage of the fathers are the same age as the girls? What percentage are older?
3. Why do programs designed to help girls deal with boys their age fail to be really effective in preventing teenage pregnancy? What do you think should be done?

QUESTIONS AND PROBLEMS

1. What factors make it difficult for adolescents to handle their emotions?
2. Why do you think the "love" that adolescents have for boyfriends or girlfriends is different than the "love" that married couples have for each other?
3. What are the advantages of sexual abstinence before marriage?
4. Why is child abuse higher among teenage parents than it is with older parents?
5. What factors contribute to increasing numbers of teenage pregnancies?
6. Of the steps listed in figure 10-18 regarding decision making, which is most important? Why?
7. Who are people who may be affected by a teenage pregnancy?
8. Why is it important to learn refusal skills before a situation arises?
9. Why is it difficult to stop sexual activity once it has started?
10. What kind of difficulties come if a pregnant teen decides to get an abortion? What difficulties come if she decides to have the baby adopted? What difficulties come if she decides to keep the baby and raise it herself?

RESEARCH

1. Find out how many teenage pregnancies occurred each year in the United States or Canada over the past five years. Create a graph that summarizes this information.
2. Create a skit, complete with dialogue and props, based on the information in figure 10-4 regarding refusal skills. Enlist some of your classmates to help you perform the skit.
3. Make a creative and colorful bulletin-board display that teaches the steps in decision making.
4. Make a series of color posters on the subject of building friendships.
5. Use library resources to learn the impact of teenage pregnancy on society. Write a report on your findings.

REVIEW

HIGHLIGHTS

1. Sexual abstinence involves choosing not to have sexual intercourse.
2. The benefits of sexual abstinence before marriage include maintaining a good reputation, no guilt, no STDs, no unwanted pregnancy.
3. Ways to help reinforce a decision to be sexually abstinent include: making a decision to be sexually abstinent, avoiding situations where there are opportunities for progressive sexual behavior, stating the reasons for your decision, reinforcing your decision with your behavior, sticking with your decision, acting firmly, finding other ways of showing affection, breaking off a relationship if the other person does not respect your decision.
4. Teenage pregnancy affects girls by getting in the way of their social life, increasing stress and frustration, affecting their work or school, usually causing poverty, encouraging marriages that usually do not last.

5. Teenage pregnancy affects boys because the girl can abort or adopt out the child without their consent, and it encourages marriages that usually do not last.
6. Children born to teenagers often are abused by their parents.
7. Normal emotional changes during adolescence include dramatic mood swings, difficulty with handling emotions, insecurity about physical appearance, sensitivity to peer pressure, increased interest in the opposite sex.
8. Ways of building friendships are outlined in figure 10-16.
9. The steps in decision making include choosing from among alternatives, considering the consequences, considering what God says, considering what is most important to you, affirming your decision by speaking about, and acting on, your decision.

VOCABULARY LIST

adolescence   sexual abstinence   virgin

PRACTICE

Multiple Choice. Choose the best answer.
1. Which of the following will help you to be sexually abstinent until marriage?
   a. being alone as a couple   c. early dating
   b. making a decision in advance   d. watching television
2. To support your decision to be sexually abstinent, you must
   a. state your reasons   c. choose freely
   b. talk to your best friend   d. all of these
3. What would have been the *best* thing Karen and Kevin could have done to prevent pregnancy?
   a. taken another couple along
   b. used birth control
   c. made a decision in advance to be sexually abstinent
   d. gone to college
4. Which is never part of a teenage pregnancy?
   a. guilt   c. unwanted child
   b. abstinence   d. consideration of abortion
5. Teenage fathers usually have
   a. guilt   c. stress
   b. few rights to the child   d. all of these
6. One of the biggest jobs a teenager has to learn is
   a. how to work   c. how to study
   b. how to handle emotions   d. how to drive
7. Which of the following is a poor way to build friendships?
   a. share good times and bad   c. being caring
   b. thinking of yourself first   d. protecting values

8. Which is a normal emotional change that takes place during adolescence?
   a. insecurity about physical appearance
   b. decreased interest in the opposite sex
   c. indifference to what peers think
   d. ability to handle changing emotions
9. Most normal teenagers at some time will feel
   a. stress, awkward, jealous
   b. obsessed, awkward, unhappy
   c. in love, like crying
   d. all of these
10. The skill of decision making is best done by
    a. asking someone for advice
    b. practicing the seven steps
    c. doing it quickly
    d. being independent

Matching. Match each word with its definition or description.
1. time during which puberty occurs
2. these often trigger emotional changes
3. refraining from sexual activity
4. a benefit of sexual abstinence
5. a time of physical and emotional changes
6. results in sexual maturity
7. time during which puberty occurs
8. a problem often associated with teenage parents
9. reduces the risk of STDs and pregnancy
10. an individual who has never had sexual intercourse

a. adolescence
b. child abuse
c. hormones
d. puberty
e. self-respect
f. sexual abstinence
g. virgin

CHAPTER 11

SEXUALLY TRANSMITTED DISEASES

INTRODUCTION

The organism on page 254 is a spirochete. It causes syphilis, a disease transmitted through sexual contact. Syphilis produces sores, a rash, fever, and headache. If not treated, it can go into hiding, only to come back and attack and destroy body organs and sometimes cause insanity. Health officials estimate that every year, 90,000 people in the United States and Canada become infected with syphilis.

Syphilis is just one of several sexually transmitted diseases that are serious and potentially life threatening. No immunizations can protect a person from them.

In this chapter you will learn about these diseases and how they can be prevented.

SECTION TITLES

This small organism causes the STD syphilis.

11-1 DISEASE-CAUSING ORGANISMS

VOCABULARY

VOCABULARY
communicable disease
epidemiologist
infectious disease
  specialist
microbiologist
normal flora bacteria
pathogen
surveillance
toxin

OBJECTIVES

- Define the term **communicable disease**.
- Define the term **pathogen**.
- Describe several types of pathogens.
- Identify several communicable diseases.
- Explain how agencies monitor communicable diseases.

Communicable (kə myōō′ ni kə bəl) **diseases** can be spread from one person to another through **pathogens**, the organisms that cause such diseases.

You may recall from your study of Unit 1 that there are four kinds of pathogens: viruses, bacteria, protists, and fungi (fig. 11-1).

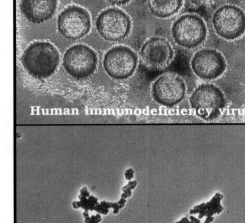

Viruses

Viruses are the smallest pathogens known. They are so small that they can be seen only by using an electron microscope. More than a million viruses can fit on the head of a pin. Viruses can live and multiply only within living cells. Measles, polio, and HIV are examples of virus-caused diseases.

Human immunodeficiency virus

Bacteria

Bacteria are somewhat larger than viruses. They are one-celled organisms that can be seen through a light microscope. There are thousands of different kinds of bacteria, but only about 100 of them are causes of common disease in humans. For example, one kind of bacteria, streptococcus, produces a severe sore throat. Some bacteria cause disease by releasing poisonous substances called **toxins** into the body. Some bacteria live in our bodies all the time but usually do not make us sick; such bacteria are called **normal flora bacteria**.

Streptococcus

Fig. 11-1 Disease-causing organisms include viruses, bacteria, protists, and fungi.

Fig. 11–1 Continued

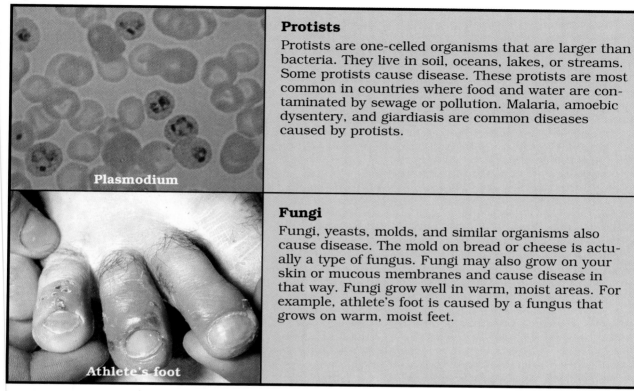

Protists

Protists are one-celled organisms that are larger than bacteria. They live in soil, oceans, lakes, or streams. Some protists cause disease. These protists are most common in countries where food and water are contaminated by sewage or pollution. Malaria, amoebic dysentery, and giardiasis are common diseases caused by protists.

Plasmodium

Fungi

Fungi, yeasts, molds, and similar organisms also cause disease. The mold on bread or cheese is actually a type of fungus. Fungi may also grow on your skin or mucous membranes and cause disease in that way. Fungi grow well in warm, moist areas. For example, athlete's foot is caused by a fungus that grows on warm, moist feet.

Athlete's foot

The pathogens that cause sexually-transmitted diseases are most commonly viruses or bacteria. Each pathogen is unique in its pattern of behavior, the way in which it causes disease, and the kind of environment in which it thrives. Several kinds of scientists study pathogens and the diseases they cause. A **microbiologist** studies microscopic organisms and how they behave (fig. 11-2). An **epidemiologist** (ep ə dē mē äl′ ə jist) traces the spread of communicable diseases in a population. An **infectious disease specialist** treats people who have communicable diseases (fig. 11-3).

Fig. 11–2 Microbiologists study microorganisms.

The United States and Canadian governments have public health organizations, which monitor the number, kind, and location of most communicable diseases. Their records show the rates of disease in any part of the country.

For example, the U.S. Centers for Disease Control and Prevention (CDC), located in Atlanta, Georgia, identified the epidemic of AIDS as the early reports of this new disease came from doctors in Los Angeles, San Francisco, and New

Fig. 11–3 Infectious disease specialists treat people infected by communicable diseases.

York City (fig. 11-4). As reports of patients with similar symptoms came in from other cities, the CDC traced the course of the epidemic in a process called **surveillance** (sər vā′ ləns). They shared information about the disease, its prevention, and its treatment with government agencies in other parts of the world. Surveillance is an important scientific tool to help health-care workers control epidemics.

Fig. 11–4 The scientists at the Centers for Disease Control study the causes, transmission, treatment, and prevention of disease.

REVIEW IT

1. What is a communicable disease?
2. What is a pathogen?
3. List several types of pathogens.
4. List several communicable diseases.
5. How are communicable diseases monitored?

11–2 HOW DISEASES ARE SPREAD

OBJECTIVES

- Contrast direct contact with indirect contact.
- Identify the role of animals in transmission of disease.
- Give examples of diseases spread by direct contact, by indirect contact, and by insects.

VOCABULARY
direct contact
indirect contact

Judy sneezed throughout the entire class period (fig. 11-5). She went through a whole packet of tissues in an attempt to stifle her runny nose.

"It's just an allergy," she kept reassuring her classmates. "I get it every spring."

"Are you sure?" asked Joan.

Why was Joan concerned? Because she knew that the virus that causes the common cold can be transmitted through the air by the droplets of a sneeze. That's why you've always been told to cover your mouth when you cough or sneeze.

Pathogens can be transmitted in three ways: by direct contact, by indirect contact, and by animals. Study figure 11-6 to learn about the methods of disease transmission.

The Centers for Disease Control and Prevention continuously conduct studies to identify factors contributing to the

Fig. 11–5 One sneeze can release thousands of disease-causing microorganisms.

DIRECT CONTACT

Direct contact occurs when a pathogen from one person is carried to another person. Touching, kissing, and sexual intercourse are examples of direct contact. Diseases transmitted by sexual activity, such as gonorrhea, syphilis, and AIDS, are transmitted by direct contact. Medical technologists and those who draw blood wear gloves to prevent the transmission of pathogens by direct contact.

Fig. 11–6

Fig. 11-6 Continued

INDIRECT CONTACT

Indirect contact means that the pathogens move from the infected person to some object, perhaps a glass, doorknob, or telephone, and then to the next person. Drug abusers who share needles may infect each other through indirect contact. Diseases such as chickenpox, tuberculosis, and the flu can be transmitted by indirect contact.

ANIMALS

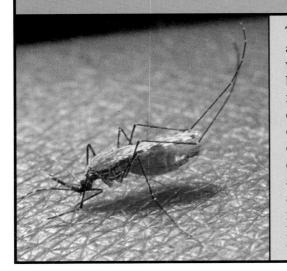

The bite of animals is a third way pathogens are spread to people. Animals become infected with pathogens through their food, water, or the bites of other animals. In many cases an animal is not itself affected by the pathogen but simply carries the pathogen in its body. Rabies, a viral disease, is transmitted by the bite of an infected dog, skunk, or other mammal. Lyme disease is carried by the deer tick. Many other diseases are carried by insects. Mosquitos spread malaria and yellow fever. The fleas that live on some rodents transmitted bubonic plague, which killed millions of Europeans during the fourteenth century.

DID YOU KNOW?
Bubonic plague infects many animals in the southwestern United States today.

spread of disease. Such studies are another important tool in the fight against communicable diseases. If any one of the factors can be changed or removed, the spread of the disease may be stopped.

REVIEW IT

1. What is the difference between direct contact and indirect contact?
2. How do animals transmit disease?
3. List three diseases that are spread by:
   a. direct contact
   b. indirect contact
   c. animals

Alexander Fleming

Dear Friend,

I must write to tell you of an exciting discovery I recently made. As is often the case with scientific discoveries, this one happened by accident and without any plan on my part.

A few weeks ago I was cleaning several culture dishes that had accumulated in my laboratory. As I was washing and stacking the dishes, one dish caught my eye. Unlike the other dishes, which had colonies of bacteria covering the bottom, this dish appeared to have a noticeable spot where no bacteria was growing. I took the dish to my microscope to observe it more closely. As I was placing the dish on the microscope, I observed a small piece of mold that had fallen into the dish. To my amazement this speck of fungus was positioned in the center of the spot where no bacteria was growing. My analysis under the microscope confirmed this observation. Not only had the bacteria surrounding the fleck of mold died, but no new bacteria appeared to be growing in the immediate area either.

This observation stimulated my thinking. I wondered, "Could it be that the mold or something in the mold was killing the bacteria?" I began to investigate this question. First, I had to identify the mold. I found it was similar to the mold that grows on oranges and other citrus fruit. Since no name existed for the fungus, I named it *Penicillium notatum*. Once I identified the mold, I set up several experiments. As a result of this research, I have discovered that Penicillium produces a toxin lethal to most bacteria. I have also discovered that while Penicillium kills bacteria, it does not have a damaging effect on other body cells, particularly blood cells.

Many more tests and experiments must be performed to verify my findings. However, I believe that in the end, my conclusions will be confirmed. If this is the case, science will finally have an effective weapon in fighting bacterial infection. I will keep you informed as to my progress.

Signed,

Sir Alexander Fleming, Professor
Bacteriology Department

11-3 SEXUALLY TRANSMITTED DISEASES

VOCABULARY

chancre
cryotherapy
sexually transmitted
    disease
spirochete
venereal disease

OBJECTIVES

- Define the term **sexually transmitted diseases**.
- Describe several common sexually transmitted diseases.

Sexually transmitted diseases (STDs) are spread through sexual contact with an infected person. STDs, formerly called **venereal** (və nir′ ē əl) **diseases** (VD), are caused by the following pathogens: bacteria, viruses, protozoans, and fungi.

No one is immune to sexually transmitted diseases. People of all ages can become infected with an STD. Unborn babies may become infected from their mothers (fig. 11-7).

Fig. 11–7 Unborn babies become victims of STDs when their mothers are infected.

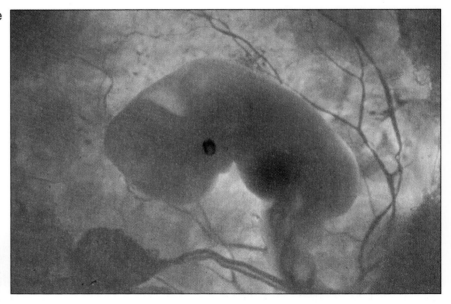

Fig. 11–8 The most dramatic rise in the number of STD infections is occurring in the teenage population.

It is even possible to become infected with more than one STD at the same time. More than 12 million people in the United States and Canada become infected with an STD every year. Teenagers, however, show the most rapidly rising number of infections (fig. 11-8). This increase is due to several factors: teenagers are becoming more sexually active,

262

they often have a greater number of sexual partners, their use of drugs and alcohol is increasing, and they often refuse to take any protective measures.

You need to know what these diseases are, their symptoms and treatment, and ways of protecting yourself from getting them. The most common sexually transmitted diseases are chlamydia, genital herpes, genital warts, gonorrhea, syphilis, vaginitis, and AIDS. (AIDS will be discussed in chapter 12.) Figure 11-9 describes each of these diseases.

DID YOU KNOW?
Some varieties of bacteria that cause sexually transmitted diseases are becoming immune to penicillin.

Fig. 11-9

CHLAMYDIA (klə mid′ ē ə)	GENITAL HERPES
• The fastest growing STD in the U.S. • Caused by bacteria. • In males, it produces inflammation of the urethra, causing a thin mucous discharge and a burning sensation when urinating, or there may be no symptoms. • In females, no symptoms occur until the disease is in late stages. • If untreated, chlamydia may cause damage to the reproductive organs or sterility. • An infected mother can pass the disease to her baby; can cause blindness. • Can be cured with antibiotics.	• Caused by the herpes simplex virus, which also causes cold sores. • Once infected, a person is infected for life. • Causes red, tender skin in the genital area. One or more blisters or bumps form, which may burn or itch; may cause flulike symptoms. • An infected mother can pass the disease to her baby; can cause severe brain fever, which can be fatal. • No cure exists, but it can be treated with antiviral drugs.
GENITAL WARTS	GONORRHEA (găn ə rē′ ə)
• Caused by human papilloma virus, which also causes cancer of the cervix. • Warts on other parts of the body are caused by a different virus. • Appear on genitals. • Can be treated by **cryotherapy** (krī′ ō ther ə pē) (freezing the wart with liquid nitrogen) or with lasers, electrocautery, or antiviral drugs.	• Most common STD worldwide. • Caused by bacteria. • Can cause sterility and insanity. • In males, gonorrhea causes a discharge and painful urination. • In females, gonorrhea shows no early symptoms, but discharge, abdominal pain, fever, and pelvic inflammatory disease may develop. • Can be passed to baby during birth, causing blindness. • Can be treated with antibiotics.

Fig. 11–9 Continued

SYPHILIS (sif′ ə lis)	VAGINITIS (vaj ə nīt′ is)

• Caused by a corkscrew-shaped bacteria called a **spirochete**.
 	
• The disease occurs in stages:
  Stage 1. A **chancre** (shaŋ′ ker), a painless sore, forms on the genitals or mouth.
  Stage 2. A month to a year later, a rash covers the entire body, accompanied by fever, headache, and weight loss. When these symptoms disappear, the bacteria go into hiding.
  Stage 3. If untreated, the bacteria enter the body organs and destroy them. Sometimes bacteria enter the nervous system, causing insanity.
 	
• A blood test can detect the infection.
 	
• Can be passed to baby during birth.
 	
• Can be treated with antibiotics in the early stages.
	• Occurs only in women.
	
	• Infection of the vagina.
	
	• Not all forms of vaginitis are sexually transmitted.
	
	• Includes a group of diseases: trichomoniasis (trīk ō mō nī′ ə sis)—a protozoan.
	  • Produces a yellow discharge.
	  • Causes itching and burning.
	  Candidiasis (kan di dī′ ə sis)—a yeast.
	  • Produces a cottage cheeselike discharge.
	  • Causes intense itching.
	  Gardnerella—a bacteria.
	  • Produces a grayish, watery, strong-smelling discharge.
	
	• Can be treated with specific drugs.
	
	• Good personal hygiene and cotton undergarments that ensure air circulation reduce the risk of vaginitis.

REVIEW IT

1. What are sexually transmitted diseases?
2. List six common sexually transmitted diseases.

CLASS ACTIVITY 11-3: Hey! This Is Serious!

Question: How serious are sexually transmitted diseases?

Materials:
   none needed

Procedure:
1. Use the information in figure 11-9 to complete the table.
2. Determine the cause of the disease. If the disease is caused by a virus, put an X in the V column. If bacteria cause it, put an X in the B column. If it is caused by another organism, put the X in the O column.
3. Determine who is most affected by the disease, male or female. If you think women and girls are most affected, put an X in the F column. If men and boys are most affected, place an X in the M column.
4. Briefly describe the symptoms of the disease. Write your description in the column labeled "Symptoms."
5. Briefly describe the treatment of the disease. Write the treatment in the column labeled "Treatment."
6. Rate each disease as to its seriousness, using the following rating:

   1 = extremely serious (life threatening)   3 = moderately serious
   2 = serious   4 = not serious

Data:

Disease	V	B	O	M	F	Symptoms	Treatment	Rating
Chlamydia								
Genital herpes								
Genital warts								
Gonorrhea								
Syphilis								
Vaginitis								

Questions:
1. Which STDs are caused by viruses? Which are caused by bacteria?
2. Which STDs affect only men? Which affect only women?
3. Which STDs are life threatening?
4. Which STDs can be passed to an unborn baby?
5. What is the best way of preventing STDs?
6. Does a person always know when he or she is infected with an STD? Explain.

Conclusion: Write 3–5 sentences about what you learned from this activity.

11–4 PREVENTING STDs

- Identify ways of preventing the transmission of STDs.

Did you notice which of the STDs can make a person sterile, never able to reproduce? And which can damage an unborn baby?

Most of the STDs can be treated (fig. 11-10). However, early detection can be difficult. One may have the disease without knowing it. In these cases, the treatment may come too late to prevent the serious effects of the disease. Often, an STD comes back to haunt a person years later. Married couples find out that the diseases they had as teenagers make it impossible for them to have children. Or a woman discovers she has a disease that has infected her unborn baby.

Fig. 11–10 The public health department works to treat and prevent the spread of STDs.

The best way to deal with STDs is to prevent them. The responsible choice for teenagers is sexual abstinence. Choosing not to have sexual contact outside of marriage reduces the risk of having sexual contact with an infected person. Later, when you are ready to marry, choose a faithful marriage partner who is not infected. While it is true that barriers such as condoms may prevent transmission of some STDs, they are not 100 percent effective.

When you are ready to marry, learn all you can about your prospective partner. Both of you should have a physical examination, including tests for STDs.

If an individual has been infected with an STD organism, early treatment is the best means of preventing further damage or transmission to another person. People who have had several sexual partners and are diagnosed with an STD should take the responsibility to tell their sexual partners, who may have become infected without knowing it. In most states and provinces, public health workers trace such contacts to be sure everyone is treated.

Fig. 11–11 Pregnant women should be checked for STD infection.

Pregnant women should be checked for STD infection (fig. 11-11). In most cases, early treatment can protect the unborn baby. In one of the most serious kinds of STD, however, it is difficult to protect the unborn baby. That disease is AIDS.

REVIEW IT

1. Why is it important to prevent STDs?
2. Describe several ways of preventing the transmission of an STD.

CHAPTER 11 WRAP-UP

THINKING SKILLS: Interpreting Data

Scientists conduct experiments and make observations to gather data about objects or events. The data is usually recorded in a table or chart. Sometimes the data is put into a graph. Whatever the form, scientists must analyze and interpret the data. Doing so allows them to draw conclusions and form theories that help explain what they observe.

Refer to the graph on common sexually transmitted diseases to answer the questions.

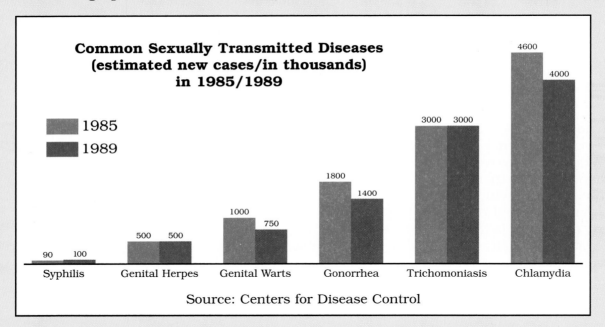

1. Which STDs increased during the period of 1985 to 1989? Which decreased? Which stayed about the same?
2. How many more cases of Chlamydia were there in 1989 than in 1985?
3. How many more cases of gonorrhea were there in 1989 than in 1985?
4. According to the graph, which STD is the most common? Does this disease affect men or women more?
5. What percent increase was there in the number of cases of syphilis between the years 1985 and 1989?
6. Why do you think there are so many more cases of chlamydia than syphilis?
7. Of the STDs that affect both men and women, which showed the greatest increase between 1985 and 1989?

QUESTIONS AND PROBLEMS

1. How are genital warts different from other warts?
2. How do microbiologists keep from getting the diseases they study?
3. Name two diseases that are communicable and two that are not communicable.
4. What are "normal flora bacteria"? Why don't they make a person sick?
5. Why do so many people with STDs avoid medical treatment?
6. Which STDs can cause insanity or blindness?
7. How can washing your hands prevent the spread of disease?
8. Are condoms the solution to the spread of STDs? Explain your answer.
9. How are viruses different from the other pathogens?
10. Why should a pregnant woman be tested for STDs even though she does not appear to have an STD?
11. Why is the rate of STD infection so high in teenagers?

RESEARCH

1. Find the number of new syphilis and gonorrhea cases for each of the past five years in your state or province. Graph the results.
2. Use library resources to learn how the spread of malaria was stopped during the building of the Panama Canal. Present an oral report on your findings.
3. Make a bulletin-board display on the subject of insect-borne disease.
4. Make a series of color posters that could be used to teach K-3 students ways of preventing communicable diseases. Make a presentation to a group of younger students and report on your experience.
5. Find out about the CDC and what it does. Write a report that summarizes its work in North America.

REVIEW

HIGHLIGHTS

1. Communicable diseases are diseases that are spread from one person to another.
2. Pathogens are disease-causing microorganisms.
3. Pathogens include viruses, bacteria, protozoans, and fungi.
4. Common communicable diseases include measles, AIDS, polio, sore throat, malaria, amebic dysentery, giardiasis, and athlete's foot.
5. Health agencies monitor diseases through a process called surveillance, in which information is gathered and then shared with agencies in other areas of the world.
6. Some pathogens are spread by direct contact from one person to another; other pathogens are spread by indirect contact from an infected person to an object and then to another person.
7. Animals usually transmit disease to people by biting them.

8. Diseases spread by direct contact include all of the sexually transmitted diseases. Tuberculosis, food poisoning, and the flu are examples of diseases passed through indirect contact. Animal-borne disease includes rabies, Lyme disease, yellow fever, malaria, and bubonic plague.
9. Sexually transmitted diseases (STDs) are diseases spread by sexual contact with an infected person.
10. Common STDs include chlamydia, genital herpes, genital warts, gonorrhea, syphilis, and vaginitis. Figure 11-9 describes the cause, symptoms, and treatment of each of these diseases.
11. Abstinence, early diagnosis and treatment, and condoms help prevent the spread of STDs. However, only abstinence can guarantee that a person will not become infected with an STD.

VOCABULARY LIST

chancre	infectious disease	sexually transmitted
communicable disease	specialist	disease
cryotherapy	microbiologist	spirochetes
direct contact	normal flora bacteria	surveillance
epidemiologist	pathogen	toxin
indirect contact		venereal disease

PRACTICE

Multiple Choice. Choose the best answer.
1. Viruses are
   a. the same as bacteria
   b. used in cryotherapy
   c. the smallest fungi
   d. the smallest pathogen
2. Communicable diseases are caused by
   a. pathogens
   b. cryotherapy
   c. acne
   d. all of these
3. STD stands for
   a. standard treatment disease
   b. sexual trichoid disease
   c. severe trauma disease
   d. sexually transmitted disease
4. What does the US Centers for Disease Control do?
   a. stops epidemics
   b. monitors diseases
   c. controls malaria
   d. controls STDs
5. Direct contact means a disease is spread by
   a. doorknobs
   b. insects
   c. toilet seats
   d. person to person
6. Sexually transmitted diseases are spread by
   a. direct contact
   b. indirect contact
   c. animals
   d. normal flora bacteria

7. Which is not a pathogen?
   a. viruses
   b. bacteria
   c. prototype
   d. fungi
8. The only sure way to prevent the spread of STDs is
   a. marriage
   b. abstinence
   c. condoms
   d. none of these
9. Diseases contracted through sexual activity are
   a. syphilis, malaria, AIDS
   b. AIDS, gonorrhea, syphilis
   c. AIDS, genital warts, malaria
   d. chlamydia, syphilis, toxins
10. A painless open sore on the genitals is called
   a. chancre
   b. gardnerella
   c. toxins
   d. surveillance

Matching. Match each word with its definition or description.
1. how flu and tuberculosis are spread
2. spread by sexual contact
3. any disease-causing microorganism
4. freezing with liquid nitrogen
5. traces spread of communicable disease
6. disease spreads from person to person
7. tracking of disease
8. corkscrew-shaped bacteria
9. studies microscopic organisms
10. present in the body but do not cause sickness or disease

a. cryotherapy
b. direct contact
c. epidemiologist
d. indirect contact
e. normal flora bacteria
f. microbiologist
g. pathogen
h. sexually transmitted
i. spirochete
j. surveillance

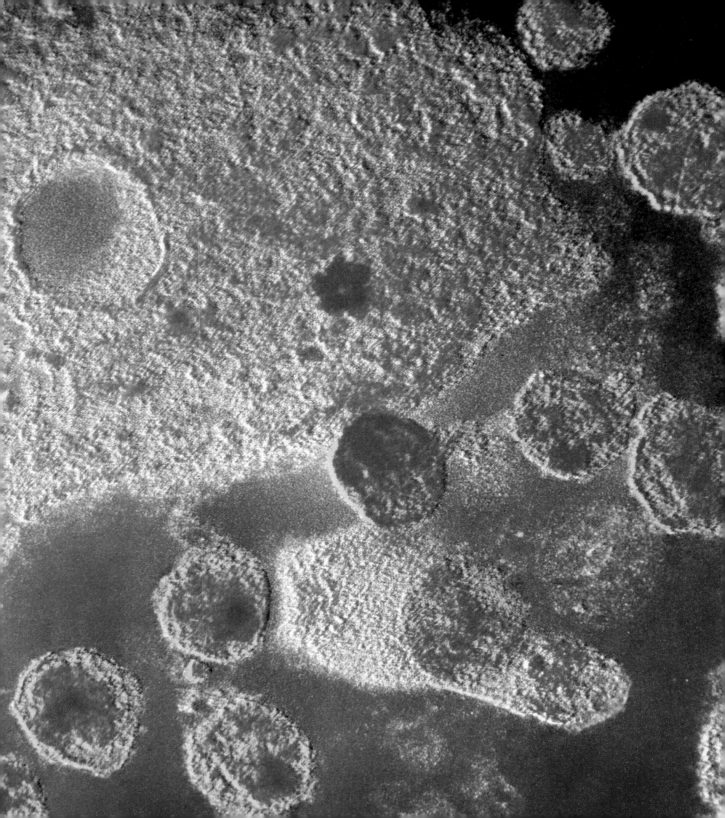

CHAPTER 12

A DEADLY VIRUS

INTRODUCTION

In 1981, a new disease was discovered. When young men in several parts of the United States began dying of a rare type of cancer called Kaposi's sarcoma, physicians suspected that something was damaging their immune systems. These cases first occurred among homosexual men. As scientists found out more about the disease, it was named acquired immune deficiency syndrome, or AIDS. In 1983, the virus that caused the disease was identified, and in 1985 it was named the human immunodeficiency (im′ myōo nō dē fish′ ən sē) virus, or HIV.

Since many of the people who develop AIDS become infected during their teenage years, this chapter tells you how to avoid getting this fatal disease.

SECTION TITLES

This microphotograph shows the human immunodeficiency virus, the virus that causes AIDS.

12–1 HIV AND AIDS

VOCABULARY
AIDS
HIV
opportunistic infection
retrovirus

OBJECTIVES

- Define the term **AIDS**.
- Describe HIV.
- Describe the action of HIV in the body.

AIDS, the acronym for acquired immune deficiency (dē fish′ ən sē) syndrome, is a disease in which the immune system can no longer protect the body against invasion by pathogens and opportunistic infections.

Opportunistic infections are caused by microbes commonly present in or on the human body or in the environment (fig. 12-1). Normally, these microbes do not cause illness in a person with a healthy immune system. However, if the body's immune system is damaged, these microbes gain a foothold and cause infections. AIDS allows such opportunistic infections to occur.

DID YOU KNOW?
The genetic blueprint for the structure of the HIV is about 100,000 times smaller than the genetic blueprint contained in a human cell.

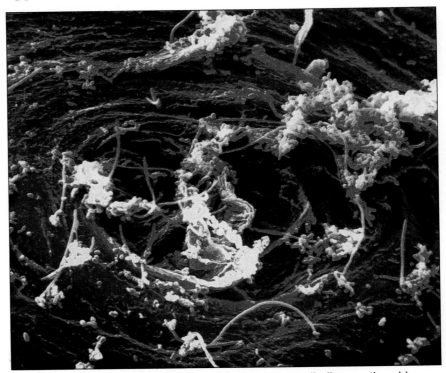

Fig. 12–1 As many as six different bacteria normally live on the skin.

274

In the 1980s, epidemiologists began to trace the number of persons with the symptoms of AIDS. They discovered cases in Europe, Africa, North and South America, and the Caribbean. Within five years, AIDS was found in nearly every country in the world.

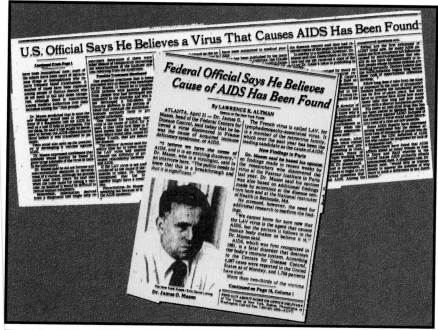

Fig. 12-2 The HIV was first identified in 1984.

When the first cases of AIDS were diagnosed, medical scientists immediately began to look for a cause. Researchers in the United States and France both discovered the virus in 1984 (fig. 12-2). The name given to the virus, **HIV** (human immunodeficiency virus), describes the action of the virus: it makes the immune system deficient. It also distinguishes the virus from similar animal viruses such as the simian immunodeficiency virus (SIV), which infects monkeys (fig. 12-3).

You have learned that viruses are capable of reproducing only in living cells. Viruses have a host cell preference. The common cold viruses attack only the cells of the respiratory tract, the hepatitis virus attacks liver cells, and the rabies virus uses nerve cells for its growth and reproduction. HIV prefers invading the cells that play a major role in defending the body against infection—the white blood cells.

Fig. 12-3 Monkeys are affected by the simian immunodeficiency virus.

TRY THIS 12-1: You Call It

Materials:
   none needed

Procedure:

1. Form a group of two or three. With your group read the scenario below.

> Gary has AIDS. He has Kaposi's sarcoma, and some of the purplish blotches
> from the disease show on his face. He has just boarded a bus and paid his
> fare. The bus driver, recognizing the blotches as a sign of AIDS, says, "I am
> not going to let you on this bus because you have AIDS. I have other passen-
> gers to protect. You will have to get off the bus." The other passengers get
> angry because they are trying to get somewhere, and the bus is just sitting
> there. Some of them yell at the driver; some yell at Gary.

2. Decide as a group how you would answer each question.
   - If you were one of the passengers on the bus, what would you do? Why?
   - What would have been the best thing for Gary to do in this situation?
   - What should the bus driver have done in this situation?
   - Should people who have HIV/AIDS be allowed to ride public transportation? Why?
   - If you were the director of transportation, what kind of policy do you think you might set for situations like this one?
   - Suppose Jesus had been trying to get on the bus behind Gary. What do you think He would have done?

Normally, in a viral infection, the flow of genetic information is from the DNA of the virus to the RNA of the host cell
(fig. 12-4). HIV reverses this flow. The genetic material of HIV
is encoded in RNA. When HIV attacks a cell, the genetic information of the virus passes from its RNA to the host cell's
DNA. Because of this reverse flow of genetic information, HIV
and similar viruses are called **retroviruses** (re′ trō vī rəs).

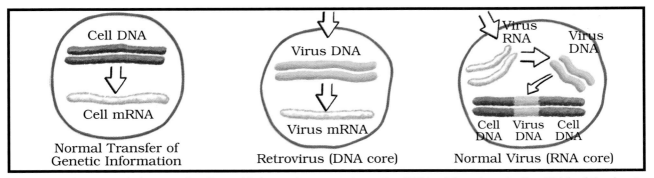

Fig. 12–4 In normal viruses, the flow of information goes from the DNA of the virus to the RNA of the host
cell. In retroviruses the flow is from the RNA of the virus to the DNA of the host cell.

When HIV takes over the cells of the human immune system, it enters into the genetic material of the cells. It acts like a pirate, taking over the cells of the immune system by inserting itself into the DNA of the host cell. HIV grows quietly in the lymph system, gradually destroying white blood cells called T-helper cells. When enough of these cells are destroyed, the infected person begins to have the symptoms of AIDS. Figure 12-5 summarizes how HIV affects the body.

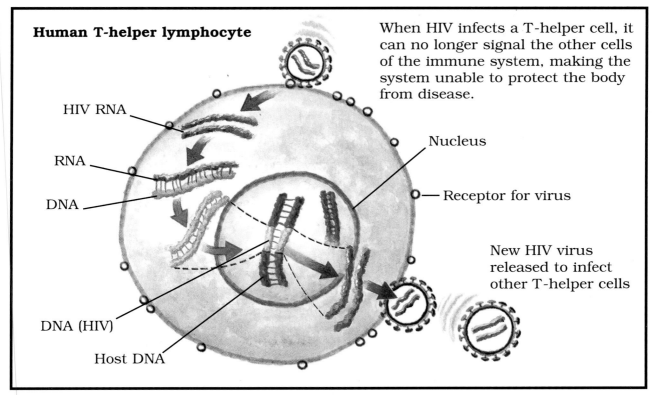

Human T-helper lymphocyte

HIV RNA

RNA

DNA

DNA (HIV)

Host DNA

When HIV infects a T-helper cell, it can no longer signal the other cells of the immune system, making the system unable to protect the body from disease.

Nucleus

Receptor for virus

New HIV virus released to infect other T-helper cells

Fig. 12-5 HIV attacks the body by attacking the T-helper cells, causing them to produce copies of HIV virus.

REVIEW IT

1. What does the acronym AIDS stand for?
2. How is HIV different from other viruses?
3. What cells in the body are attacked by HIV?

12–2 TRANSMISSION OF HIV

HIV cannot multiply outside of living cells. It is unable to survive for more than a few hours outside the body. Only in stored blood, blood products, or a laboratory viral culture can it survive longer.

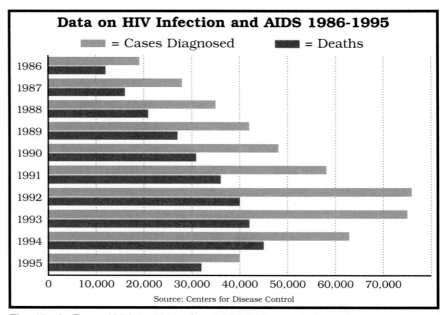

Fig. 12–6 From 1986 to 1995 about 500,000 people have been diagnosed with AIDS, and more than 300,000 have died from the disease.

Once a person is infected with HIV, he or she is infected for life (fig. 12-6). Since there is no cure for HIV infection and the treatment extends life for only a short while, AIDS is a fatal disease. Research is being conducted in many countries to find a vaccine that will protect against HIV and treatment that will be effective in halting the disease (fig. 12-7). Since the virus directly attacks the body's means of fighting off disease and infection, this research is very difficult.

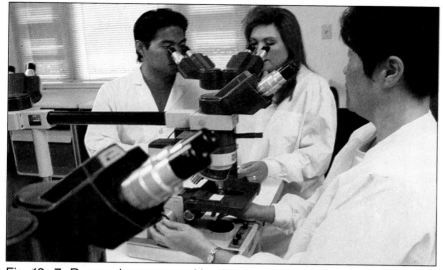
Fig. 12–7 Researchers are working hard to find ways of treating and preventing AIDS.

Infected persons can transmit HIV to other individuals as long as they live. Figure 12-8 summarizes how HIV is and is not transmitted.

HIV is spread by direct contact between people, through certain body fluids, and between mother and unborn baby.

Not all body fluids transmit HIV. Those which contain enough viruses to transmit HIV are semen, blood, vaginal fluid, and pus. Body fluids such as saliva and tears occasionally have the virus in very low concentrations; but scientists believe these are not sufficient to transmit HIV.

RESEARCH IT

Find the number of health professionals infected with HIV as a direct result of their work.

| TRANSMISSION OF HIV ||
No	Yes
Mosquitoes	Sexual intercourse
Touching hands	Blood transfusion
Hugging	IV drug use
Food	Mother to baby
Dishes	Exposure to body fluids
Clothing	blood
Toilet seats	semen
Sneezing	vaginal fluids
Coughing	pus

Fig. 12–8

Body fluids are shared when persons have any kind of sexual intercourse: vaginal, anal, or oral. Blood may also be shared by using the same needles (as in drug abuse) or by health-care workers who get stuck with an infected needle. Blood is also shared when individuals receive a transfusion of blood or blood products. In the United States and Canada, however, blood banks have been testing donated blood to make this risk very small (about 1/150,000). Although some people think you can get HIV by donating blood, this is a mistaken belief (fig. 12-9).

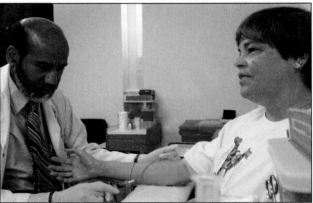

Fig. 12–9 HIV is not spread by donating blood.

HIV has been shown not to be transmitted by mosquitoes or other biting insects (fig. 12-10). HIV survives only a short time outside the human body and does not multiply in mosquitoes, according to laboratory tests.

Neither is there any evidence that HIV can be transmitted by indirect contact—on hands, food, dishes, clothing, or toilet seats. Airborne transmission by dust or droplets, as in sneezing, has never been documented by health scientists.

Fig. 12–10 Mosquitoes and other biting insects do not pass HIV from person to person.

However, you should be aware that epidemiologists discuss risks and probabilities, rather than certainties, about HIV transmission. There is no risk so low that it is zero. In other words, no scientist can guarantee that a person will never get HIV in any way other than those listed. They can only tell you ways in which HIV can be transmitted, which factors are high risk, and which ones are low.

REVIEW IT

1. How is HIV transmitted?
2. How is HIV *not* transmitted?

CLASS ACTIVITY 12-2: Hey, Wanna Trade?

Question: How is HIV spread?

Materials:
> construction paper (5 cm x 5 cm)
> Special Master R319

Procedure:
1. Obtain a square of colored construction paper.
2. When given the signal, you may trade your square of construction paper with anyone else in exchange for theirs, or you may choose not to trade. If you choose to trade squares, record the color you traded for in the data table.
3. Continue trading as many times as you want during the time allotted. Be sure to record the color traded for each time.
4. When time is called, stop all trading. Record the color of paper you ended up with and complete the rest of the table.
5. When the data table is complete and all questions have been answered, get a copy of the Special Master.

Data:

Trade Number	Red	Orange	Yellow	Green	Blue	Purple
1						
2						
3						
4						
5						
6						
7						
8						
9						
10						

Questions:
1. Was the number of trades you made average, above average, or below average for the class?
2. Did anyone not want to trade with you?
3. Did anyone try to get you to trade even though you didn't want to? How?
4. What color did you trade for the most? What color did you trade for the least?
5. Is the color you ended up with the same color you started with?
6. Explain how this activity illustrates the spread of HIV.

Conclusion: Write 3–5 sentences about what you learned from this activity.

In the spring of 1995 information came out of the African country of Zaire that a mysterious disease had broken out in small town of Kikwit. According to early reports, 59 people had died, and panic had gripped the area. Within days of the first reports, scientists from the World Health Organization (WHO) and the Centers for Disease Control (CDC) arrived in the small town and found preliminary evidence that the Ebola virus was responsible.

Ebola, named for the Ebola River area in northern Zaire where the first documented case occurred, is one of a family of viruses called hemorrhagic viruses because of the internal bleeding they cause. The symptoms of Ebola infection include fever, muscle pain, headache, sore throat, vomiting, diarrhea, rash, and severe internal bleeding. It is transmitted by direct contact with infected blood, body fluids, organs, or contaminated needles. While treatment can be given to relieve symptoms, there is no known cure for Ebola.

In the Kikwit outbreak, WHO and CDC experts developed a plan of attack. This plan consisted of three goals: halt the spread of infection, develop techniques for early diagnosis, and determine the origin of the virus.

Investigators found that many victims of Ebola were family members of infected vic-

tims, who had contracted disease as they had cared for their sick family members. They also found a large number of health-care providers infected as a result of caring for Ebola patients. Education, improved sanitation, and adequate supplies helped halt the spread of infection.

Early diagnosis of Ebola depended upon observable symptoms, but since the incubation period could be up to 21 days, this did little to prevent the transmission of the disease. Then it was discovered that fresh tissue samples could be tested for the presence of the virus. A CDC pathologist developed a technique for testing preserved samples of skin. This technique allowed field workers to collect a skin sample of a suspected Ebola victim.

Finally, scientists searched for the source of the Ebola virus. They had suspected that the virus resided in a local species of animal that, while carrying the disease, did not get sick from it. Scientists trapped hundreds of different species but were unsuccessful in finding the host.

By the fall of 1995, the Ebola epidemic that killed nearly 250 people in Kikwit was over. However, scientists believe that the deadly virus is just hiding and that it is just a matter of time before another outbreak occurs. But this time, they will be ready with effective tools for fighting Ebola.

Questions:

1. What is a hemorrhagic virus?

2. How is Ebola spread?

3. Why was observing the symptoms not a useful tool in the diagnosis of the disease?

4. What tools do health official now have to fight future Ebola outbreaks that they did not have at the beginning of the Kikwik outbreak?

12–3 RESPONSIBLE SEXUAL BEHAVIOR

OBJECTIVES

- Explain how teenagers can prevent the transmission of HIV.
- Describe how health-care and emergency workers can prevent the spread of HIV.
- Identify ways of obtaining current information about HIV and other viral diseases.

VOCABULARY

promiscuous

Since many persons with AIDS contracted the virus when they were teenagers, teenagers hold a key to controlling the epidemic. You will rarely see a teenager with AIDS, because the time from infection to symptoms of AIDS can be eight to ten years (fig. 12-11). During that time, however, the person can infect anyone with whom he or she has sexual intercourse or shares blood through needles or syringes. Also, a pregnant woman infected with HIV can pass the virus to her unborn baby.

DID YOU KNOW?

Blood tests will miss only 1 infected person out of every 10,000 tested.

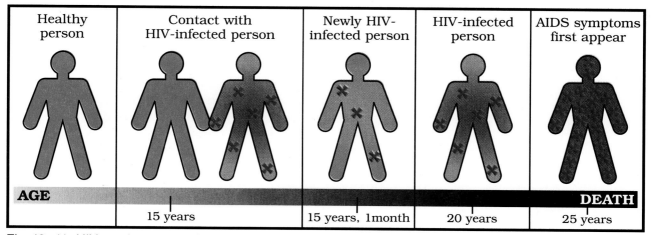

Healthy person	Contact with HIV-infected person	Newly HIV-infected person	HIV-infected person	AIDS symptoms first appear

AGE

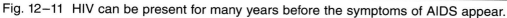

| | 15 years | 15 years, 1month | 20 years | 25 years | DEATH |

Fig. 12–11 HIV can be present for many years before the symptoms of AIDS appear.

As you have learned, the sexual urge is one of the strongest in human nature. Yet, deciding to remain abstinent and postpone sex until marriage is the best way to avoid the transmission of HIV. When you are ready to get married, learn all you can about your prospective partner. Ask questions about any previous history of sex and drug abuse. Ask for an HIV blood test even if you trust the other person; people who trust each other should be willing to find out for sure.

People who are **promiscuous**, who have sex with numerous sexual partners, or those who have sex with individuals of the same sex, or who have sexual relations with someone other than their marriage partner greatly increase their risk of getting HIV. They may think they can hide their activity, but the virus has no favorites. While it appears that males can transmit the virus more readily than females, there is no safety in that information.

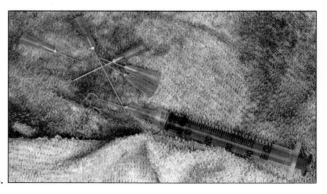

Fig. 12–12 The HIV can be passed through used IV needles.

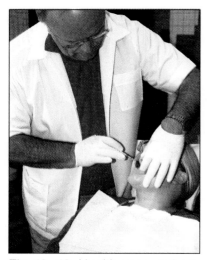

Fig. 12–13 Health care workers take precautions to prevent HIV infection when working with patients.

You may have heard that using a condom provides "safe sex." This is not safe sex; it is really sex that is somewhat safer than high-risk sex. While condoms may give some protection against the exchange of body fluids, they are not totally safe. Studies have found that the tiny pores present in condoms, which are 50 times larger than the HIV, allow the virus to leak through about 33 percent of the time. In other studies condoms have been shown to break approximately 14 percent of the time. The unreliability of condoms is an important reason for choosing abstinence as the only sure protection against HIV infection.

Sharing needles for intravenous drug use is another high-risk behavior for the transmission of HIV (fig. 12-12). Being a sexual partner of an IV drug abuser is also high risk. Even experimenting one time can be one time too many.

Health-care and emergency workers have to take special precautions to avoid HIV. They need to wear gloves whenever they are handling blood, and face masks if they expect blood to splash or splatter (fig. 12-13). Dentists and dental hygienists wear gloves and masks for this reason. They also have to adequately sterilize their instruments so they do not transmit the virus from one patient to another. Blood-bank technicians and others who draw blood need to wear gloves and to handle their syringes, needles, and vials with care (fig. 12-14).

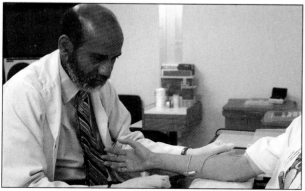

Fig. 12–14 Gloves and careful handling of syringes and needles help protect blood-bank workers.

You can obtain current scientific information about HIV and AIDS by reading magazines and newspapers and by watching TV programs. These media report the latest discoveries made by epidemiologists and other health scientists, who continue to study the virus and the worldwide epidemic it has caused (fig. 12-15). It pays to keep informed about this virus, for knowledge may save your life or the life of someone you love.

God's plan for this world never included diseases such as AIDS. All disease came when Satan changed God's perfect world. Until Christ comes again, there will be epidemics such as AIDS. God's plan is not an arbitrary limitation of our liberty or pleasure. It is a guideline for our happiness and well-being as a teen, as a young adult, and as a potential marriage partner.

While sin and its effects continue to plague Earth, Christians will show their love for Christ by caring for those with disease, including AIDS. They also look forward to Earth made new, where there will be no disease and no death.

Fig. 12–15 Magazines and newspapers present new findings about HIV and AIDS.

REVIEW IT

1. How can teenagers prevent the spread of HIV?
2. How can health-care and emergency workers prevent the spread of HIV?
3. Where can you find current information about HIV and other diseases?

CHAPTER 12 WRAP-UP

THINKING SKILLS: The Main Idea

Although experimenting, observing, and recording data are important activities of science, reading is just as important. Most scientists spend more time reading articles and papers of other scientists than they do in any other activity. When scientists read, they must be able to identify and understand the main ideas and the supporting details.

Read the text below and identify the main idea and the supporting details for each paragraph.

AIDS kills. This disease is sweeping the world. In 1981, the United States had only 265 reported cases of AIDS. But by 1992, more than 100,000 people had died from AIDS—double the number of Americans killed in the Vietnam War. This epidemic threatens all of us. But each one of us has the power to stop the spread of AIDS.

This can be done by changing behavior. In the early 1980s, doctors saw their first cases of AIDS. They warned people to change their behaviors, or there would be more cases. But not many people listened. Persons with the AIDS virus didn't feel sick or look sick. So they didn't believe AIDS could happen to them. They were wrong. Soon, first one and then another got sick and sicker—and died.

Today doctors continue to warn people about risky and deadly behaviors. But some people refuse to change their lifestyles. So AIDS, once found in only a few cities, has spread to smaller communities around the world. Now, it is not only deadly, it is also common throughout the world.

But there is something we can do. We can take control. We can rise to the challenge, and we can fight back. We can stop deadly behaviors that will kill us, avoid risky behaviors that put us in danger, and practice healthful behaviors to stay AIDS-free and worry-free. And we can do more. We can promote healthful behaviors to our friends and explain healthful behaviors to others. Working together, we can stop the spread of AIDS.

Paragraph	Main Idea	Supporting Details
1		
2		
3		
4		

QUESTIONS AND PROBLEMS

1. Why are condoms not always a safe protection against the spread of HIV?
2. Why can't you get AIDS by donating blood?
3. How do teenagers hold the key to stopping the spread of HIV?
4. What is the difference between HIV and SIV?
5. Why does the term *safe sex* contradict itself?
6. Why don't all people who are infected with HIV have AIDS?
7. How would following God's plan for sexuality change the spread of diseases such as AIDS?
8. Why is the spread of HIV more difficult to stop than the spread of other STDs?
9. Why are promiscuous people more likely to get an STD?
10. How likely is it that a person could get AIDS from using a public restroom? Why?
11. Why are people who do not have AIDS rarely affected by opportunistic infections?

RESEARCH

1. Make a series of color posters that shows how the HIV attacks the immune system.
2. Find out what resources are available in your community for people with HIV and AIDS. Write a report on your findings.
3. Use a current *Reader's Guide to Periodical Literature* to find at least three articles on current AIDS research and treatment. Write a reading report on each article you read.
4. Develop a creative bulletin board entitled "Ways you don't get AIDS—ways you do get AIDS."
5. Study to find various treatments and drugs used to treat AIDS patients. Make an oral presentation on your findings.

REVIEW

HIGHLIGHTS

1. AIDS is the acronym for acquired immune deficiency syndrome, which is a disease of the human immune system.
2. HIV is a retrovirus that attacks the human immune system, making the immune system unable to protect the body against infection.
3. HIV is transmitted through direct contact with blood, semen, vaginal fluid, and pus during sexual intercourse or by using infected needles.
4. HIV is not transmitted by casual contact such as shaking hands or hugging; through food, dishes, clothing, or toilet seats; or by mosquitoes.
5. Teenagers can help prevent the spread of HIV by abstaining from sexual activity until marriage.
6. Health-care and emergency workers wear gloves and masks, and they sterilize instruments to prevent HIV from spreading.
7. You can learn about HIV and other viral diseases by paying attention to the media (newspapers, magazines, radio, TV, etc.).

VOCABULARY LIST

AIDS   opportunistic infection   retrovirus

HIV   promiscuous

PRACTICE

Multiple Choice. Choose the best answer.

1. AIDS attacks the
   a. respiratory system
   b. integumentary system
   c. immune system
   d. none of these

2. HIV is transmitted
   a. by sexual contact
   b. in certain body fluids
   c. from mother to baby
   d. all of these

3. AIDS is associated with
   a. drug use
   b. opportunistic infections
   c. homosexual behavior
   d. all of these

4. Once a person is infected with HIV, he or she
   a. is infected for life
   b. has AIDS
   c. will give it to others
   d. will know right away

5. To prevent the transmission of HIV, teenagers should
   a. be promiscuous
   b. remain abstinent
   c. get married
   d. stay in school

6. "Safe sex" really means
   a. safer than high-risk sex
   b. mom didn't find out
   c. using a condom
   d. none of these

7. HIV is not transmitted by
   a. indirect contact
   b. body fluids
   c. sexual intercourse
   d. direct contact

8. Where should you learn about HIV?
   a. TV, friends, radio
   b. friends, newspapers, TV
   c. TV, older brother or sister
   d. TV, newspapers, magazines

9. The time from infection with HIV to the first symptoms of AIDS ranges from
   a. 6 months to 1 year
   b. 1 to 2 years
   c. 8 to 10 years
   d. 2 days to 2 weeks

10. Health-care workers prevent the spread of HIV
    a. with masks
    b. with sterilized instruments
    c. with gloves
    d. all of these

Matching. Match each word with its definition or description.
1. transmitted by exposure to body fluids
2. uses the DNA of the host cell
3. allows other diseases to occur
4. gives an infection for life
5. diseases that occur because of a weakened immune system
6. attacks the T-cells of the immune system
7. people who have sex with numerous partners
8. genetic information is coded in the RNA
9. is not transmitted by casual contact
10. caused by pathogens commonly present in the body

a. AIDS
b. HIV
c. opportunistic infections
d. promiscuous
e. retrovirus

CAREERS

AIDS Counselor

Description of Work
AIDS counselors provide support and assistance for those suffering from AIDS. They also provide instructions for AIDS prevention to high-risk groups and information to the general public. Some AIDS counselors talk to people who are about to have an AIDS test. If the test is positive, they then provide advice and counseling.

Personal Qualifications
AIDS counselors must be good communicators. They must be able to work with people who are very ill and severely depressed due to the effects of the disease. They must be compassionate and caring to their patients.

Requirements
A high-school diploma. Experience is more important than education. Four to six years of college is required for paid positions.

Career Information
American Foundation
   for AIDS Research
5900 Wilshire Boulevard,
2nd Floor
Los Angeles, CA 90036

Pathologist

Description of Work
Pathologists are life scientists who study the nature, causes, and effects of disease in all forms of plant and animal life. They concentrate on the changes that disease causes in organs, tissues, and cells. Pathologists work in hospitals and medical laboratories and at colleges, universities, and medical schools. They do laboratory tests to diagnose disease in the patients of other physicians.

Personal Qualifications
Pathologists should be able to absorb a great deal of information and have the patience to complete lengthy research projects. They must be careful and precise workers. Pathologists must be able to express their ideas well orally or in writing.

Requirements
A high-school diploma and four years of college. They must continue education to obtain an advanced degree.

Career Information
American Board of Pathology
P.O. Box 25915
Tampa, FL 33622

School Counselor

Description of Work
School counselors help students understand their abilities, interests, talents, and personality characteristics so that the students can develop realistic academic and career options. They use interviews, counseling sessions, tests, or other tools to assist them in evaluating and advising students. They work with students individually, in small groups, or with entire classes.

Personal Qualifications
School counselors must like to work with people. They must maintain the privacy and confidentiality of the students' concerns. They also must be very good listeners and communicators. Counselors must be able to provide encouragement and help to their clients.

Requirements
A high-school diploma and four to six years of college. It is also advised to be nationally certified by the National Board for Certified Counselors (NBCC).

Career Information
American Association for
   Counseling and Development
5999 Stevenson Avenue
Alexandria, VA 22304

School Nurse

Description of Work
School nurses provide health-care services to students. They plan school health programs and participate in medical examinations and reviews. They also administer immunizations, provide first aid, and maintain health records of students.

Personal Qualifications
School nurses must be caring and responsible. They must also enjoy working with children. Nurses must be able to take care of emergencies, as well as providing compassion to sick students.

Requirements
A high-school diploma and two to four years of college. A license is also required in most states.

Career Information
American Nurses Association
2420 Pershing Road
Kansas City, MO 64108

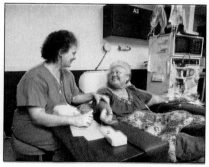

Licensed Practical Nurse

Description of Work
Licensed practical nurses (LPNs) help physicians and registered nurses (RNs) care for patients. They have the technical knowledge to perform routine nursing duties. Most licensed practical nurses work in hospitals, nursing homes, other health-care institutions, and private homes.

Personal Qualifications
Licensed practical nurses must enjoy working with people. They must be able to keep patients in good spirits. They must be able to follow directions accurately and keep correct, up-to-date records. Licensed practical nurses must keep an even temper at all times.

Requirements
A high-school diploma is preferred and one year at an accredited school. LPNs must also obtain a license.

Career Information
National Federation of
   Licensed Practical Nurses
P.O. Box 18088
Raleigh, NC 27619

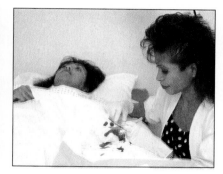

Nurse Practitioner

Description of Work
Nurse practitioners provide general medical care and treatment under the direction of a physician to patients in medical facilities, such as clinics, health centers, or public health agencies. They perform physical examinations and preventive health measures. Practitioners record findings and discuss cases with the physician to formulate patient care plans.

Personal Qualifications
Nurse practitioners must be able to work with people. They must be able to give and take responsibility. They must be good communicators and listeners. Nurse practitioners must be able to take information and settle on a diagnosis of the patient's problem.

Requirements
A high-school diploma and two to four years of college. A license is also required in most states.

Career Information
American Nurses Association
2420 Pershing Road
Kansas City, MO 64108

UNIT III

FORCES AND MOTION

INTRODUCTION

Near the top of a mountain, a skier races down a steep slope. Fresh powdery snow sprays from her skis. It's cold here, but the thrill of speeding downhill brings millions of people out to ski resorts every year. They buy boots, wax, goggles, and hats. They dream of powdery snow and perfect turns. They imagine smooth, fast runs. But a scientist may look at the same hill and think of forces and motion, acceleration and friction.

When you have finished this unit, you should understand what makes the skiers move downhill and stop at the bottom. You will also discover why gliding down the hill is work.

CHAPTER TITLES

Skiing through fresh powder is exhilarating.

293

CHAPTER 13

FORCE

INTRODUCTION

The huge scraper is used to smooth uneven areas of land. One week it may level land, preparing for a building project. The following week it may be used to build a highway, part of a dam, or level a field for planting. Scrapers are strong, heavy pieces of machinery used to move soil and level land. They are a symbol of power and force.

This chapter will teach you about the idea of force and what it does and about work and how it happens.

SECTION TITLES

Machines such as this large scraper help move soil and level land.

13-1 FORCE

force
mechanical force
newton

Fig. 13–1 The girl at the plate uses the force of her swing and the mass of the bat to send the ball into the outfield.

OBJECTIVES

- Define the term **force**.
- Identify several forces active in the universe.

The softball player is standing at home plate. The pitcher pitches the ball toward her. She swings, hits the ball, and sends it into the outfield (fig. 13-1). The softball player used the bat and the speed at which it was swung to force the ball to fly over the third baseman. In science, a **force** is a push or a pull on any object. In the softball player's case, the force was largely due to the size of the bat. When you shoot marbles with your thumb, the force is small (fig. 13-2). In both of these examples, people use their muscles to create the pushing force. The force created by muscles is called **mechanical force**.

When people row a boat, they pull on the oars to make the boat move through the water (fig. 13-3). In some activities, such as bicycle racing, people create force by pushing and pulling. As the girl races on her bicycle, she pushes down with the bottom of her foot while pulling up with the toes of her other foot.

Mechanical force is also produced by most machines (fig. 13-4). For example, when a carpenter plugs in a power saw, the motor produces a mechanical force and turns the saw blade. A similar force is produced when the robotic arm of an assembly machine is activated (fig. 13-5).

Fig. 13–4 Electric can openers and similar appliances provide a mechanical force.

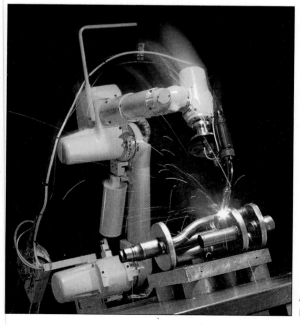

Fig. 13–5 Robotic machines in assembly plants produce a mechanical force.

TRY THIS 13-1: The Lazy Coin

Materials:

index card (3" x 5")   styrofoam cup
quarter

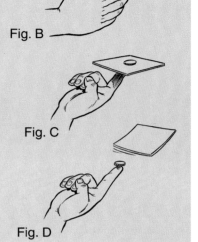

Fig. A

Fig. B

Procedure:

1. Cut the index card in half so it is about 6 cm x 6 cm square.
2. Cover the cup with the card and put the coin on the card as shown in figure A.
3. Flick the card sideways so the coin falls into the cup as shown in figure B.
4. Place the card and the coin on the tip of your index finger as shown in figure C.
5. Flick the card sideways so the coin stays on the end of your finger as shown in figure D.
   - What causes the coin to drop into the cup when the card is flicked away?
   - Why doesn't the coin move with the card as it is flicked?
   - What causes the coin to stay on the end of your finger when the card is flicked away?
   - What would happen if the card were pulled slowly?

Fig. C

Fig. D

Fig. 13-6 A spring scale is used to measure force.

You are familiar with mechanical force because you experience it every day in the things you do. Other forces also affect you every day, but you may not be as familiar with them. These forces include gravity, friction, atomic force, electrical force, and magnetic force. They are active throughout the universe and have strong influence on the activities that take place in space and on Earth. These forces will be discussed later in this chapter.

Force is measured in **newtons** (in honor of Sir Isaac Newton). The symbol N is used to identify this unit of force. Various types of spring scales can be used to measure force (fig. 13-6). The greater the mass of an object, the more force it takes to get it moving or to stop it once it is moving. For example, it takes more force to throw a softball 50 m than it does to throw a tennis ball the same distance. Also, the faster an object is to be propelled, the more force it takes.

REVIEW IT

1. What is force?
2. What forces are active in the universe?

13-2 GRAVITY, MASS, AND WEIGHT

OBJECTIVES

- Define the term **gravity.**
- Identify the factors that affect gravitational attraction.
- Distinguish between mass and weight.
- Explain the center of gravity.

VOCABULARY
center of gravity
gravity
mass
weight

A skier races down the hill, water drops 100 m (330 ft) down a waterfall, and an egg falls and smashes on the floor (fig. 13-7). Long ago you learned that gravity causes objects to move, flow, or fall. You probably learned that gravity is the pull of Earth on all objects. But gravity is more than what Earth does.

Fig. 13-7 Skiing down a hill, water flowing over a waterfall, an egg dropping to the floor—all demonstrate the effects of gravitational attraction.

Gravity, or gravitational attraction, is the force of attraction that exists between any two objects. The amount of gravity between two objects depends on their masses and the distance they are apart. An object's **mass** is the amount of matter it has. The greater the mass an object has, the greater force of gravity between it and another object. Since the mass of this book is fairly small, the gravitational attraction you feel for it is unnoticeable. However, since Earth's mass is so great, you feel a strong gravitational attraction for it.

DID YOU KNOW?
Jumping 1 meter (3 ft) on Earth would equal a jump of nearly 5.8 m (19 ft) on the moon. The one-meter jump on Earth would be only 3.2 cm (1 1/4 in) on the sun.

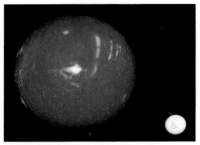

Fig. 13−8 The bowling ball (left) has more mass than the Ping-Pong ball (right).

Earth is so large that it has much more gravity than any object on its surface. The sun has a million times more mass than Earth and therefore has even more gravity than Earth (fig 13-8). The moon, in contrast, is much smaller and has less mass; therefore, it has less gravitational attraction than Earth. In fact the moon has only one-sixth of Earth's gravity (fig. 13-9).

While the mass of an object determines the amount of gravity it has, the gravitational pull an object exerts is not only influenced by mass but also by the distance between one mass and another. Newton discovered that the distance between two objects affects the amount of attraction each is

Fig. 13−9 Because the moon's mass is less than Earth's, you would be able to jump higher on the moon than on Earth.

able to exert on the other. He found that when the distance between two objects increased, their pull on each other decreased. When the distance decreased, the gravitational pull increased (fig. 13-10).

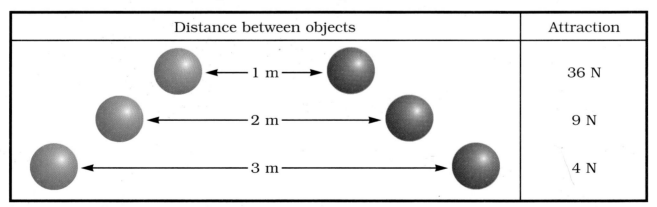

Distance between objects	Attraction
←— 1 m —→	36 N
←——— 2 m ———→	9 N
←———— 3 m ————→	4 N

Fig. 13−10 An English scientist, Sir Isaac Newton, discovered that the distance between objects affected their gravitational attraction.

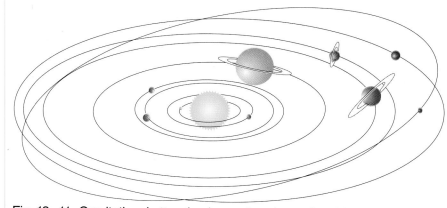

Fig. 13–11 Gravitational attraction keeps the planets in orbit around the sun.

Fig. 13–12 Because the student's finger is at the center of mass of the meterstick, the meterstick balances.

The sun's mass and gravitational pull are so gigantic that they keep Earth and other planets in orbit around it (fig. 13-11). But because Earth is very close to you and the sun is very far away, the sun's gravitational attraction does not pull you from Earth.

Gravity not only helps to keep planets in orbit around the sun and holds us to Earth, it also enables us to balance things. In figure 13-12 a student is pointing at the midpoint of a meterstick. Half the meterstick's mass is on the left side, and half is on the right side. The midpoint of the meterstick represents the center of its mass. Figure 13-13 shows a student balancing a meterstick and a hammer. Her finger is located exactly in the middle of the meterstick, just below the center of mass of the meterstick. The hammer is balanced on her finger very near the head of the hammer, just below the hammer's center of mass. Gravity pulls down on the left side of each object exactly as hard as it does on the right side. This point of balance is called the **center of gravity** and is located exactly at the center of mass.

DID YOU KNOW?

You would weigh less on the top of Mt. Everest, at an elevation of 8 882 m (29 141 ft) than you would standing on the floor of Death Valley, at an elevation of 86 m (282 ft) below sea level. The reason is that on the top of Mt. Everest, you are farther away from Earth's center of gravity, resulting in a smaller gravitational pull and less weight. Standing on the floor of Death Valley, you are closer to the center of gravity, resulting in a greater gravitational pull and a greater weight.

Fig. 13–13 Any object will balance if it is supported at its center of mass.

RESEARCH IT
Find the geographic centers of the United States and Canada and mark them on a map of North America.

Fig. 13–14 Neither the apparatus (left) nor the boulder (right) looks as though it should balance.

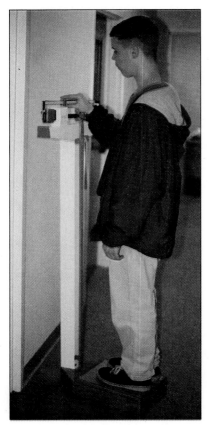

Fig. 13–15 On Earth you weigh more than you would on the moon.

Any object that balances must be positioned so that its center of gravity is directly above or below the point on which it is balancing. For example, in order for you to balance on the toes of one foot, your center of gravity must be directly above your toes. The apparatus and rock in figure 13-14 both look as though they should fall, but, as you can see, their center of gravity is directly in line with the point of balance. This alignment causes the objects to balance.

In addition to affecting balance, gravity also affects weight. For example, suppose that on Earth when you stand on your bathroom scale, you have a weight of 420 N (92 lbs) (fig. 13-15). Now imagine that you can travel to the moon in just a few minutes. When you step out of the spaceship that transported you and stand on the bathroom scale, it reads 70 N (15 lbs). Amazing! how could you lose 350 N (77 lbs) in just the few minutes it took to get from Earth to the moon?

The difference is gravity. On Earth and on the moon you have exactly the same mass. But the gravitational pull of Earth on your mass is six times as great as the moon's gravitational force, so you weigh six times more on Earth than on the moon.

The pull of gravity, or the gravitational attraction of gravity, is determined by the mass of an object and the closeness of that object to the center of gravity. The **weight** of an object is a measure of the pull of gravity on the object. Unlike mass,

Planet	Wt (lbs)	Planet	Wt (lbs)
Earth	100	Saturn	132
Mercury	38	Uranus	93
Venus	90	Neptune	123
Mars	38	Pluto	3
Jupiter	287	The Moon	16
		The Sun	2790

Fig. 13-16

which does not vary, weight varies according to mass and distance. Because the objects in our solar system, the sun, planets, moons, have different masses and sizes, your weight would vary, depending on which you were standing (fig. 13-16).

RESEARCH IT
Construct a line graph that depicts the Olympic records for the men's long jump from 1920 to today. Explain what happened in 1968 that might be related to gravity.

TRY THIS 13-2A: Falling Pennies

Materials:
> index card (3" x 5")
> pennies - 2

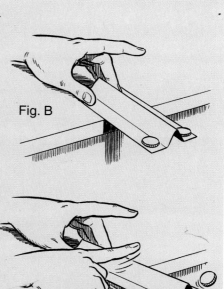

Fig. A

Fig. B

Procedure:
1. Fold the index card in half; then fold each side one-third from the end outward as shown in figure A.
2. Place the pennies on each side of the center ridge of the card and place one end of the card over the edge of a desk or table as shown in figure B.
3. You are going to flick the card with your index finger against the side of the ridge so that penny A will be projected forward and penny B will drop straight down to the floor as shown in figure C. Before you do this, predict which penny will hit the ground first.
   - Which penny do you think will hit first? Why?
4. Flick your finger against the ridge of the card.
   - Did you hear one or two clicks of the falling pennies?
   - What would it mean if you heard one click?
   - Does the direction of a falling object have any influence on its rate of fall?
   - What can you conclude from this experiment?

Fig. C

	SI System	English System
Mass	kilogram	slug (rarely used)
Weight	newton (rarely used)	pound

Fig. 13–17 The kilogram is a measure of mass, not of weight. The SI unit for weight is the newton.

Very often the unit kilogram (kg) is used to refer to weight. In fact, this measurement refers to mass, not weight (fig. 13-17). Pounds are units of weight. Sometimes they are incorrectly compared to kilograms, which is a mass unit. Often kilograms are multiplied by 2.2 to change them to pounds. For practical purposes, this is a useful conversion. But this value works only on Earth. If you were on the moon or another planet, a different conversion would be necessary.

To find weight from mass, you must multiply the mass of an object times gravity. On Earth, gravity is expressed as 10 N/kg. This means that for every kilogram there is a gravity force of 10 newtons acting on it. Therefore, if the mass of an object is 5 kg, its weight is 5 x 10 N/kg, or 50 newtons. Using this method of calculating weight from mass, a person who has a mass of 80 kg would have a weight of 800 newtons on Earth. On the moon the gravity would be 1.7 N/kg. Therefore, a person with a mass of 80 kg would have a weight of 136 N on the moon.

TRY THIS 13-2B: Extend It

Materials:
  metersticks - 6

Procedure:
1. Stack the metersticks any way you wish to get a meterstick to extend as far as possible beyond the edge of a desk or table without falling.

   • How far were you able to get a meterstick to extend beyond the edge?

   • How does your try compare with that of your classmates?

   • What was the greatest distance anyone got a meterstick to extend beyond the edge?

   • Under normal conditions what causes a meterstick to fall when it extends more than half its length?

REVIEW IT

1. What is gravity?
2. What two factors affect the gravitational pull between two objects?
3. What is the difference between mass and weight?
4. In order for an object to balance, where must it rest?

MINIBIOGRAPHYMINIBIOGRAPHYMINIBIOGRAPHYMINIBIOGRAPHYMINIBIOGRAPHY

Henry Cavendish

Henry Cavendish, an English scientist, was born in Nice, France, where he lived until he traveled to England to attend Cambridge University. As a university student, Henry enjoyed investigating a variety of scientific phenomena. His years of observation and experimentation yielded a number of important scientific discoveries. He discovered many of the basic laws of electricity. In the field of chemistry, he discovered the properties and characteristics of hydrogen, an element he called "inflammable air." He also demonstrated that water is a compound made of oxygen and hydrogen.

Perhaps one of Henry Cavendish's most important discoveries occurred in 1798, when he decided to try to determine the density of Earth. In the process of trying to find this answer, he had to determine how to measure the gravitational attraction between objects. Cavendish used a bar with a small mass of lead attached to each end and suspended from a a wire. He placed a large mass of lead near each small lead mass. The bar twisted very slightly as the masses pulled together. Cavendish measured the force of attraction between the two masses and used this information to calculate Earth's density. Cavendish's investigations and the data he collected showed that Sir Isaac Newton's earlier calculations regarding gravity had been correct.

MINIBIOGRAPHYMINIBIOGRAPHYMINIBIOGRAPHYMINIBIOGRAPHYMINIBIOGRAPHY

13-3 FRICTION

OBJECTIVES

- Explain friction
- Describe the types of friction.
- Explain how friction can be increased and decreased.

The bowler takes careful aim, walks up to the toe-line, takes her stride, and releases the ball. The gymnast jumps up and grasps one of the uneven parallel bars and begins his routine. In both of these instances, friction is at work (fig. 13-18). **Friction** is the force opposing motion between two objects that are in contact. The bowler wants the ball to slide easily out of her fingers when she releases it. She may make sure her hands are dry or use a little talcum powder to reduce the friction. The gymnast wants to make sure that his hands do not slip off when he grasps the bar and may use rosin on his hands to increase friction.

Fig. 13-18 Friction is present between the bowling ball and the floor and between the gymnast's hands and the bar.

Fig. 13-19 Friction keeps bike tires from slipping around on the road.

Friction keeps your feet from slipping out from under you, allows you to pick up objects, keeps the tires of your bike gripping the road, and causes the brakes to stop your bike when necessary (fig. 13-19). Friction also causes the lead of your pencil or ink of your pen to rub off onto your paper when you write. As you can see, life without this force would be difficult.

Scientists identify three types of friction: static friction, sliding friction, and rolling friction (fig. 13-20).

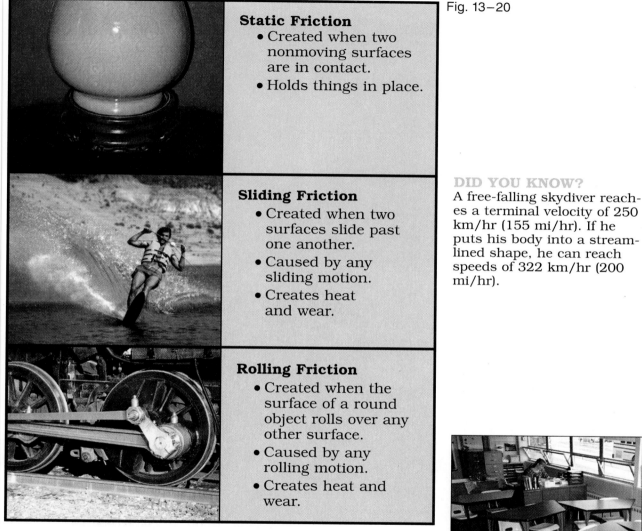

Fig. 13—20

Static Friction
- Created when two nonmoving surfaces are in contact.
- Holds things in place.

Sliding Friction
- Created when two surfaces slide past one another.
- Caused by any sliding motion.
- Creates heat and wear.

Rolling Friction
- Created when the surface of a round object rolls over any other surface.
- Caused by any rolling motion.
- Creates heat and wear.

Imagine that you have the job of sweeping the floor of the classroom in figure 13-21. To do this, you must slide all the desks to one side of the room. As you push the desks, they rub against the floor. The friction force between the floor and the desks makes it difficult to move them. How could you make the desks slide across the floor more easily? One way would be to smear oil all over the floor, but this is quite messy. Another way would be to wax the floor.

Fig. 13—21 Reducing the friction between the desks and the floor makes moving them an easier job.

Both oil and wax reduce friction and make it easier to slide the desks. Substances that reduce friction in this way are called **lubricants** (lōō′ bri kənts) (fig. 13-22).

Fig. 13–22 Lubricants such as these help reduce frictional forces.

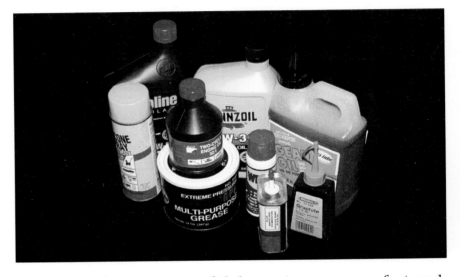

Many different types of lubricants are manufactured. Each one is designed to be used under certain conditions. The heat and wear caused by the friction between moving parts in engines and machines can be reduced by using lubricants. Scientists and engineers are constantly working to find better lubricants that will reduce friction and make engines and machines last longer. Friction can also be decreased by decreasing the force pushing the surfaces together or by making surfaces smoother (fig. 13-23).

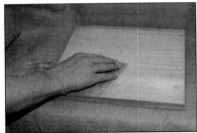

Fig. 13–23 Sanding helps smooth the surfaces of furniture.

While in many cases it is important to reduce friction, there are times when it is necessary to increase friction. For example, driving on an icy road, braking a car, and sanding a piece of wood are all instances in which frictional forces must be increased. Friction can be increased on the road by sprinkling sand, salt, or other de-icers on the ice (fig. 13-24). Friction in braking can be increased by applying more force. Both applying more force and using coarser sandpaper will increase friction when sanding a piece of wood.

Fig. 13–24 People use various de-icers on driveways and sidewalks to increase friction.

REVIEW IT

1. What is friction?
2. What are the types of friction?
3. How is friction decreased? Increased?

CLASS ACTIVITY 13-3: Friction

Question: How does sliding friction compare to rolling friction?

Materials:

board (1 x 10) - 1 m
block
spring scale

twine - 1 m
wooden dowels (0.5 x 15 cm) - 10

Procedure:

1. Tie the twine to the screw eye in the block so that when the twine is pulled, the block moves.

2. Pull the block slowly across a rough surface, such as a sidewalk or parking lot. (Make sure the area used is level.) Determine the force needed to keep the block moving (fig.A). Record.

3. Repeat step 2, this time placing the dowels under the block. Keep the dowels under the block as it is pulled by removing the dowels in the back and putting them in the front of the block as it moves along (fig. B).

4. Repeat steps 2 and 3, this time pulling the block along the top (length) of the board, then rolling the block along the top of the board.

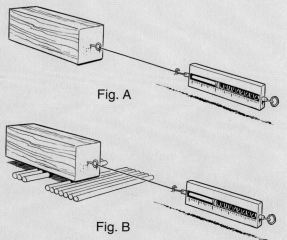

Fig. A

Fig. B

Data:

Surface	Type of Friction	Amount of Force
Concrete	Sliding	
Concrete	Rolling	
Board	Sliding	
Board	Rolling	

Questions:

1. Which of the four trials required the greatest force to keep the block moving? Which required the least?

2. How did the amount of force compare between the sliding friction and rolling friction for each surface?

3. Would more force be required to keep the block moving using two dowels rather than 10? Test your hypothesis and find out.

4. Would more force be required to pull the block over a piece of hardwood or softwood? Explain.

Conclusion: Write 3-5 sentences about what you learned from this activity.

13-4 OTHER FORCES

elastic force
electrical force
magnetic force
magnetite
nuclear force

OBJECTIVES

- Describe elastic force.
- Explain nuclear force.
- Distinguish between electrical and magnetic forces.

Although mechanical force, gravity, and friction are three common forces, they are not the only forces at work in the universe. Other forces include elastic force, nuclear force, electrical force, and magnetic force. Study figure 13-25 to learn what these forces are and how they affect things on Earth and in the universe.

Fig. 13-25

Elastic Force

- Created by objects that are stretched, bent, twisted, or compressed that return to their original shape.

- Demonstrated by stretching a rubber band or a coiled spring and releasing it.

Nuclear Force

- Holds the protons in the nucleus of an atom together.

- When an atomic nucleus is split, large amounts of energy are released, showing the enormous strength of the nuclear force.

- When nuclear energy is released all at once, a nuclear explosion occurs.

- When nuclear energy is released under controlled conditions, it can be used to generate electrical energy.

Fig. 13–25 Continued

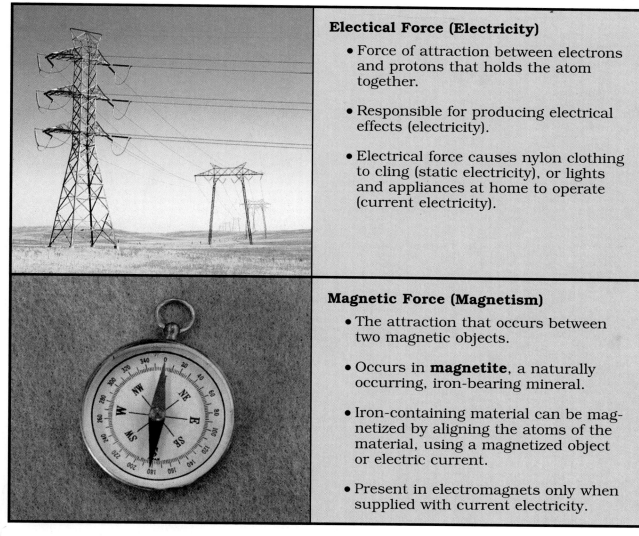

Electical Force (Electricity)

- Force of attraction between electrons and protons that holds the atom together.

- Responsible for producing electrical effects (electricity).

- Electrical force causes nylon clothing to cling (static electricity), or lights and appliances at home to operate (current electricity).

Magnetic Force (Magnetism)

- The attraction that occurs between two magnetic objects.

- Occurs in **magnetite**, a naturally occurring, iron-bearing mineral.

- Iron-containing material can be magnetized by aligning the atoms of the material, using a magnetized object or electric current.

- Present in electromagnets only when supplied with current electricity.

God created the many different types of forces in the universe to keep things running in an orderly fashion. These natural forces operate day after day and year after year.

REVIEW IT

1. What is elastic force?
2. What force holds the nucleus of atoms together?
3. How is magnetic force different from electrical force?

CHAPTER 13 WRAP-UP

THINKING SKILLS: Using Numbers

A characteristic of good scientists is that they can use numbers given them to determine an unknown variable. By adding, subtracting, multiplying, or dividing, scientists can use numbers to obtain a desired outcome.

Using the formula given below, find out how weight, a force, and mass are related to each other. F is the force measured in N (newtons), m is mass measured in kg, and g is gravity measured in N/kg.

$$F = m \times g$$

Use the numbers in the table below and determine the unknown force in each case.

Trial	Mass (kg)	Gravity (N/kg)	Force (N)
1	2.0	10.0	
2	10.5	10.0	
3	8.1	10.0	
4	18.0	10.0	
5	18.0	6.0	

1. If gravity is constant, what happens to the force if the mass of the object increases?
2. If a person moves from one planet to another planet of a lower gravity, what will happen to his or her weight?
3. If the force was equal to 25 N and the mass was 15 kg, what would the pull of gravity be?
4. If you had a mass of 50.2 kg and a gravity pull of 5.0 N/kg, what would the force be?
5. If you had a pull of gravity of 3 N/kg and a force of 150 N, what would the mass be?

QUESTIONS AND PROBLEMS

1. What is the difference between a pound and a kilogram?
2. Would you weigh more on Jupiter or on one of its moons? Explain.
3. How does friction help you walk or run?
4. Which type of musical instrument produces sound as a result of friction. Explain.
5. Can a large planet have less gravitational attraction for you than a small planet? Explain.
6. Does something with more mass always weigh more?
7. How does the presence of natural forces support the idea of a Creator?
8. What happens to friction when objects become wet?
9. What two factors affect the amount of force it takes to act on an object?
10. How do gymnasts increase friction on their hands and feet?
11. What is a newton?
12. How is electrical force created?
13. What is the center of gravity?

RESEARCH

1. Prepare a series of color posters that shows 10 different forces that are observed every day.
2. Research to find out what type of equipment is used in various professional sports to reduce injury due to forces. Prepare an oral report on your findings.
3. Make a photographic study of cars, showing examples of streamlined design. Use the pictures to make a bulletin-board display on streamlining.
4. Research to find out the difference between synthetic motor oils and natural motor oils. Make a poster-sized chart that compares the advantages and disadvantages.
5. Find out how rolling friction is reduced in cars and bicycles. Make one or more drawings to accompany your report.

REVIEW

HIGHLIGHTS

1. Force is any push or pull on an object.
2. Forces active in the universe include gravity, friction, nuclear force, electrical force, and magnetic force.
3. Gravity, or gravitational attraction, is the pull of an object on any other object.
4. The strength of a gravitational attraction is affected by the mass of the objects and their distance apart.
5. An object's center of gravity is the point at which the object can be balanced; this point is located exactly at the center of mass.
6. Mass is the amount of matter in an object and is constant. Weight is the measure of the pull of gravity on an object and varies, depending on distance between the object and the source of gravity.

7. Friction is the force opposing motion between two objects that are in contact.

8. There are three kinds of friction: static friction—friction created when two nonmoving surfaces are in contact; sliding friction—friction created when two surfaces slide past each other; and rolling friction—friction created when the surface of a round object rolls over any other surface.

9. Friction can be reduced by various lubricants, by reducing pressure, and by making surfaces smoother. Friction is increased by increasing pressure and by making surfaces rougher.

10. Elastic force is created when objects are stretched and return to their original shape.

11. Nuclear force is the powerful force that holds the protons together inside the nucleus.

12. Electrical force is created by the flow of electrons through an object; magnetic force is the attraction of magnetic objects on each other.

VOCABULARY LIST

center of gravity	lubricant	nuclear force
elastic force	magnetic force	rolling friction
electrical force	magnetite	sliding friction
force	mass	static friction
friction	mechanical force	weight
gravity	newton	

PRACTICE

Multiple Choice. Choose the best answer.

1. Force is a(n)
   a. imaginary concept
   b. a push or pull
   c. power
   d. none of these

2. Force is measured in
   a. Hertz
   b. Proton units
   c. Newtons
   d. Edisons

3. The pull of any object on another is
   a. gravity
   b. weight
   c. inertia
   d. friction

4. Weight is determined by mass and
   a. gravity
   b. friction
   c. inertia
   d. none of these

5. Friction
   a. causes heat
   b. resists motion
   c. is reduced by lubricants
   d. all of these

6. Which are the three types of friction?
   a. inertia, heat, weight
   b. sliding, rolling, static
   c. elastic, sliding, heat
   d. nuclear, elastic, electrical

7. What does nuclear force do?
   a. destroys atoms
   b. is quite small
   c. holds protons in the nucleus
   d. none of these
8. Electromagnets have a magnetic force only if
   a. electric current is running through the magnet
   b. the object being attracted is small
   c. the object is made of magnetite
   d. there is high humidity
9. Gravity is stronger when objects are
   a. close together
   b. have more mass
   c. both a and b
   d. none of these
10. Electrical force exists only when
   a. voltage is high
   b. electrons flow
   c. days are cold and dry
   d. objects have low mass

Matching. Match each word with its definition or description.
   1. pull of any object on another
   2. force that resists motion
   3. any push or pull
   4. an object's point of balance
   5. the flow of electrons
   6. reduces friction
   7. unit of force
   8. caused by the pull of gravity
   9. between two nonmoving objects
   10. force created by muscles

   a. center of gravity
   b. current electricity
   c. force
   d. friction
   e. gravity
   f. lubricant
   g. mechanical force
   h. newton
   i. static friction
   j. weight

CHAPTER 14

MOTION

INTRODUCTION

During the time-lapse photograph of Chicago, the camera lens was left open for several seconds. The colored lines were made by the lights of cars traveling on the freeway at night. As the cars moved through the scene, they left a trail of light on the film, allowing the camera to capture a picture of motion.

The previous chapter explained various ideas about force. In this chapter you will study what happens when forces are put to use.

SECTION TITLES

The motion of these cars, on the North Lake Shore Drive in Chicago, is captured by time-lapse photography.

14-1 THE BASICS OF MOTION

OBJECTIVES

- Define the term **motion**.
- Distinguish between balanced and unbalanced forces.
- Distinguish between distance and displacement.

Imagine that you are riding in a car that is traveling on the freeway at 80 km/hr (50 mi/hr). In your hand you are holding a glass of water filled to the brim (fig. 14-1). Why doesn't the glass appear to be moving? As you look out the window, you see trees and fence posts moving by. Why do they appear to be moving when you know they are attached to the ground?

Fig. 14-1 Is the glass of water moving or not moving?

When an object changes position in relation to another object or point, the object is said to be moving, or in **motion**. The car and everything in it is in motion at 80 km/hr. The water in the glass is also traveling at 80 km/hr and is not sloshing over the edge of the glass. Why not? Because the glass of water is not moving in reference to the car. The trees and fence posts are attached to the ground, but they appear to be moving because of the motion of the car. So motion is not always as it appears. It depends on your frame of reference. In fact, the objects all around you that appear to be motionless are moving nearly 1600 km/hr due to Earth's rotational speed.

All motion results from a force, either a push or a pull, that moves an object. Soccer balls move from a kicking force, sailboats by the force of the wind, and race cars by the force of powerful engines (fig. 14-2).

Motion does not always occur when a force pushes or pulls on an object. For example, suppose all of your classmates are evenly divided into two tug-of-war teams (fig. 14-3). If both teams pull with equal force, the flag on the rope does not move because the forces are balanced. **Balanced forces** pull in opposite directions but are equal, hence there

Fig. 14−2 A soccer ball, a sailboat, and a race car all move because a force is acting on them.

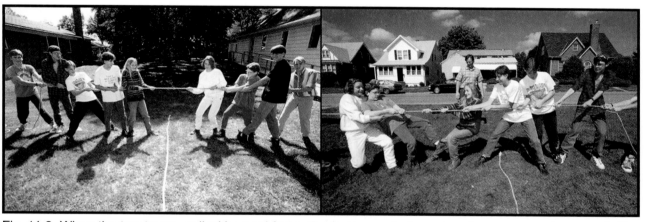

Fig. 14-3 When the two teams pull with equal force, the forces are balanced and no movement occurs (left). When one team begins to tire, the forces of the two teams become umbalanced and movement occurs (right).

is no motion. However, if one team pulls with a greater force, the other team and the flag move toward the opposing team because the forces are unbalanced. **Unbalanced forces** can also pull in opposite directions, but if the forces are unequal, there is a change in movement.

Opposing forces can be illustrated by airplane flight (fig. 14-4). When a plane takes off, the force of the jet engine pushing the plane forward is greater than the friction and air resistance pushing backward on the plane. When the plane is cruising at a constant speed, the forward and backward forces are equal. When an airplane lands, the plane slows because the backward forces are greater than the forward forces.

Fig. 14−4 A jet plane takes off because the force of the engine is greater than the force of the wind resistance pushing against it.

Forces	Result	Example
Balanced	no change in motion	tug of war with equal teams
Unbalanced	change in motion	tug of war with unequal teams
Balanced	no change in motion	airplane cruising at a constant speed
Unbalanced	changing speed or new direction	airplane takeoff or landing

Fig. 14—5

The chart in figure 14-5 shows how balanced and unbalanced forces affect motion.

Two other aspects of motion deal with a change of location—distance or displacement. These can be illustrated by the following example. In a soccer game, the ball must enter the blue goal for the red team to score (fig. 14-6). But the blue players would not let the ball travel directly to the net. To get the goal, the red team had to kick the ball in several directions to various players. In this example, **distance**, or total length of travel by the ball, is shown by the red arrows. This distance is about 60 m. In the same figure is a black arrow. This arrow shows the ball's **displacement**, or the span between the starting and finishing point along a straight line. A sailboarder tacks (zigzags) as he sails into the wind (fig. 14-7). Like the soccer ball, his displacement is much less than the distance traveled. A track team member runs one lap around a 400 m track. Her distance is 400 m, but since she ends up at the same place she started, her displacement is zero.

Fig. 14—6 The red line shows the distance the ball traveled. The black line shows the displacement.

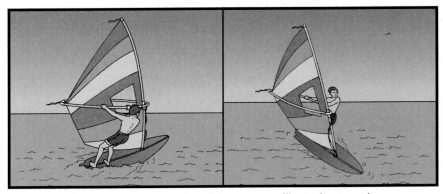

Fig. 14—7 Tacking increases the distance a sailboarder travels

Galileo

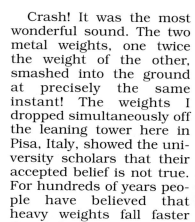

Crash! It was the most wonderful sound. The two metal weights, one twice the weight of the other, smashed into the ground at precisely the same instant! The weights I dropped simultaneously off the leaning tower here in Pisa, Italy, showed the university scholars that their accepted belief is not true. For hundreds of years people have believed that heavy weights fall faster than light ones. Today my demonstration proved otherwise. Yet even after they saw it happen, many of the professors and students argued that their parchments are correct and that what they observed is untrue. It is hard to believe that educated people deny the plainest of evidence.

Enough of that. My recent studies on the rate of falling objects is progressing nicely. I have been rolling a brass ball down a ramp and timing how long it takes for the ball to reach the bottom of the ramp. This has proved difficult to measure until recently, when I reasoned that I could measure one event with another event.

Let me explain. I acquired a pail and bore a hole in the bottom. I fill the pail with water. As I release the ball at the top of the ramp, I start to catch the stream of water in a cup placed underneath the pail. When the ball reaches the bottom of the ramp, I remove the cup. This approach has proven most exciting, because I can time the quickest of events and compare the different amounts of water collected in the cup. The quicker the events, the less water in the cup. The levels of water have proven to compare very accurately with my visual observation of the rates of falling objects.

REVIEW IT

1. What is motion?
2. What is the difference between balanced and unbalanced forces?
3. What is the difference between distance and displacement?

14–2 MEASURING MOTION

VOCABULARY
acceleration
momentum
speed
velocity

VOCABULARY
acceleration
momentum
speed
velocity

OBJECTIVES

- Explain the difference between speed and velocity.
- Explain what acceleration is.
- Identify what momentum is and the factors that affect it.

The announcer called out on the loudspeaker, "And the winner of the womens' division of the New York City Marathon is Wanda Panfil, with a time of 2 hours, 30 minutes, and 44 seconds" (fig. 14-8). Ms. Panfil won the 42.2 km race because she had the highest average speed of any of the runners in her division. **Speed** is the rate of motion, which is calculated by dividing the distance by the time it took to go that distance (fig. 14-9).

Fig. 14–8 Wanda Panfil is seen here winning the New York City Marathon.

SPEED EQUATION		
$$\text{Speed} = \frac{\text{Distance}}{\text{Time}}$$		
Example $$\text{Speed} = \frac{\text{Distance}}{\text{Time}} = \frac{42\ 200\ \text{m}}{9044\ \text{sec}} = 4.7\ \text{m/sec}$$		

Fig. 14–9

All moving objects have a speed that can be measured, just as the woman who won the race with a speed of 4.7 m/sec. She also had an average velocity of 4.7 m/sec north. **Velocity** (və läs′ ə tē) is both the speed and the direction that an object is moving.

When the starting gun fired, Wanda was stationary and had a speed of 0 m/sec. During the race, she kept increasing her speed up to 4.7 m/sec (fig. 14-10). Her speed of 4.7 m/sec was an average of slower speeds near the start and faster speeds later on.

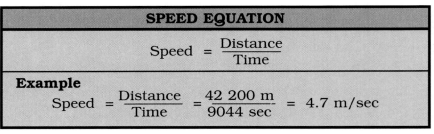

PANFIL'S SPEEDS DURING THE 100 M RACE			
Start	10 m	20 m	30 - 42 200 m
0 m/sec	2.5 m/sec	3.5 m/sec	4.7 m/sec

Fig. 14–10

TRY THIS 14-2A: Velocity

Materials:

    graph paper   Special Master R370

    metric ruler

Procedure:

1. Obtain a copy of Special Master R370. The time interval between each position of the ball is 1/30th of a second.
2. Place a piece of graph paper on top of the drawing on the Special Master. Mark each position of the ball with a dot.
3. Remove the graph paper and use the ruler to draw a straight line connecting every fourth position of the ball (three intervals). The time between three intervals of the ball is 0.1 second. The length of each straight line (to the nearest mm) can be used to show the distance traveled during each 0.1 second of flight. The distance divided by time can be used to determine an average velocity for each interval.

   - What is the average velocity for each interval?

     Interval 1 =   Interval 4 =

     Interval 2 =   Interval 5 =

     Interval 3 =   Interval 6 =

   - At what interval is the velocity the smallest?
   - When does the vertical acceleration of the ball have a positive value?
   - When does the acceleration of the ball have a negative value?
   - How does the velocity of the ball change during its flight?

Between the 0 m and the 10 m mark in the race, she increased her speed from 0 m/sec to 2.5 m/sec. In the next ten-meter length, she increased her speed to 3.5 m/sec. In the remaining 9014 m of the race, her speed remained fairly constant at 4.7 m/sec. Ms. Panfil's change in speed, or any change in speed, is called **acceleration** (ak sel ər ā' shən). Acceleration is calculated by dividing the change in speed by the time. In the first 10 m of the race, Ms. Panfil's acceleration was 2.5 m/sec^2. The time it took to reach this speed was 4 seconds. Dividing the change of speed (2.5 m/sec^2) by the elapsed time (4 sec), an acceleration of 0.6 m/sec^2 can be calculated (fig. 14-11).

ACCELERATION EQUATION		
$\text{Acceleration} = \dfrac{\text{Change in speed}}{\text{Time}}$		
Example		
$\text{Acceleration} = \dfrac{\text{Change in Speed}}{\text{Time}} = \dfrac{2.5 \text{ m/sec}}{4 \text{ sec}} = 0.6 \text{ m/sec}^2$		

Fig. 14–11

Fig. 14–12 The baseball has greater momentum than the Ping-Pong ball.

Another measure of motion is called momentum. **Momentum** (mō men′ təm) depends on the mass of an object and its velocity (fig. 14-12). For example, if a Ping-Pong ball with a velocity of 30 m/sec strikes your hand, it bounces off harmlessly. If a baseball with the same velocity hits your hand, it causes pain. The different effects are caused by the different mass of each object. If instead of hitting your hand, they both hit a window, the Ping-Pong ball would bounce off, but the baseball would break the window. The baseball has more momentum than a Ping-Pong ball. Due to its greater mass, it takes more force to get the baseball up to speed than it does for the Ping-Pong ball. Figure 14-13 shows how the mass of each ball, times its velocity, equals the momentum.

MOMENTUM EQUATION		
mass x velocity = momentum		
Examples		
Ping-Pong ball	0.005 kg X 30 m/sec	= 0.15 kg m/sec
Baseball	0.140 kg X 30 m/sec	= 4.20 kg m/sec

Fig. 14–13

TRY THIS 14-2B: Hey! Slow Down!

Materials:

candle · matches
kite string · quart jar/lid
lead sinker (small) · water

Procedure:

1. Cut the string so it is about 1 cm shorter than the height of the jar.
2. Tie the sinker to one end of the string.
3. Use melted candle wax to attach the other end of the string to the center of the bottom of the lid (fig. A).
4. Allow the wax to harden and check to make sure the string is securely attached to the lid. If it is not, add more wax and allow it to cool.
5. Fill the jar full with water.
6. Place the sinker in the water and screw the lid on tightly (fig. B).
7. Hold the jar steady and start walking. Observe the position of the sinker as you accelerate and as you move at a constant speed.

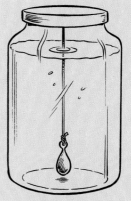

Fig. A

Fig. B

- What is the direction of the sinker as you accelerate from rest?

- What is the direction of the sinker when you are walking at a constant speed in a straight line?

- What is the position of the sinker when you are walking at a constant speed and you make a turn to the left? When you make a turn to the right?

- When you accelerate, does the sinker move backward, or does the jar move forward?

- Does the sinker point toward or away from the direction of acceleration? Why?

REVIEW IT

1. What is the difference between speed and velocity?
2. What is acceleration?
3. What is momentum and what factors affect it?

CLASS ACTIVITY 14-2: Faster, Faster

Question: How does height of release affect the speed of a marble?

Materials:

clay	metric ruler
corner molding - 0.5 m	meterstick
marble	stopwatch

Fig. A

Procedure:
1. Form a group of two or three. Find a hard surface that provides a level distance of at least 1.5 m.
2. Use the corner molding to construct a ramp that is 2 cm high. Use clay to help hold the ramp stationary as shown in figure A.
3. From the top of the ramp, roll the marble down onto the level surface. Determine the distance the marble rolled from the bottom of the ramp in 2 seconds. Record.
4. Repeat step 3 two more times.
5. Calculate the average distance and speed of the marble.
6. Repeat steps 3 to 5, raising the ramp to a height of 4 cm.
7. Repeat steps 3 to 5, lowering the ramp to a height of 1 cm.

Data:

Ramp Height	Distance	Speed
2 cm - Trial 1		
Trial 2		
Trial 3		
Average		
4 cm - Trial 1		
Trial 2		
Trial 3		
Average		
1 cm - Trial 1		
Trial 2		
Trial 3		
Average		

Questions:
1. What was the marble's slowest speed? What was the fastest speed?
2. What force caused the marble's speed to increase?
3. What is the overall average speed of the marble?
4. Leaving the height of the ramp the same, what could have been modified to increase the speed of the marble?

Conclusion: Write 3-5 sentences about what you learned from this activity.

14-3 THE LAWS OF MOTION

OBJECTIVES

- Describe Newton's laws of motion.
- Explain the law of the conservation of momentum.

VOCABULARY
inertia
law of acceleration
law of action-reaction
law of inertia
law of the conservation of momentum

High atop the slide at Wonder Water Park, the seventh-grader jumps onto his plastic mat (fig. 14-14). He pushes himself into the stream of water and begins to move. As he gains speed, he shoots through the first three turns and races for the next two. He explodes out of the last turn and splashes into a pool, spraying water everywhere. "This is great! I fly down this slide," he tells his friends. He can have this fun because of the laws of motion.

In 1665, long before water-slide parks, Sir Isaac Newton discovered three different laws of motion to help describe how moving objects behave (fig. 14-15).

Fig. 14—14 Riding down a waterslide is a great summertime activity.

THE LAWS OF MOTION
Law of Inertia (in ʉr′ shə) **(Law 1)** Moving objects keep moving, and resting objects remain at rest unless acted on by an unbalanced force.
Law of Acceleration (ak sel ər ā′ shən) **(Law 2)** The acceleration of an object is determined by its mass and the size of the unbalanced force.
Law of Action/Reaction (Law 3) For every action, there is an equal and opposite reaction.

Fig. 14—15

LAW OF INERTIA

The **law of inertia**, also called the first law of motion, states that, unless acted on by an unbalanced force, an object at rest will remain at rest, and that an object in motion will remain in motion (fig. 14-16). This property of matter is called **inertia.** In other words, objects act as if they are lazy. They seem to want to keep doing what they are already doing. Inertia is what keeps moving cars traveling in a straight line, even when there is a

DID YOU KNOW?
An American parachutist jumped from a balloon at 29 000 m (95,000 ft). Thin air allowed him to fall at a speed of 1040 km/hr (646 mi/hr).

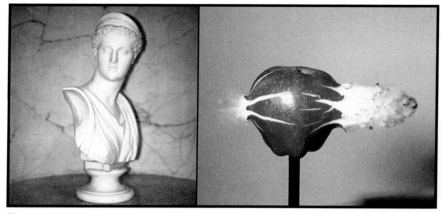

Fig. 14–16 Inertia causes the stationary statue to remain stationary and the speeding bullet to keep speeding.

curve in the road or a stop sign ahead. If the car is stopped at an intersection, inertia is what keeps the car from moving.

The inertia of an object depends on its mass. Objects with a large mass resist change more than objects with a smaller mass (fig. 14-17).

Fig. 14–17 Moving or stopping a car requires more force than moving or stopping a small wagon.

LAW OF ACCELERATION

The **law of acceleration**, or the second law of motion, states that acceleration of an object depends on the mass of the object and the size of the force acting on the object. Acceleration can be increased by either increasing the force or by decreasing the mass. Decreasing the force and increasing the mass both decrease acceleration. For example, if a boy on a pier pushed a toy sailboat (small mass) as hard as he could, the sailboat would accelerate and move away quickly (fig. 14-18). If the boy pushed just as hard on a larger boat, such as a ski boat (large mass), acceleration would be small, and the boat would move slowly away.

The second law of motion is used in different ways every day. If you want a baseball player who can hit home runs, you hire a strong player who can deliver the greatest possible force to a baseball. You must get strong players because you cannot change the mass of the baseball. To design a faster race car, you must reduce the mass of the car or develop a stronger engine so the force of the engine can give the car greater acceleration (fig. 14-19).

Fig. 14–18 Because it has a small mass, it takes a small force to push a toy sailboat out into a lake.

Fig. 14–19 A large, powerful engine can provide a large force to propell a racecar down a track.

LAW OF ACTION/REACTION

The **law of action/reaction**, or Newton's third law of motion, states that for every action there is an equal and opposite reaction. If you kick a boulder, you will learn about this law. When your foot pushes hard on the boulder (active force), the boulder pushes back (reactive force) just as hard (fig. 14-20).

You are very familiar with the third law of motion in your daily life. For instance, when you walk, your foot pushes against the ground, and the ground pushes back. This allows you to move. This example may seem silly, but if you

Fig. 14–20 When you kick a large boulder, it pushes back against your foot with an equal force.

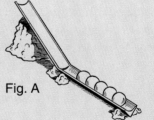

Fig. 14–21 When you walk in loose sand, your foot slips because the sand does not push back with an equal force.

have tried to walk fast in loose sand, you have found that as your foot pushes on the sand, the sand collapses under your foot, causing your foot to slip. Your foot continues to slip backward until the sand is compacted enough to push back with a force equal to your weight. When the force of the sand equals the force of your weight, you move forward (fig. 14-21).

Hitting a racquetball with a racket also demonstrates Newton's third law of motion. The racquetball bouncing off the racket pushes back on the racket with the same force as the racket exerted on the ball (fig 14-22). Running a race demonstrates this law as well. As you round a curve on the track, your feet seem to push outward against the ground, but the ground pushes back on you with the same force and allows you to go around the curve.

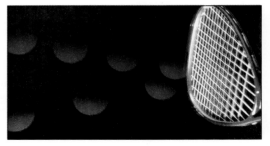

Fig. 14–22 The racquetball moves away with about the same force as it struck the racket with.

Closely related to the third law of motion is the **law of the conservation of momentum**. This law states that momentum is neither gained nor lost during a collision of two or more objects. You will remember from Section 14-2 that momentum is the velocity of an object multiplied by its mass (m x v). A 10 kg ball moving at 5 m/s has a momentum of 50 kg m/s (10 kg x 5 m/s). When dealing with several objects bouncing off each other, the total momentum just before the collision equals the total momentum just after the collision. Figure 14–23 shows ball A before it hits balls B and C, and also just after it hits the other two balls. As you can see, the total momentum before equals the total momentum after.

Fig. 14–23 The momentum of the cue ball (white) is transferred to the ball it hits, which passes it the next, and so on.

In many cases, friction makes an object slow down; thus a small amount of momentum is transferred elsewhere and is not found in the objects involved. In such cases there may be a slight difference in the momentum before and after a collision.

REVIEW IT

1. What are Newton's three laws of motion?
2. What does the law of the conservation of momentum say?

CHAPTER 14 WRAP-UP

THINKING SKILLS: Interpreting a Diagram

Diagrams are drawings that show important structures and details of things they depict. Scientists used diagrams to show people specific features or to illustrate specific processes. Sometimes diagrams are made to allow scientists to measure and analyze certain features. Scientists also interpret the evidence illustrated by diagrams.

Study carefully the diagram of Niagara Falls. Then answer the questions.

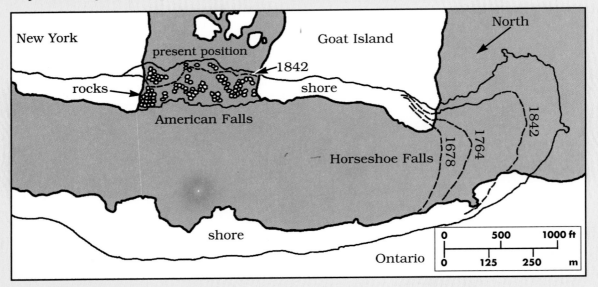

1. Draw a large, dark arrow to show which way the water is flowing.
2. How do American Falls and Horseshoe Falls differ? Why?
3. How far have Horseshoe Falls receded since 1678? How far has American Falls receded since 1842?
4. What is the rate of recession in meters per year for each of the falls?
5. Why have the falls eroded at different rates?
6. How has the shape of Horseshoe Falls changed in the last 300 years?
7. Do all parts of the crest line (edge of the cliff) change at the same rate? Why?
8. Draw a blue line to show where you predict the falls will be in 100 years. Draw a red line to show where you think they will be in 1000 years.

QUESTIONS AND PROBLEMS

1. When does an object have no momentum?
2. How do seat belts help to balance forces?
3. Can a moving object have velocity but no acceleration?
4. Why is the gas pedal of a car called the accelerator?
5. In order for a moving bowling ball and a moving Ping-Pong ball to have the same momentum, what must happen to the speed of both balls?
6. When would you use your muscles in an unbalanced way?
7. Why is displacement usually less than distance?
8. If two objects move together, is there any motion?
9. Is deceleration a type of acceleration?
10. How are velocity and speed different?
11. What could you do to have your muscles create balanced forces?
12. Suppose you and your best friend travel from Boston, Massachusetts, to San Diego, California. You make the trip by car; your friend makes the trip by train. Who travels the greatest distance? Who has the greatest displacement? Explain.

RESEARCH

1. Research to find the world record for the 100-m, 1500-m, and 10 000-m races. Calculate the runner's average speed and construct a graph to show the speed for each event. Have your classmates see how close they can come to world record times.
2. Make a model of an airplane. Use the model to identify parts of the airplane that control direction, speed, and lift. Draw a detailed diagram of the airplane. On the diagram identify the forces that affect an airplane in flight. Use arrows to show the directions in which these forces act.
3. Find out how the third law of motion is involved in a game of Air Hockey. Draw a series of diagrams that display your findings.
4. Research the winning times for the quarter-mile race with dragsters. Make a poster that displays your findings. Be sure to show data in table and graph form and provide artwork.
5. Use library resources to discover information about the work of Sir Isaac Newton. Develop a bulletin board that summarizes his life and accomplishments.

REVIEW

HIGHLIGHTS

1. Motion occurs when an object changes position in relation to another object or point.
2. Balanced forces are opposite and equal and result in no motion. Unbalanced forces are opposite but not equal and result in motion.
3. An object's distance is the total length of the path followed by the object. The displacement of an object is the span between the starting point and the finish point along a straight line.

4. The speed of an object is simply its rate of motion, independent of its direction of movement. Velocity includes both an object's speed and its direction of movement.
5. Acceleration refers to the change in the speed of an object.
6. The momentum of an object describes its strength of movement. It is determined by the object's mass and its velocity.
7. The law of inertia (first law of motion) states that moving objects keep moving, and resting objects remain at rest unless acted on by an unbalanced force. The law of acceleration (second law of motion) states that the acceleration of an object is determined by its mass and the size of the acting force. The law of action/reaction (third law of motion) states that for every action, there is an equal and opposite reaction.
8. Examples of events that demonstrate the laws of motion are identified on pages 327 - 331.
9. The law of the conservation of momentum states that momentum cannot be lost, because as one object loses its momentum, another object gains it.

VOCABULARY LIST

acceleration
balanced force
displacement
distance
inertia

law of acceleration
law of action/reaction
law of inertia
law of the conservation
   of momentum

momentum
motion
speed
unbalanced force
velocity

PRACTICE

Multiple Choice. Choose the best answer.

1. When an object changes position, it is called
   a. relocated
   b. motion
   c. balanced
   d. all of these

2. Unbalanced forces cause
   a. motion
   b. breakage
   c. inertia
   d. energy

3. Balanced forces cause
   a. motion
   b. no motion
   c. inertia
   d. calories

4. Distance and displacement
   a. are the same thing
   b. are sometimes equal
   c. never equal each other
   d. are unrelated

5. Velocity is both
   a. inertia and speed
   b. balanced and unbalanced
   c. speed and momentum
   d. speed and direction

6. Acceleration occurs when
   a. displacement takes place
   b. energy is used
   c. speed changes
   d. none of these

7. Momentum is a result of
    a. balanced forces
    b. inertia
    c. acceleration
    d. mass and speed
8. Objects are lazy because they don't want to change speed.
    a. law of inertia
    b. law of acceleration
    c. law of action-reaction
    d. none of these
9. The law of acceleration says objects accelerate because of
    a. weight of object
    b. speed
    c. mass and force acting on it
    d. all of these
10. The law of the conservation of momentum says
    a. do not waste momentum
    b. momentum cannot be lost
    c. momentum is invisible
    d. none of these

Matching. Match each word with its definition or description.
1. usually less than distance
2. the rate of motion
3. cause no motion
4. change in speed
5. opposite and unequal, causes motion
6. both speed and direction
7. first law of motion
8. third law of motion
9. mass times velocity
10. change in position of an object

    a. acceleration
    b. action-reaction
    c. balanced force
    d. displacement
    e. inertia
    f. momentum
    g. motion
    h. speed
    i. unbalanced force
    j. velocity

CHAPTER 15

ENERGY AND WORK

INTRODUCTION

The water wheel on page 336 once powered the main saw at Sutter's Mill on the American River, east of Sacramento, California. Some of the water from the river was diverted into a flume that carried water through the bottom of the mill. As the water passed through, it turned the water wheel as it pushed on the paddles of the wheel. This movement of the water wheel was transferred through a system of gears and pulleys to turn the massive saw blade.

Water wheels such as this were used in many parts of the world to provide the energy to drive machinery. In this chapter you will learn about energy and work and how both are related to the concepts of force and motion.

SECTION TITLES

Before gas engines and electric motors, water wheels were used to power machines such as this sawmill.

15–1 ENERGY

VOCABULARY
energy
joule
kinetic energy
potential energy

OBJECTIVES

- Distinguish between potential and kinetic energy.
- Describe the factors that affect the potential energy of an object.
- Describe the factors that affect the kinetic energy of an object.

"Five, four, three, two, one, contact," were the words spoken just before the dynamite exploded, and the building collapsed exactly as planned (fig. 15-1). Later, work crews began to clear the area where the new fifty-story office building was to be constructed.

DID YOU KNOW?
According to Einstein's theory $E = mc^2$, one pound of anything, when completely converted to energy, will produce 11 400 000 000 kilowatt-hours of energy.

Fig. 15–1 Engineers carefully plan the placement of explosives so the force created by the explosion results in the safe demolition of the building.

It takes a force to move an object, and energy is required to cause the force. In science we give energy a special definition; **energy** is the ability to do work. This definition tells what energy does, rather than what it is. Energy is measured in units called **joules** (jo͞ol) (J), named for the scientist James Joule, who worked with the concepts of work and energy.

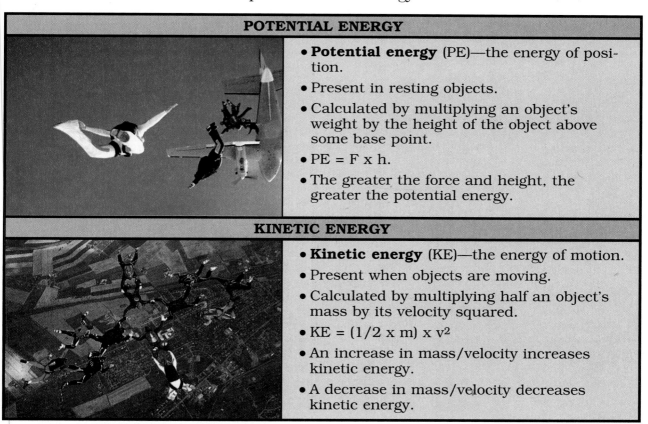

POTENTIAL ENERGY

- **Potential energy** (PE)—the energy of position.
- Present in resting objects.
- Calculated by multiplying an object's weight by the height of the object above some base point.
- PE = F x h.
- The greater the force and height, the greater the potential energy.

KINETIC ENERGY

- **Kinetic energy** (KE)—the energy of motion.
- Present when objects are moving.
- Calculated by multiplying half an object's mass by its velocity squared.
- KE = (1/2 x m) x v^2
- An increase in mass/velocity increases kinetic energy.
- A decrease in mass/velocity decreases kinetic energy.

Fig. 15—2

Energy occurs as either potential or kinetic energy (fig 15-2). **Potential** (pō ten′ shəl) **energy** is the energy of position. It is the amount of energy a resting object has, based on how high the object is above a point and the object's force, or weight, in newtons. To find the potential energy of an object, multiply its weight by how high it is above the base point. This formula is **PE = F x h**. If an object's weight is 10 N, and it is 2 m above the floor, the object's potential energy is 20 joules (10 N x 2 m). If the object is lifted up to 5 m above the floor, its potential energy is 50 joules (10 N x 5 m).

Potential Energy
PE = F x h
F = Force
h = height

339

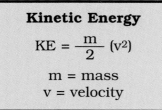

Kinetic Energy

$$KE = \frac{m}{2} (v^2)$$

m = mass
v = velocity

Kinetic (ki net′ ik) **energy** is the energy of motion. It is based on an object's mass multiplied by its velocity. To calculate the kinetic energy of an object, you must take half the mass multiplied by the velocity squared. This formula is **KE = (m/2) x (v²)**. If an object has a mass of 10 kg and a velocity of 5 m/s, its kinetic energy is 125 joules (1/2 x 10 kg x [5 m/s]²).

TRY THIS 15-1: Pokin—kinpo

Materials:

index cards (3" x 5") - 3   masking tape
kite string - 80 cm   pencil
lead sinker   scissors

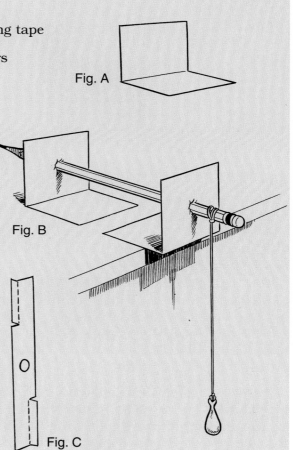

Fig. A

Fig. B

Fig. C

Procedure:

1. Bend two of the index cards in the middle as shown in figure A.
2. Use the scissors to make a small hole through the center of each folded card. The holes should be lined up and large enough for the pencil to rotate freely.
3. Tape the two folded cards to your desk or a table about 5 cm apart. Insert the pencil through the two cards as shown in figure B.
4. Make a fan blade out of part of the third card. Do this by cutting a 2 x 10 cm strip. Make two cuts as shown in figure C and bend the edges down as shown.
5. Make a small hole in the center of the fan blade so it can be slipped tightly over the end of the pencil. If the blade rotates freely, use a small amount of tape to hold the fan blade to the pencil so it does not rotate.
6. Tie one end of the string to the lead sinker as shown in figure B. Tie the other end of the string securely to the end of the pencil between the fan blade and the card support.
7. Wind the full length of the string up on the pencil. Let the weight drop.
8. Repeat step 7 three more times.

- What kind of energy does the weight have when the string is wound up?

- What kind of energy does the fan blade have while the weight is dropping?

- Will all potential energy of the weight be changed into kinetic energy? Explain.

340

It is important to remember that any object can have both potential or kinetic energy at any one time. A 100 N skier at the top of a 100 m high ski run has 10 000 joules of potential energy (fig. 15-3). As he starts his run, the potential energy begins to change to kinetic energy. At first only a small amount of potential energy is changed to kinetic energy, but by the time the skier reaches maximum speed at the bottom of the run, almost all the potential energy has been changed into kinetic energy.

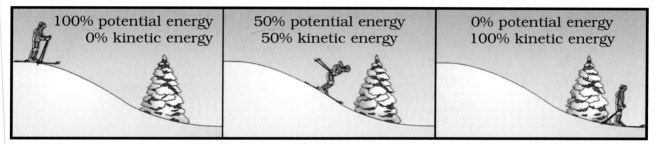

Fig. 15-3 An object can have potential energy, kinetic energy, or both forms of energy at the same time.

When the skier comes to a stop at the bottom of the run, what has happened to the potential energy he started with at the top of the run? Most—but not all—of the potential energy has gone into the kinetic energy of the skier as he coasted down the hill. Some of the potential energy was lost to wind friction, and a little was lost to the friction of the skis against the snow.

The total kinetic energy the skier had at the bottom of the hill was consumed by the friction of the skis and the flying snow, created when the skier skidded to a stop.

REVIEW IT

1. How are kinetic and potential energy different?
2. How do mass and distance affect potential energy?
3. What effect do mass and velocity have on kinetic energy?

15-2 WORK AND POWER

OBJECTIVE

- Distinguish between work and power.

The backhoe shown in figure 15-4 is used to dig trenches and holes, lift pipe, and move dirt and gravel. Heavy equipment such as this help construction companies accomplish much of the work they do. Homework assignments or a test are often referred to as being work, even hard work. You may have had someone ask you, "Does that pen work?" *Work* has many different meanings.

Fig. 15-4 The backhoe is doing work, filling the truck with rock and dirt.

When scientists use the word *work*, it means something very different from what most people mean. For scientists, **work** occurs when force is exerted on an object, and the object moves in the direction of the force.

In figure 15-5, the girl is lifting boxes that weigh 10 N each. She lifts them 1 m high onto a shelf. The amount of work she does on each box is 10 N times 1 m, or 10 joules of work (fig. 15-6).

DID YOU KNOW?

The space shuttle's engines develop 33 000 000 watts of power at liftoff.

Fig. 15-5 The girl is working by lifting the box up to the shelf.

Fig. 15-6

WORK EQUATION
Work = Force (F) x Distance (d)
Example
$W = 10 N \times 1 m$
$W = 10$ joules (J)

Fig. 15–7 Even though the boy is pushing hard against the wall, no work is being done.

If the girl could not have lifted the box, then she would have done no work because the box would have moved no distance. Look at the boy pushing the wall in figure 15-7. Even though he may get tired as he pushes the wall, he is doing no work on the wall. Why? Because the wall does not move. If there is no movement, there is no work.

If the girl lifted one of the 10 N boxes 1 m high, walked across the room, and placed it on another shelf, she still would have done only 10 J of work. Because when she held the box and walked across the room, she did no additional work on the box. In this case, she moved the box in a direction different from the box's weight, so no work was done on it. To do work, the motion must be in the same direction as the force (fig. 15-8). The girl used an upward force to lift the box, and then she moved horizontally. Since the force was not in the direction of the motion, no work was done. Even though she did no work on the box, her arms would get tired, because she is holding the weight of the box.

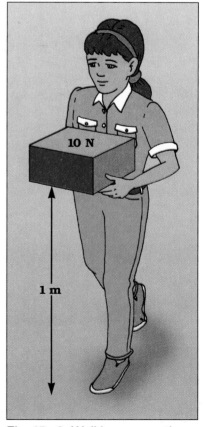

Fig. 15–8 Walking across the room carrying a box represents the same amount of work as simply lifting the box.

Fig. 15–9 The truck is able to produce more power than the sports car.

Fig. 15–10 Stairs or an elevator can be used to get to the top of this building.

A concept related to work is power. **Power** is the rate at which work is done and is measured in watts. A **watt** is defined as 1 J of work per second. A large truck engine is more powerful than a car engine because it can do more work each second it is working (fig. 15-9).

Suppose that a girl wants to get on the roof of a building (fig. 15-10). She can either walk up stairs or ride the elevator. Which will require more power? To calculate power, the power equation is used (fig. 15-11).

POWER EQUATION
Power = Work (J)/time (t)
Example $$P \ (\text{power}) = \frac{4500 \text{ J}}{50 \text{ sec}} = 90 \text{ W (watts)}$$ $$P \ (\text{power}) = \frac{4500 \text{ J}}{10 \text{ sec}} = 450 \text{ W (watts)}$$

Fig. 15–11

Because the girl weighs 300 N and the roof is 15 m high, for her to reach the roof will take 4500 J of work (300 N x 15 m = 4500J). It takes 50 seconds for her to run up to the roof and only 10 seconds to ride the elevator to the roof.

Fig. 15–12 Riding an elevator to the top of a building requires more power than climbing the stairs to the top of the same building.

The electric motor that runs the elevator has more power, so it can lift her quickly to the roof (fig. 15-12). The girl is not as powerful, so it takes her longer to climb the stairs.

If you had to dig the hole for a swimming pool in three months, you could use a shovel. If you needed to dig the hole in one day, you would need a backhoe. Since the backhoe can deliver more power, the job can be done more quickly.

REVIEW IT

1. How is work different from power?

CLASS ACTIVITY 15-2: Human Power

Question: How much power can you produce?

Materials:
Special Master R391

Procedure:
1. Obtain a copy of Special Master R391.
2. Use the information on the Special Master to complete the table in the data section.
3. Compute the average time (sec) it took each person to climb the steps. Record.
4. Calculate the average amount of force each person exerted in climbing the steps. (REMEMBER: FORCE IS MEASURED IN NEWTONS. POUNDS CAN BE CONVERTED TO NEWTONS BY MULTIPLYING THEM BY 4.4). Record.
5. Calculate the average work each student performed in climbing the stairs. Use this equation: Work = Force x Distance. Record.
6. Calculate the power produced by each student using the equation Power = Work (J)/time (sec). Record. Round all answers to the nearest 0.1.

Data:

Student	Average Time (sec)	Force (N)	Distance (m)	Work (J)	Power (W)
1					
2					
3					
4					

Questions:
1. Who used the greatest force in climbing the steps? Who used the least?
2. Who produced the greatest amount of work? Who produced the least?
3. Did the person who works the most produce the most power? Why or why not?
4. How much horsepower did the most powerful student produce (746 watts = 1 horsepower)?
5. How could a student improve his or her performance in this activity?
6. If there had been more steps, do you think the power produced by each student would have been more or less? Why?

Conclusion: Write 3–5 sentences about what you learned from this activity.

James Watt

Imagine what life would be like if there were no lights, no cars, no microwave ovens, no computers, no refrigerators, no trains, no TVs. It is hard to imagine life without these machines, but it is likely that your grandparents or great-grandparents may remember what it was like before these machines were invented. Prior to the mid-1700s century, powered machines simply did not exist. Work that needed to be done was performed by people or animals.

With the beginning of the industrial Revolution in the mid-1700s, people began to see the potential of powered machines. One such person was James Watt. James was born on January 19, 1736, in Greenock, Scotland. James's early education occurred at home. Later, he attended grammar school, where he learned Latin, Greek, and mathematics. However, the most important part of young James's education took place in his father's workshops, where he was given his own set of tools, a workbench, and a forge. James used these to build models of may different things manufactured by his father's ship- and house-building business.

At the age of 17, James decided to attend university in Glasgow. After his training was completed, he returned to his home and set up shop, making various mathematical instruments. James became interested in improving the newly developed steam engines. Through experimentation, Watt determined the properties of steam and designed several improvements that prevented the large loss of steam from the engine. He patented his improved design and became partners with John Roebuck, who financed his continued research. This research resulted in patents on several other inventions, including a rotary engine, a double-action engine, and a steam indicator to record the steam pressure inside the engine.

After his retirement from the steam-engine company, James continued to invent new devices to improve his steam engines. Perhaps the most important of these inventions was the flyball governor, which automatically regulated the speed of an engine. This invention led the way to automation in manufacturing.

James Watt died on August 25, 1819, at the age of 83. Because of the many contributions he made to the development of powered machines, the watt, the SI unit for power, was named in his honor.

15–3 FORMS OF ENERGY

law of the conservation
of energy

• Identify the forms of energy.
• Explain how energy can change from one form to
another.

It was a cold, windy night, and the rain was changing to
snow. Suddenly, about eight o'clock, the lights went out,
and the electric furnace stopped. Dad went outside and
brought in some firewood. Soon he had a warm fire roaring
in the fireplace, and everyone gathered around to stay warm
(fig. 15-13). The fire supplied the energy the family needed
to keep warm.

DID YOU KNOW?

Breaking ocean waves pro-
duce pressure as great as
6000 lbs per square inch. A
four-foot swell moving along a
hundred-mile front produces
enough energy to supply a
city the size of Seattle for 24
hours.

Fig. 15–13 The fire in the fireplace produces heat and light energy.

RESEARCH IT

Bend a paper clip back and
forth rapidly; then quickly
put the clip against your
forehead. What happens?
Explain why.

To understand how energy affects us, you must remember
that while energy exists as either potential or kinetic energy,
it can be exhibited in several forms, including nuclear,
chemical, electrical, heat, radiant, and mechanical. These
forms can be further classified as to whether they store the
energy, allow it to be transferred, or do both. Nuclear energy
and chemical energy are examples of stored energy. Heat
and radiant energy are examples of transferred energy.

Electrical and mechanical energy both store and transfer energy. Study figure 15-14 as you learn about the forms of energy.

Fig. 15-14

Nuclear Energy
- Stores energy only.
- Comes from nuclear reactions within the atomic nucleus.
- Usually occurs in the nuclear reactor of nuclear power plants or nuclear-powered machines.
- Uncontrolled nuclear reactions are created by nuclear weapons.
- Small amounts of matter produce large amounts of energy.
- Always stored as potential energy until released by nuclear reaction.

Chemical Energy
- Stores energy only.
- Produced during chemical reactions.
- May produce heat (fire) or electricity (battery).
- Always stored as potential energy until released during chemical reaction.

Heat Energy
- Transfers energy only.
- Energy transferred by contact among molecules.
- Energy produced by infrared radiation, the sun, warm objects, and chemical reaction.
- It makes things feel warm or hot.
- Heat energy is kinetic energy.

Fig. 15–14 Continued

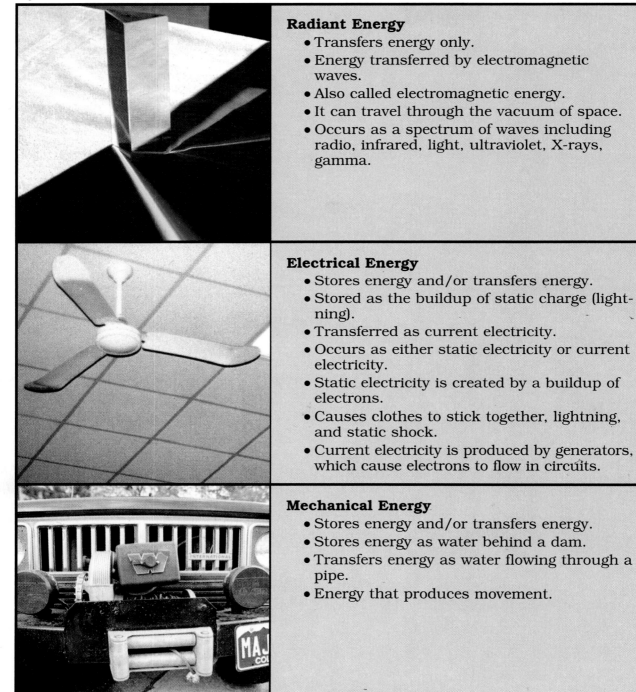

Radiant Energy
- Transfers energy only.
- Energy transferred by electromagnetic waves.
- Also called electromagnetic energy.
- It can travel through the vacuum of space.
- Occurs as a spectrum of waves including radio, infrared, light, ultraviolet, X-rays, gamma.

Electrical Energy
- Stores energy and/or transfers energy.
- Stored as the buildup of static charge (lightning).
- Transferred as current electricity.
- Occurs as either static electricity or current electricity.
- Static electricity is created by a buildup of electrons.
- Causes clothes to stick together, lightning, and static shock.
- Current electricity is produced by generators, which cause electrons to flow in circuits.

Mechanical Energy
- Stores energy and/or transfers energy.
- Stores energy as water behind a dam.
- Transfers energy as water flowing through a pipe.
- Energy that produces movement.

Fig. 15–15 The mechanical energy of the windmill is converted to electricity, which is converted to light energy produced by the lamp.

Energy can appear in all of these forms because it can be changed from one form to another (fig. 15-15). For example, the wind blows and turns the blades of a windmill (mechanical energy). The blades turn the generator to create electricity (electrical energy). The electricity flows through wires to your house and makes a light bulb glow (radiant and heat energy). In this example, energy appeared in four different forms. In a similar way a flashlight battery contains chemicals that react to release energy that flows from the battery as electricity through a light bulb to produce light (fig. 15-16).

The **law of the conservation of energy** states that energy is neither created nor destroyed. However, as energy changes from one form to another, some of it is used to overcome friction or resistance and is released as heat. Subsequently, not all energy is changed into a useful form. In the example of the windmill, all the energy of the turning blades does not become electricity as the generator turns (fig. 15-17). Some is used to overcome friction of the moving parts and is lost as heat. Electricity running through a light bulb does not all become light. In fact, only about 10 percent of it becomes light; the rest becomes heat, making the light bulb hot.

REVIEW IT

1. Name the six forms of energy.
2. State the law of the conservation of energy.

Fig. 15–16 In a flashlight, chemical energy in the battery is converted into electricity and finally into light.

Fig. 15–17 In a windmill, the wind energy is converted into mechanical energy and electrical energy.

CHAPTER 15 WRAP-UP

THINKING SKILLS: Computer Skills

Computers are important tools of science. They are used to design and test models, to record and analyze data, and to make calculations. The job that a scientist needs to have accomplished by a computer must be put into a form the computer can understand. This set of directions, called a program, must be written by the scientist so the job can be completed. Writing computer programs that accomplish specific jobs is an important part of science.

In this activity you will write a computer program that calculates work and power when force and distance are entered. Type in the BASIC program that follows. Start the program by typing "RUN" and then pressing the "ENTER" key. After each question is answered, press the "ENTER" key again.

BASIC PROGRAM:

```
10    REM Calculate Work and Power
20    Input "A. What is the amount of force used?";F
30    Input "B. What is the distance the object moves?";d
40    Let W = F * d
50    Input "C. How much time in seconds did it take?";t
60    Let P = W/t
70    Print "The work done is " W "joules."
80    Print "The power done is " P "watts."
90    Print
100   Input "D. Do you want to do another? Yes/No";A$
110   If A$ = "Yes" GOTO 20
120   Print "Goodbye from Joules and Watts."
```

Run the program, using the following data:

1. F = 25 N, d = 50 m, t = 30 sec

2. F = 12 N, d = 34 m, t = 10 sec

3. F = 5 N, d = 35 cm, t = 16 sec

4. F = 16 N, d = 5 m, t = 19 sec

5. F = 75 N, d = 2 km, t = 2.5 hrs

6. F = 14 N, d = 1 m, t = 15 sec

7. F = 1575 N, d = 450 m, t = 5 min

QUESTIONS AND PROBLEMS

1. Is wind energy kinetic energy or potential energy?
2. Where would a boulder have more potential energy, at the top of a mountain or at the bottom?
3. A feed-store worker must exert 30 N of force to lift one bag of dog food. How much power is produced by the worker who moves a pile of 100 bags of dog food to a new location 20 m away in 30 minutes?
4. Why does a small car generally get better gas mileage than a large car?
5. Can something with less power do the same amount of work?
6. If you stand and hold a box of oranges for very long, you will become tired. But if holding the box is not work, why do you become tired?
7. Does a flashlight battery have potential energy or kinetic energy? Explain.
8. Which would have more kinetic energy, a person in a moving car or the car? Why?
9. List the changes in energy that take place in a nuclear generating plant.
10. How is heat energy produced in the body? Where does this energy come from?
11. When does a rubber band have potential energy?
12. Is current electricity potential energy or kinetic energy? Explain.

RESEARCH

1. Make a model windmill that actually generates electricity.
2. Draw a simple floor plan of your house, showing all rooms and light fixtures. Show the wattage of each light fixture. Contact your local utilities company to find out the cost per kilowatt/hour of electricity. Calculate how much power would be used if all the lights in your house were left on for a period of four hours.
3. Use library resources to research the work of James Watt. Write a biographical report on the life and work of this scientist. Be sure to include artwork with your report.
4. Develop a series of colored posters that can be used to teach younger students about potential and kinetic energy. Use your posters to teach a class of younger students about energy.
5. Research the horsepower and mileage of several domestic and foreign trucks and cars. Make a large poster that displays a graph of your findings.

REVIEW

HIGHLIGHTS

1. Potential energy is the energy of position and is contained in most resting objects. Kinetic energy is the energy of moving objects and is contained in all moving objects.
2. Potential energy is determined by the mass of the object and the distance the object can move. The greater the mass and distance, the greater the potential energy.
3. Kinetic energy is determined by the mass of the object and its velocity. Kinetic energy increases as mass or velocity increases.
4. Work is the force acting on an object multiplied by the distance the object is moved. Power is a measure of the rate at which the work is done.

5. The six forms of energy include nuclear, chemical, electrical, heat, mechanical, and radiant energy.

6. The law of the conservation of energy states that while energy can change forms, these changes do not create or destroy any energy in normal situations. However, when energy changes from one form to another, some energy escapes the system.

VOCABULARY LIST

energy	law of conservation	power
joule	of energy	watt
kinetic energy	potential energy	work

PRACTICE

Multiple Choice. Choose the best answer.

1. Potential energy is the energy of
   - a. resting objects
   - b. power
   - c. probability
   - d. potentates

2. The ability to do work is called
   - a. power
   - b. chemical strength
   - c. energy
   - d. none of these

3. The unit used to measure energy is
   - a. newton
   - b. joule
   - c. slug
   - d. watt

4. The energy of a moving object is referred to as
   - a. chemical energy
   - b. nuclear energy
   - c. radiant energy
   - d. kinetic energy

5. Force times distance is
   - a. energy
   - b. work
   - c. joules
   - d. newtons

6. The rate at which work is done is called
   - a. potential energy
   - b. speed
   - c. power
   - d. pulse

7. The unit of measure for power is
   - a. what
   - b. watt
   - c. work
   - d. none of these

8. Which set includes a wrong name for a form of energy?
   - a. nuclear, ballistic, heat
   - b. mechanical, chemical, heat
   - c. chemical, radiant, nuclear
   - d. chemical, electrical, nuclear

9. The law of the conservation of energy states that energy
   - a. is able to be made
   - b. changes forms without loss
   - c. is all nuclear energy
   - d. all of these

10. Chemical energy is the source of energy in
   a. batteries
   b. atoms
   c. kinetic energy
   d. none of these

Matching. Match each word with its definition or description.
   1. energy of moving objects
   2. energy of resting objects _pe_
   3. force times the distance
   4. the ability to do work
   5. the rate at which work is done
   6. affected by an object's velocity
   7. unit of measure for energy
   8. equals mass times distance
   9. 1 joule of work per second
   10. decreases as potential energy increases

   a. energy
   b. joule
   c. kinetic energy
   d. potential energy
   e. power
   f. watt
   g. work

CHAPTER 16

MACHINES

INTRODUCTION

Imagine what it would be like if the pencil sharpener had never been invented. Even though pencils could be sharpened in other ways, using a well-maintained pencil sharpener like this one makes the job of keeping a sharp point on a pencil a simple one. The pencil sharpener is an example of a machine. But it is not just one machine; it is a combination of several simple machines. These simple machines include the handle, gears, and spiral cutting blades, all of which work together to sharpen pencils.

You are familiar with many different kinds of machines. What you may not know is that most machines are made up of other simpler machines. You may also be surprised to learn that items such as a butter knife, screwdriver, and tweezers are machines. As you study this chapter, you will discover what machines are and why they are used.

SECTION TITLES

The common pencil sharper that you may often use is a combination of several different simple machines.

16–1 SIMPLE MACHINES

OBJECTIVES

- Define the term **simple machine.**
- Identify the characteristics of each type of simple machine.

You use different machines every day (fig. 16-1). Your clothes were washed by a washing machine, you probably rode to school in a car or on a bus, and some of you used a lawn mower to cut your family's lawn. These are some of the machines you are familiar with. But there are machines that are made of one or two parts and are very easy to use. They are referred to as simple machines.

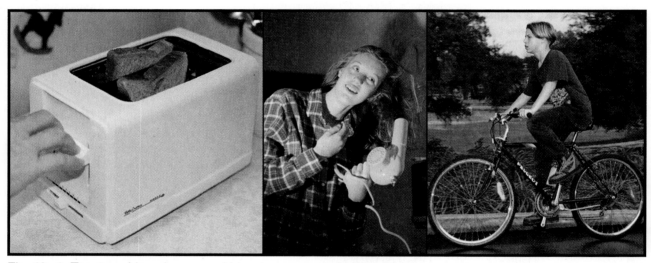

Fig. 16–1 Toasters, blow dryers, and bicycles are common machines.

DID YOU KNOW?
Hero, a Greek born in 20 B.C., was perhaps the earliest mechanical engineer. This early inventor constructed several mechanical devices, including a taximeter and a steam engine. In addition, he wrote books on mechanics, air, mirrors, and light.

Simple machines are devices that change the strength or direction of a force. The force that must be applied to cause these changes is called the **effort force**. The force that resists these changes is called the **resistance force**. Machines are most useful when the effort force is smaller than the resistance force. When this occurs with these machines, work is done that may have been impossible to do without the machine. There are three basic types of simple machines: the lever, the inclined plane, and the pulley (fig. 16-2).

Fig. 16–2

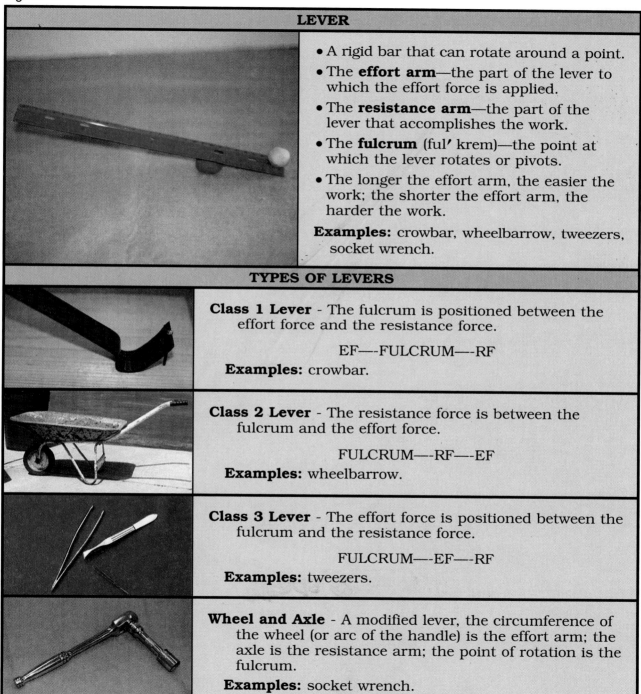

LEVER

- A rigid bar that can rotate around a point.
- The **effort arm**—the part of the lever to which the effort force is applied.
- The **resistance arm**—the part of the lever that accomplishes the work.
- The **fulcrum** (ful′ krem)—the point at which the lever rotates or pivots.
- The longer the effort arm, the easier the work; the shorter the effort arm, the harder the work.

Examples: crowbar, wheelbarrow, tweezers, socket wrench.

TYPES OF LEVERS

Class 1 Lever - The fulcrum is positioned between the effort force and the resistance force.

EF—-FULCRUM—-RF

Examples: crowbar.

Class 2 Lever - The resistance force is between the fulcrum and the effort force.

FULCRUM—-RF—-EF

Examples: wheelbarrow.

Class 3 Lever - The effort force is positioned between the fulcrum and the resistance force.

FULCRUM—-EF—-RF

Examples: tweezers.

Wheel and Axle - A modified lever, the circumference of the wheel (or arc of the handle) is the effort arm; the axle is the resistance arm; the point of rotation is the fulcrum.

Examples: socket wrench.

Fig. 16–2 Continued

INCLINED PLANE

- A slanted surface used to raise objects.
- The longer the slanted surface and the lower the height, the easier the work; the shorter the slanted surface and the higher the height, the harder the work.

Examples: ramp, splitting wedge, knife, and screw.

TYPES OF INCLINED PLANES

Wedge - Two inclined planes attached back to back.

Examples: splitting wedge and knife.

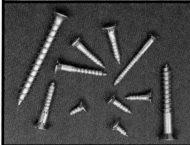

Screw - A spiraled inclined plane.
- **Threads**—the spiraled incline plane
- **Pitch**—the number of threads per cm
- The greater the pitch, the harder it is to turn the screw; the smaller the pitch, the easier it is to turn.

Examples: screw, nut/bolt, and drill bit.

PULLEY

- A grooved or flat wheel with a rope or belt that passes over it.
- The more ropes supporting the weight, the easier the pulley lifts; the fewer ropes supporting the weight, the harder the pulley lifts.

Examples: hoist, block and tackle.

TRY THIS 16-1: Balance Your Money

Materials:

    metric ruler   pennies - 3
    pencil

Procedure:

Fig. A

1. Lay the ruler on the pencil so it is balanced.
2. Place one penny on the 10 cm mark of the ruler.
3. Place a second penny on the opposite side of the ruler from the first penny, as shown.
4. Move the second penny until the ruler is balanced again.
    - What is the position of the second penny when the ruler is balanced?
    - How does the length of the effort arm compare to the length of the resistance arm?
5. Lay two pennies on top of each other at the 10 cm mark of the ruler.
6. Move the third penny on the opposite side of the ruler until the ruler is balanced.
    - What is the position of the third penny when the ruler is balanced?
    - How does the length of the effort arm compare to the length of the resistance arm?

REVIEW IT

1. Define the term *simple machine*.
2. How are simple machines helpful?
3. Name and give an example of each type of simple machine.

16–2 MECHANICAL ADVANTAGE

VOCABULARY
efficiency
mechanical advantage
theoretical mechanical
    advantage
work input
work output

OBJECTIVES

- Explain the term **mechanical advantage.**
- Explain the term **efficiency.**

The students in figure 16-3 are getting ready to take the engine out of their car. This isn't an easy job. All wires, hoses, and tubes must be identified and disconnected. Then the engine must be unbolted from the motor mounts and transmission. Next, the engine must be supported in some way so it can be lifted out of the engine compartment and be suspended over the floor while it is being repaired or over-hauled. In shop class the students have learned that they must attach the safety chain of an engine hoist to the engine. Once this is done and everything is disconnected, the pulley of the engine hoist can safely lift the engine out of the car.

Fig. 16–3 Lifting out an engine to work on it can be difficult.

Fig. 16–4 Using a pulley makes removing an engine a much easier task.

Simple machines, such as levers and pulleys, help do work by changing the direction or amount of a force (fig. 16-4). While changing the direction of the force makes work simpler, it is really the second aspect, that of increasing a force, that makes machines so useful. The man in figure 16-5 is using a lever that is 3 m long. If used as shown, it cre-

Fig. 16–5 Using a lever can accomplish work that otherwise could not be done.

ates an effective force of 3000 N on the rock. A 3000 N force is far greater than the man's weight, and, therefore, he can move more than he could without the lever.

The ability of this lever or any other machine to multiply force is referred to as mechanical advantage. The **mechanical advantage** (MA) of a machine is identified as the number of times a machine multiplies the effort put into it. It identifies how effective the machine will be at performing the work desired (fig. 16-6).

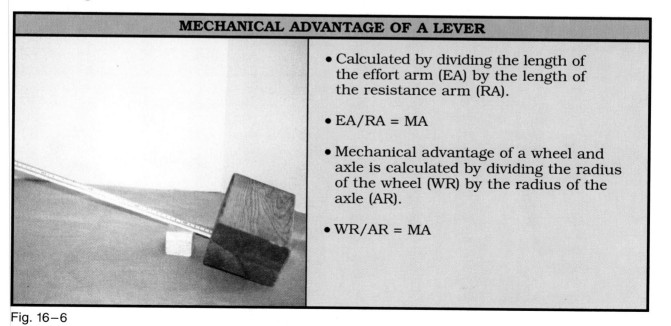

MECHANICAL ADVANTAGE OF A LEVER

- Calculated by dividing the length of the effort arm (EA) by the length of the resistance arm (RA).

- EA/RA = MA

- Mechanical advantage of a wheel and axle is calculated by dividing the radius of the wheel (WR) by the radius of the axle (AR).

- WR/AR = MA

Fig. 16–6

Fig. 16-6 Continued

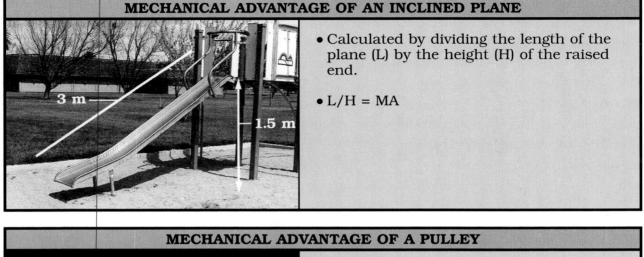

MECHANICAL ADVANTAGE OF AN INCLINED PLANE

- Calculated by dividing the length of the plane (L) by the height (H) of the raised end.

- L/H = MA

3 m

1.5 m

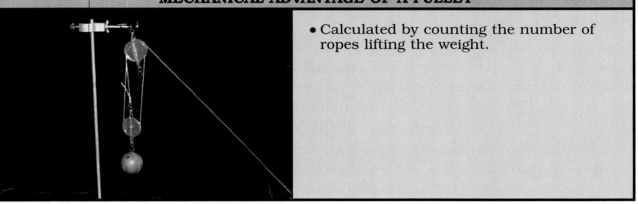

MECHANICAL ADVANTAGE OF A PULLEY

- Calculated by counting the number of ropes lifting the weight.

Look at the playground slide in figure 16-6. The slide has a length of 3 m and a height of 1.5 m. The theoretical mechanical advantage is equal to 2. According to this calculation, how much work should it take to pull a 50 N bag of dog food up the slide? If you said "25 joules," you are correct. However, if you actually tried this, you would find that it takes nearly 35 joules of work to actually pull the dog food up the slide rather than the predicted 25 joules. Why? The reason is friction, which interferes with the brick's movement up the plane. If the board is sanded or a lubricant is added, friction is reduced, and less work will be needed to pull the brick.

The mechanical advantage calculated for each machine, called the **theoretical mechanical advantage**, rarely equals the actual mechanical advantage obtained from a machine.

This is because other forces—such as friction, gravity, or wind resistance—interfere with the working of the machine.

Because there is a difference between theoretical and actual mechanical advantage, another value, efficiency, is used to measure the work of machines (fig. 16-7). **Efficiency** is the measure of the actual work a machine can do compared to the energy put into it. Efficiency (E) is usually represented as a percent (%). It is calculated by dividing the amount of work gotten out of a machine, called **work output** (WO), by **work input** (WI), or the amount of work put into the machine.

In the example of the brick and inclined plane, it should take 10 joules of work to pull the brick up the plane, but it actually requires 14 joules of work. Therefore, the efficiency of this inclined plane is 71 percent (fig. 16-8).

Fig. 16-7 The actual mechanical advantage of the loading ramp may be different from its theoretical mechanical advantage.

$$\text{E (efficiency)} = \frac{WO}{WI} \times 100\% = \frac{10 \text{ J}}{14 \text{ J}} \times 100\% = 71\%$$

Fig. 16–8

An efficiency of 71 percent means that 71 percent of the work put in helps you, and 29 percent is lost to friction or other force. No machine is 100 percent efficient, but the machines rated closest to 100 percent are the most helpful. Many household appliances are labeled with their efficiency ratings. Designers and manufacturing companies are constantly researching ways of making these items more efficient (fig. 16-9).

Fig. 16–9 Technologists constantly look for ways to make machines more efficient.

Fig. 16–10 The more efficient an automobile is, the less often it must be refueled.

Automobiles are usually less than 10 percent efficient (fig. 16-10). This is because the chemical energy in the fuel is not completely converted into mechanical energy. Some is lost as heat when the fuel ignites. Of the mechanical energy that is produced, some is lost to the friction of moving parts, and some is lost to wind resistance as the car moves along the road. Other large machines, such as cranes, trains, bulldozers, tractors, and airplanes, are even less efficient than automobiles, but the jobs they perform probably would never get done without them.

REVIEW IT

1. What does the term *mechanical advantage* mean?
2. What does the term *efficiency* mean?

CLASS ACTIVITY 16-2: Inclined Planes

Question: What is the mechanical advantage of an inclined plane?

Materials:

board (1" x 8") - 1 m   spring scale
books - 5   string
brick   talcum powder
meterstick

Fig. A

Procedure:

1. Tie the string to the brick. Tie the free end of the string to the spring scale and measure the weight of the brick. Record.
2. Place one end of the board on a stack of two or three books to form an inclined plane as shown in figure A. Record the length and height of the inclined plane.
3. Calculate the theoretical mechanical advantage of the inclined plane. Record.
4. Holding the spring scale, pull the brick up the inclined plane at a constant speed. Read the spring scale while the brick is moving. Record.
5. Increase the height of the inclined plane by adding another book to the stack. Repeat steps 2 to 4.
6. Decrease the height of the inclined plane by removing all but one of the books. Repeat steps 2 to 4.
7. Sprinkle talcum powder on the board and repeat steps 2 to 4.

Data:

Inclined Plane	Length (cm)	Height (cm)	Theoretical MA	Force Used to Move Brick	Actual MA
1					
Powder					
2					
Powder					
3					
Powder					

Questions:

1. Which ramp required the least amount of force to pull the brick up? Which required the most?
2. How did the theoretical mechanical advantage compare to the actual mechanical advantage of the inclined plane?
3. What happens to the mechanical advantage of an inclined plane as its height is increased?
4. What happens to the mechanical advantage of an inclined plane as its length is increased?
5. What effect did sprinkling talcum powder on the inclined plane have on the mechanical advantage of the plane? Why?

Conclusion: Write 3–5 sentences about what you learned from this activity.

16–3 COMPOUND MACHINES

VOCABULARY
compound machine

OBJECTIVE

- Describe the relationship between simple and compound machines.

The girl stood up from playing the piano in the store, rode the escalator down to the first floor, zipped up her coat, and walked outside through the automatic door. She was glad to be outside but was totally unaware that all the equipment she had just used—the piano, escalator, zipper, and automatic door—were considered compound machines (fig. 16-11).

Fig. 16–11 The piano, the escalator, the zipper, and the automatic door are all examples of compound machines.

Compound machines are combinations of two or more simple machines. They are combined so that tasks can be accomplished that would be more difficult or even impossible without them. For example, scissors are a combination of two class 1 levers that share the same fulcrum (fig. 16-12).

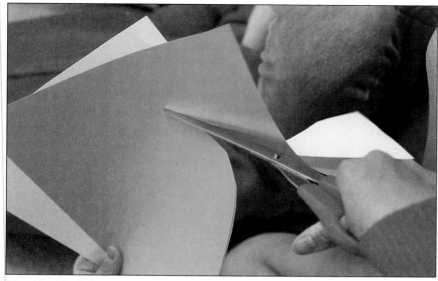

Fig. 16–12 Scissors are a combination of two levers.

Both a shovel and an ax are combination machines. The blade of each is a wedge; the handle of each acts as a lever (fig. 16-13). In both cases, the wedge cuts through material, and the handle allows the user to move the wedge more easily.

Fig. 16–13 Both the ax and shovel are compound machines.

Fig. 16–14 Wheels and axles, inclined planes, and screws are simple machines used to make a pencil sharpener.

The pencil sharpener is figure 16-14 is also a compound machine. Inside are two sets of spiral cutting blades, which are turned by a wheel and axle—the handle. Even the fishing pole of the fly fisherman in figure 16-15 is a compound machine. In this example the fishing pole is a class 3 lever with a wheel and axle—the fishing reel—attached to hold the line.

Fig. 16–15 The fly rod is a combination machine made up of a lever (the actual rod) and a wheel and axle (the reel).

Fig. 16–16 The muscles in your legs allow them to work as levers and help you to jump.

The compound machine you probably use most is your body. It is a specially designed lever system that helps you move (fig. 16-16). Each movement that you make with your arms and legs involves class 3 levers. Your bones are the lever;

Benjamin Franklin

Benjamin Franklin did many things in his life. He helped to write the Constitution of the United States. He was one of the five men who drew up the Declaration of Independence in July of 1776. He was a member of the Royal Society of London. Only the greatest scientists belonged to this society. Franklin was a member because of his experiments with lightning and electricity. He wrote many scientific articles that were printed in Europe.

Franklin knew four successive British kings. He was also the ambassador from America to France. At the end of the War for Independence, he negotiated a treaty with England.

Franklin founded a newspaper called *The Pennsylvania Gazette*. Through this newspaper, he helped organize police, militia, and fire departments. He raised support for street paving and helped establish the first public library for Philadelphia.

He established a school, which later became the famous University of Pennsylvania. Franklin invented bifocal glasses, the sewing machine, the lightning rod, and is credited with the idea of daylight saving time.

Franklin wrote: "I believe in one God, the Creator of the Universe. That He governs it by His providence. That He ought to be worshiped. That the most acceptable service we render to Him is doing good to His other children."

Benjamin Franklin did not ask payment for his writings, his inventions, or his service to his country. He did not lay up treasures on Earth. He gave his life for his country and humanity.

your muscles supply the effort; your joint is the fulcrum; and you move your body or some weight, such as a book.

Compound machines such as watches, blenders, and bicycles are made of many simple machines. Other compound machines, such as wheelbarrows and doorknobs, are made of only two or three simple machines.

REVIEW IT

1. How are compound machines different from simple machines?

CHAPTER 16 WRAP-UP

THINKING SKILLS: Making Predictions

Making a prediction is a way of trying to figure out how future events will turn out. It is not a wild guess or unfounded statement. A prediction is a statement based on information that has been collected and analyzed.

By looking at recorded data, scientists can often predict the outcome of a future event. In this activity you are to look over the fuel-consumption graph of a race car. Study the graph and make your predictions.

The graph shows the gallons of fuel used per trial race of 10 laps (2.5 mi/lap). The race car has a 30-gallon fuel tank and ran 5 trial races. The actual race is 80 laps (200 mi) long.

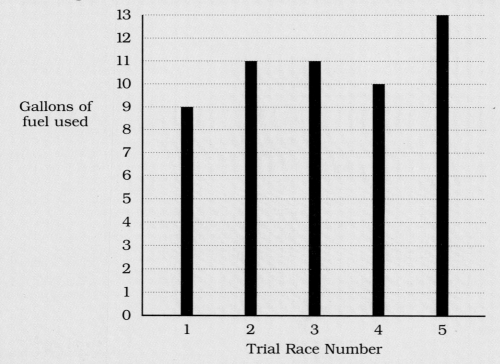

1. Why is fuel consumption less on trial 1 than on the other trials? Why is it highest on trial race 5?
2. During the trial races, how many times did the fuel tank need to be filled?
3. What is the average fuel consumption during the trial runs?
4. In the actual race how many laps will the race car be able to go before having to fuel up?
5. During the race, how many times will it have to stop to refuel?

372

QUESTIONS AND PROBLEMS

1. What are two ways of increasing the mechanical advantage of an inclined plane?
2. Why is a screw considered an inclined plane?
3. Suppose you were using a .5 m long pipe wrench to loosen a pipe fitting, and the fitting would not come loose. What could you do to increase the mechanical advantage of your machine?
4. What kind of simple machine can a screwdriver be used for?
5. A socket wrench is considered a lever. What is the effort arm? What is the resistance arm? What is the fulcrum?
6. Can efficiency ever equal 1.0 (100 percent)? Explain.
7. Examine a standard doorknob and latch. What simple machines make it up?
8. How is a class 3 lever different from a class 2 lever?
9. If you have to pull a long nail out of a piece of wood, is it better to use a long-handled hammer or a hammer with a short handle? Explain.
10. What happens to the mechanical advantage of a pulley as the number of ropes supporting the weight increases? Why?
11. If your arm and leg are levers, where are the fulcrums?
12. Which do you think would be harder to turn, a screw with a low pitch or one with a high pitch? Why?

RESEARCH

1. Make a large poster of a detailed diagram of a 10-speed bicycle. Use arrows to identify the various simple machines that make up the bike.
2. Visit a hardware store and learn how screws are categorized according to type of screw, thread, length, and diameter. Make a series of drawings to show your findings.
3. Make a mobile to hang in the classroom. Your mobile should have at least three levels and should balance when hung.
4. Use library resources to find out what is being done to make automobiles more efficient. Prepare an oral report on your findings.
5. Inventors have long sought to make perpetual-motion machines. Use library resources to discover what these machines are. Make a series of drawings that illustrate several of these machines. With each drawing include an explanation of why the machine did not work.

REVIEW

HIGHLIGHTS

1. A simple machine is a device that changes the size or direction of a force.
2. The characteristics of each type of simple machine are identified and discussed in figure 16-2.
3. Mechanical advantage is the amount a machine can multiply a force.
4. Efficiency is the measure of the actual work a machine can do.
5. A compound machine is a combination of two or more simple machines.

VOCABULARY LIST

compound machine   mechanical advantage   theoretical mechanical
efficiency   pitch   advantage
effort arm   resistance arm   thread
effort force   resistance force   work input
fulcrum   simple machine   work output

PRACTICE

Multiple Choice. Choose the best answer.

1. A simple machine
   a. has no moving parts
   b. has a fulcrum and an output
   c. multiplies force
   d. no longer exists

2. The three simple machines include
   a. lever, pulley, position
   b. lever, pulley, fulcrum
   c. inclined plane, pitch, threads
   d. pulley, inclined plane, lever

3. Levers pivot around a point called the
   a. fulcrum
   b. effort point
   c. wedge
   d. compound point

4. A spiraled inclined plane is called a
   a. screw
   b. wedge
   c. pitch
   d. none of these

5. The ability of a machine to multiply a force is called
   a. resistance force
   b. work output
   c. compound machine
   d. mechanical advantage

6. Work input compared to work output yields
   a. work done
   b. resistance arm
   c. mechanical advantage
   d. efficiency

7. A combination of two or more simple machines is a
   a. complex machine
   b. compound machine
   c. complicated machine
   d. all of these

8. Your legs and arms are examples of
   a. levers
   b. inclined planes
   c. pulleys
   d. none of these

9. An example of a simple machine would be
   a. a crowbar
   b. a bicycle
   c. pliers
   d. all of these

10. An example of a compound machine would be a
    a. pencil sharpener
    b. pair of scissors
    c. a shovel
    d. all of these

Matching. Match each word with its definition or description.

1. work put into a machine
2. work output compared to work put in
3. pivot point of a lever
4. force that resists change
5. changes the size or direction of a force
6. number of threads per cm
7. two or more simple machines
8. work produced by a machine
9. a spiraled incline
10. ability of a machine to multiply force

a. compound machine
b. efficiency
c. effort force
d. fulcrum
e. mechanical advantage
f. pitch
g. resistance force
h. simple machine
i. thread
j. work output

CAREERS

Fluid-Power Technician

Description of Work
Fluid-power technicians work with systems that use pressurized fluids to carry power from one place to another. Fluid power is one of the three basic ways that energy is transmitted, multiplied, and controlled. Fluid-power technicians work in factories, laboratories, and offices in all sections of the country.

Personal Qualifications
Fluid-power technicians must have mechanical ability. They should enjoy learning how machines and other equipment work. Technicians must also be good at mathematics and science.

Requirements
A high-school diploma and two years of college. The armed services also train some enlisted personnel in fluid power.

Career Information
National Fluid Power
  Association
3333 North Mayfair Road
Milwaukee, WI 53222

Ergonomist

Description of Work
Ergonomists assist in the design of machines, tools, and other equipment to ensure that they can be used easily and correctly. They work with companies to make the working environment comfortable and effective so that employee productivity is high.

Personal Qualifications
Ergonomists must be able to communicate well with people so they can find out what the problems are.

Requirements
A high-school diploma and four to six years of college.

Career Information
Human Factors Society
P.O. Box 1369
Santa Monica, CA 90406

Mechanical Engineer

Description of Work
Mechanical engineers are concerned with the production, transmission, and use of mechanical power and heat. They design and develop power-producing and power-using machines. Mechanical engineers design tools needed by other engineers for their work.

Personal Qualifications
Mechanical engineers should be good at science and mathematics. They should enjoy working with machinery and using it to solve problems. They also must be able to present and explain the machines they design.

Requirements
A high-school diploma and four to five years of college. They must also be licensed as a professional engineer.

Career Information
The American Society of
  Mechanical Engineers
345 E. 47th Street
New York, NY 10017

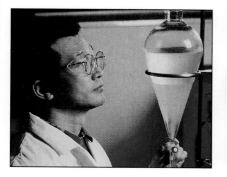

Industrial Engineer

Description of Work
Industrial Engineers determine the most effective ways for an organization to use the basic factors of production—people, machines, materials, information, and energy. They design data-processing systems and use mathematical analysis to solve problems. They deal with the management of people to increase productivity.

Personal Qualifications
Industrial engineers must be able to communicate with people. They must be able to discuss problems and come up with solutions. Industrial engineers should enjoy problem-solving and working with people.

Requirements
A high-school diploma and two to four years of college.

Career Information
Institute of Industrial
  Engineers, Inc.
25 Technology Park/Atlanta
Norcross, GA 30092

Automobile Mechanic

Description of Work
Automobile mechanics service and repair mechanical, electrical, and body parts of passenger cars, trucks, buses, and other types of gasoline-powered equipment. After making the necessary inspections and testing to determine the causes of faulty operation, they then repair or replace defective parts to restore the vehicle to proper operating condition.

Personal Qualifications
Mechanics must be able to handle physical labor and the grime and grease present in the workplace. Mechanics must keep up to date with all innovations and refinements. They must also be able to tolerate a certain amount of questions and criticism and be able to deal with people.

Requirements
A high-school diploma plus a completed apprenticeship.

Career Information
Automotive Service Industry
  Association
444 N. Michigan Ave.
Chicago, IL 60611

Flight Engineer

Description of Work
Flight engineers monitor the operation of various mechanical and electrical devices aboard an airplane. They are concerned with the condition and the performance of the plane before, during, and after the flight.

Personal Qualifications
Flight engineers require skill and training and the ability to act under a variety of circumstances. Engineers must be able to work with people.

Requirements
A high-school diploma and two years of college is recommended. They must also be licensed by the Federal Aviation Agency (FAA).

Career Information
Flight Engineers'
  International Assn.
905 16th Street, NW
Washington, DC 20006

UNIT IV

ASTRONOMY

INTRODUCTION

Have you ever gone outside on a clear, dark night and looked up at the stars? How many do you suppose you see? A hundred, a thousand, a million? Scientists estimate that you can see about 6000 stars with the unaided eye. Thousands more can be seen with the use of binoculars. Large telescopes, housed in observatories, bring billions of stars into view.

How many stars are there? How far away are they? What are they like? People have puzzled over these and similar questions for thousands of years. In this unit you will explore the study of astronomy and investigate these questions.

CHAPTER TITLES

Billions upon billions of stars make up our universe.

CHAPTER 17

LEARNING ABOUT THE UNIVERSE

INTRODUCTION

How many grains of sand are in this wheelbarrow? One million? A hundred million? A hundred billion? It would be safe to say that there are more grains of sand here than you would really want to count. Did you know that scientists estimate that there are more stars in just one galaxy than there are grains of sand in this wheelbarrow? Our sun is a very ordinary star in one such galaxy. Scientists also estimate that there are more galaxies in our universe than there are people on Earth. Some stars in these galaxies are so large that it would take a spacecraft several years to get from one side of the star to the other.

In this chapter you will explore some of what is known about the universe and learn about some of the people who contributed to our current understanding of space and the universe.

SECTION TITLES

Scientists estimate there are more stars in our galaxy
than there are grains of sand in this wheelbarrow.

17-1 WHAT WE HAVE LEARNED

OBJECTIVES

- Describe the term **universe**.
- Identify the contributions of early astronomers.
- Identify ways astronomy has been useful.
- Explain how the study of astronomy supports the concept of a Creator.

Imagine you could sit on a light beam and ride as it speeds along at about 300 000 km/sec (186,000 mi/sec). If you left the sun at 8:00 A.M. headed for Earth, you would arrive here about 8 minutes later, at 8:08 A.M. (fig. 17-1). If you left Earth on a beam of light headed for the nearest star, other than our sun, it would take you 4.5 years to make the

Fig. 17-1 It takes sunlight about eight minutes to reach Earth.

trip. Traveling on that same beam of light, it would take more than 100,000 years to travel across the Milky Way Galaxy. That means that the light we see is always "old light." The light we get from our star, the sun, is eight minutes old when we see it; the light we see from the nearest star is 4.5 years old by the time it gets to us.

The sun, the stars, and galaxies are all part of the universe. But what is the universe? The **universe** is everything that exists (fig. 17-2). The part of the universe we are most familiar with is the part we can see: Earth, planets, sun, and stars that are visible at night. But the universe is much more than this. It includes the billions of stars and galaxies that are beyond our vision. It contains asteroids, comets, and meteors. It includes dust and gas between the stars and galaxies. In addition, the universe encompasses all of the empty space and all of the energy present.

There is evidence that in ancient civilizations there were scientists who studied astronomy. The earliest scripture in the Bible, the book of Job, refers to constellations by name. It speaks of the ordinances and rules of the heavens. Two thousand years ago a group of Magi, or wise men, were studying the stars and observed the Star of Bethlehem.

Fig. 17–2 The universe includes everything on Earth, in the solar system, in the galaxy, and beyond our galaxy.

Fig. 17–3 The upright boulders at Stonehenge, in southern England, were used to mark the summer and winter solstice and to help predict seasons.

RESEARCH IT
What was the contribution of Tycho Brahe?

In southern England, long before recorded history, stones were placed in a precise pattern on a broad plain (fig. 17-3). This circle of upright boulders, called Stonehenge, was designed to catch the rays of the rising and setting sun on the day of the summer and winter solstice.

Fig. 17–4 The shaft of light marks the solstice on a rock in Chaco Culture National Historic Park, New Mexico.

Native Americans in one region of North America studied the movement of the sun and discovered that on a certain day each year, in the middle of the summer, the sun's position caused a shaft of light to shine at a particular position on a rock (fig. 17-4). They marked this spot and used it to develop a calendar. Other cultures established similar devices from which they developed accurate calendars. These calendars were used to predict yearly flooding and determine when to plant and harvest crops. During the third century A.D., the Mayan civilization of Central American made accurate written calendars based on the movement of the stars and planets. Later, during the fourteenth and fifteenth centuries, Aztec and Incan civilizations made similar calendars.

Early navigators used the position of certain stars or groups of stars to navigate as they sailed across the ocean. Some historians believe that ships from Egypt navigated by the stars to South America during the twenty-fourth century B.C. These are believed to be among the first migrations of people to the Western Hemisphere (fig. 17-5).

Fig. 17–5 Early sailors sailed the uncharted oceans, navigating by the position of the stars.

The first written explanation of the universe we have is that of Aristarchus (ar is tär' kəs), a Greek astronomer. He lived several hundred years before Christ. This early scientist believed that Earth was one of several planets that revolved around the sun. Though Aristarchus' idea was correct, it was not accepted. People did not believe Aristarchus because his idea did not agree with what they saw.

People came to many amusing conclusions based on what they saw. Thales (thā' lēz), a Greek teacher, believed that Earth was a flat disk that floated on an unending ocean of water. Xenopanes (zi näf' ə nēz) believed Earth was flat and infinite in size. He theorized that the stars were extinguished in the west and rekindled the next morning in the east. Anaximander (ə naks ə man' der), while correct about Earth orbiting the sun, incorrectly believed that everything in the universe came from water and that Earth was a cylinder floating in the center of the universe. Others, who did believe that Earth was round, still thought the sun went around Earth, rather than Earth going around the sun, because they saw the sun "cross" the sky each day.

Fig. 17–6 Early civilizations believed that the sun and other stars revolved around Earth.

In the fourth century B.C., the idea that Earth was the center of the universe was made popular by Aristotle, another Greek teacher. According to Aristotle, Earth and the heavens were spherical, and all things revolved around Earth (fig. 17-6). This theory, even though wrong, was accepted by almost everyone for over 1000 years.

Fig. 17-7 Early observations of objects in the heavens increased our understanding of the universe.

As people observed the movements of the sun, stars, and other objects in the heavens, their understanding of the universe began to change. The study of the universe, or **astronomy**, led to an understanding that was not based on superstition but rather on information gathered through observation, experimentation, and mathematics (fig. 17-7).

In 1543, a Polish astronomer named Nicholaus Copernicus (nik ə lā′ əs kō pᵤr′ ni kəs), published a new theory (fig. 17-8). Copernicus's theory stated that the sun was the center of the solar system and that Earth and other planets revolved around it.

A few years later, Galileo, an Italian astronomer, used a telescope to verify that Earth orbited the sun, just as Copernicus and others had suggested (fig. 17-9).

Fig. 17-8 Nicholaus Copernicus proposed the theory that the sun was the center of the solar system.

Fig. 17-9 Galileo used observations made with his telescope to verify the ideas of Copernicus.

Knowledge gained from astronomy helps us understand other processes and events. For example, observations of the motions of the moon and planets led to a better understanding of gravity and the forces that control all motion. This knowledge has enabled engineers to design bridges, buildings, cars, airplanes, and bicycles (fig. 17-10). The study of astronomy has contributed to the development of radios, TVs, cellular phones, and home satellite dishes.

Fig. 17–10 Knowledge gained from the study of astronomy has helped scientists and technologists to improve old designs and to develop new products.

The study of astronomy continues to help us. Observations of the sun and other stars improved our understanding of nuclear energy. In fact, astronomy suggested that such a thing as nuclear energy might exist. Studies of other planets increased our understanding of Earth's geology. The knowledge of storms on Jupiter led to a better understanding and more precise prediction of weather here on Earth (fig. 17-11).

The study of astronomy also affirms a belief in the Creator. Although space is immense, it is predictable and consistent. The movement of stars and planets is the most accurate phenomenon we have. Our clocks and watches are adjusted according to instruments that are set by the movement of

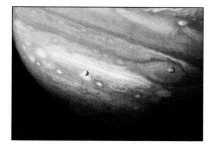

Fig. 17–11 Knowledge gained by studying storms on Jupiter has improved weather prediction on Earth.

TRY THIS 17-1: A Handy Sundial

Materials:
   pencil

Procedure:
1. Hold out your hand, palm up. Lay the pencil across the palm and hold the end with the thumb of the hand as shown in figure A.
2. Grasp one end of the pencil with your thumb. The other end of the pencil should rise to make an angle of about 30°. The pencil should point north.
3. When using your sundial in the morning, put the pencil in your left hand and point your fingers to the west. In the afternoon put the pencil in your right hand and point your fingers to the east. The pencil should always point north.
4. Read the time by looking at where the shadow of the pencil falls. Read the time from the tip of your longest finger around the edge of your hand. Begin at six and count one hour for each fingertip as shown in figure B.

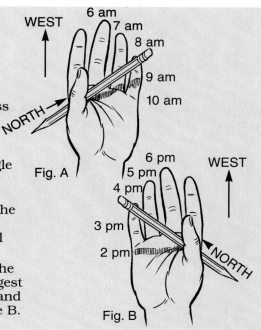

these heavenly objects. The workings of natural laws and the overall design of the universe provide strong evidence of an intelligent Creator who designed and still keeps in motion our universe.

Then the Lord answered Job out of the whirlwind: "Do you know the ordinances of the heavens? Can you establish their rule on Earth?" (Job 38:1, 33, NRSV).

MINIBIOGRAPHYMINIBIOGRAPHYMINIBIOGRAPHYMINIBIOGRAPHYMINIBIOGRAPHY

Maria Mitchell

Maria Mitchell, America's first woman astronomer, was born on the island of Nantucket, Massachusetts, on August 1, 1818. As a young girl, Maria enjoyed exploring and discovering the wonders of the natural world. She showed intense curiosity and displayed unusual powers of observation. Maria's love for nature was encouraged by her father, an amateur astronomer. Because of her father's interest in astronomy, Maria became interested in the stars and observing the night sky. Although she had little formal education, she had the opportunity to study under a local college professor, who instilled in her a passion for accuracy.

At the age of 18, Maria got a job at the local library. When she was not helping library patrons, Maria spent time teaching herself mathematics and navigation. She and her father built a small observatory on top of their home, where they spent most evenings observing the heavens through a four-inch telescope provided to them by the U.S. Coast Survey.

On the night of October 1, 1847, Maria discovered a new comet, which was named after her. Because of this discovery, Maria Mitchell won several prestigious awards, including being the first woman to be elected to the American Academy of Arts and Sciences. Her fame spread to Europe, where she traveled, giving lectures. In Europe she had the opportunity to study with many of Europe's leading scientists, including the mathematician Mary Sommerville, the geologist Alexander von Humboldt, and the inventor of the calculating machine, Charles Babbage.

On her return to the United States, Maria Mitchell was invited to become professor of astronomy at Vassar College in New York. While at Vassar, Maria continued to study astronomy. She pioneered research in the photography of sunspots and was the first to recognize that the solar features were not clouds but whirling currents of gas on the sun's surface. In addition, she studied solar eclipses, double stars, nebulas, and the satellites of Saturn and Jupiter.

MINIBIOGRAPHYMINIBIOGRAPHYMINIBIOGRAPHYMINIBIOGRAPHYMINIBIOGRAPHY

As technology develops new tools to improve our ability to observe and study the heavens, science expands its understandings of the universe. These revised theories provide the basis of new knowledge. Many discoveries of the future will undoubtedly be based on discoveries made through our study of the universe (fig. 17-12).

Fig. 17–12 Many discoveries will result from continued study of the universe.

REVIEW IT

1. What is included in the universe?
2. What was the contribution of each of the following astronomers:
    a. Aristarchus
    b. Aristotle
    c. Copernicus
    d. Galileo
3. How has astronomy helped our daily lives?
4. What aspects of the universe suggest an intelligent Creator?

17-2 TELESCOPES

VOCABULARY
observatory
optical telescope
reflecting telescope
refracting telescope
spectroscope
spectrum
telescope

OBJECTIVES

- Define the term **telescope**.
- Explain the difference between a refracting and a reflecting telescope.
- Identify the information obtained from a spectroscope.

Imagine going to school tomorrow. The sun is shining brightly. You go outside after lunch for recess and notice that the sun doesn't seem to be shining as brightly. Later you go out for P.E., and it is darker still. The darkening you

Fig. 17–13 During a total solar eclipse the moon passes in front of the sun, casting a dark shadow on Earth.

observe is like being in a big shadow. You look for clouds or smoke in the sky that might be blocking the sunlight, but none is there. The cause of this darkness is a total solar eclipse (fig. 17-13). When a solar eclipse occurs, the light that normally reaches Earth from the sun is blocked out by the moon. This casts a shadow on Earth, and the day becomes darker.

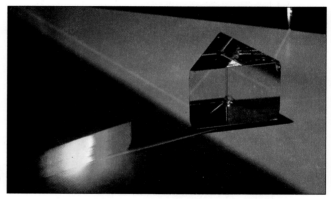

Fig. 17–14 White light is made of red, orange, yellow, green, blue, and violet light.

While visible light from the sun appears to be white, it is made up of many different colors. You can see these colors when light is separated by a prism (fig. 17-14). The visible light emitted, or given off, from other stars can be separated in a similar way. By separating a star's light, scientists can analyze the light and determine the star's composition, how hot it is, and its other features.

Telescopes are special instruments designed to study the radiation produced by objects in space. Telescopes collect radiation and feed it into scientific instruments that record the radiation and analyze it. Telescopes may be large and housed in special buildings called **observatories**, or they may be small enough to carry around by hand.

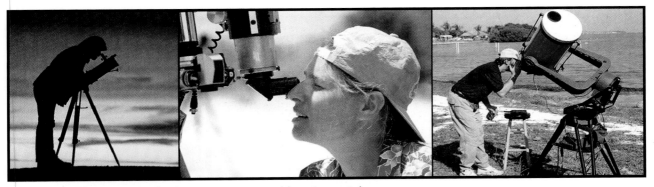

Fig. 17–15 Many types of telescopes are used by star watchers.

Most telescopes look like the ones in figure 17-15. These telescopes are called **optical telescopes** because they use lenses and mirrors to collect light and magnify the objects, forming sharp images. When you look at the stars on a dark night, your eyes collect the light from the stars you see. Because telescopes collect radiation over an area that is much larger than the pupils of our eyes, they allow us to see objects that are too faint and too far away to be seen with the unaided eye.

Though optical telescopes are interesting and fun to use, astronomers do not usually spend much time looking through them (fig. 17-16). Instead, they use the telescopes as giant cameras. Film or videotape inside the telescope cameras can be exposed for hours each night. Light from faint stars accumulates on the photographic plate and electronic monitor, and it produces a much better picture than anyone can see with the eye alone.

Fig. 17–16 Large telescopes are used as cameras, taking pictures of objects in the universe.

There are two types of optical telescopes: refracting telescopes and reflecting telescopes. Study figure 17-17 to learn the parts of each type of telescope and how each works.

Fig. 17–17

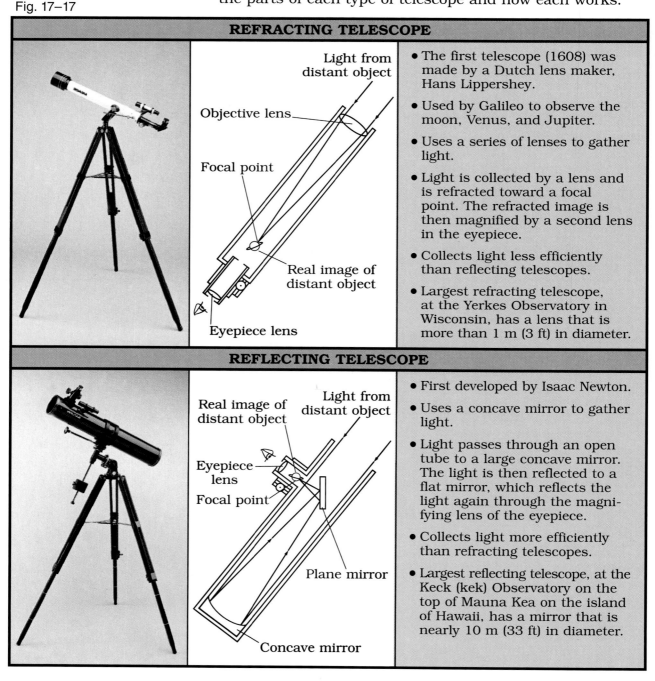

REFRACTING TELESCOPE

Light from distant object

Objective lens

Focal point

Real image of distant object

Eyepiece lens

- The first telescope (1608) was made by a Dutch lens maker, Hans Lippershey.
- Used by Galileo to observe the moon, Venus, and Jupiter.
- Uses a series of lenses to gather light.
- Light is collected by a lens and is refracted toward a focal point. The refracted image is then magnified by a second lens in the eyepiece.
- Collects light less efficiently than reflecting telescopes.
- Largest refracting telescope, at the Yerkes Observatory in Wisconsin, has a lens that is more than 1 m (3 ft) in diameter.

REFLECTING TELESCOPE

Real image of distant object

Light from distant object

Eyepiece lens

Focal point

Plane mirror

Concave mirror

- First developed by Isaac Newton.
- Uses a concave mirror to gather light.
- Light passes through an open tube to a large concave mirror. The light is then reflected to a flat mirror, which reflects the light again through the magnifying lens of the eyepiece.
- Collects light more efficiently than refracting telescopes.
- Largest reflecting telescope, at the Keck (kek) Observatory on the top of Mauna Kea on the island of Hawaii, has a mirror that is nearly 10 m (33 ft) in diameter.

TRY THIS 17-2: Collecting Light

Materials:

drawing compass
drinking straws - 40
graph paper

poster board - 10 x 10 cm
scissors

Procedure:
1. Use the compass to draw a circle 1 cm in diameter near the edge of the poster board.
2. Cut the hole out. The hole represents a telescope lens or mirror.
3. Fit straws into the hole until it is filled. Pack the straws tightly, but do not pack them so tightly that they are crushed.
   - How many straws fit into the hole?
4. Repeat steps 1 to 3, this time with a 2-cm hole.
   - How many straws fit into the hole?
5. Repeats steps 1 to 3 with a 3-cm hole and with a 4-cm hole.
   - How many straws fit into each hole?
   - Why is a large lens or mirror an advantage over a small lens or mirror?

Another instrument astronomers use to study stars and other objects in the universe is the spectroscope. A **spectroscope** is an instrument that separates light into very fine color bands of light, or a **spectrum**, much like the prism. Scientists attach spectroscopes to telescopes so they can study the composition of stars by analyzing the light produced (fig. 17-18). The spectrum of light from each star provides important information concerning the materials that make up the star, its temperature, and processes that are taking place on the star.

REVIEW IT

1. What is a telescope?
2. How is a refracting telescope different from a reflecting telescope?
3. How do astronomers use a spectroscope?

Fig. 17–18 Astronomers use spectroscopes to analyze the light emitted from objects in space.

RESEARCH IT
Who was Zacharias Janssen?

CLASS ACTIVITY 17-2: Spectroscope

Question: How does a spectroscope work?

Materials:

cardboard tube
colored pencils
construction paper (black)
diffraction grating - 2 x 2 cm
drawing compass
fluorescent lamp

incandescent lamp
metric ruler
rubber band
safety razor blade
scissors
transparent tape

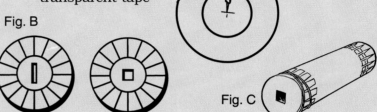

Fig. A

Fig. B

Fig. C

Procedure:
1. Measure the diameter of the tube. Use the compass to draw a circle the same diameter as the tube on the construction paper. Using the same center point, draw another circle with a diameter 2 cm larger than the first, as shown in figure A.
2. Make several equidistant cuts between the larger circle and the smaller circle.
3. In another place on the construction paper, repeat steps 1 and 2.
4. Use the safety razor blade to make a slit 2 cm by 1 mm in the center of one disk (fig. B).
5. Place the disk over the end of the tube and tape the flaps to the side of the tube as shown in figure C.
6. In the other disk cut a 1-cm-square window in the center. Center the diffraction grating over the window and tape together. Place the disk over the other end of the tube and secure the flaps with a rubber band to enable the disk to be rotated.
7. Darken the room. Point the slit-disk end of the cardboard tube toward an outside light source. Look through the diffraction-disk end of the tube. Rotate the diffraction disk slowly until you see a clear spectrum. Tape the flaps of the disk.
8. Use this newly made spectroscope to examine fluorescent light. Use colored pencils to copy the spectrum you see. Put your drawing on a separate sheet of paper.
9. Repeat step 8, examining incandescent light. Put your drawing on a separate sheet of paper.

Data: Use sparate sheet of paper.

Questions:
1. What is the difference between the two spectrums? Why are they different?
2. How would the spectrum of a 60-watt light bulb compare to the spectrum of a 150-watt bulb? Explain.
3. What advantage does a spectroscope have over an optical telescope?

Conclusion: Write 3–5 sentences about what you learned from this activity.

The 10-meter Keck Telescope is the world's largest optical and infrared telescope. Built on Mauna Kea on the Island of Hawaii, the telescope takes advantage of the best astronomical site in the world. Located high above the atmospheric pollution and background light of populated areas, the Keck Telescope offers astronomers an unequaled view of the night sky. Although the 200-inch telescope at the Mt. Palomar Observatory can detect objects with the magnitude of 25 (That's equivalent to a 25-watt light bulb, the kind in your mom's oven, seen from a million kilometers away), the Keck Telescope can see objects 20 to 50 times fainter.

The reason the 10-meter telescope can "see" so well is that it has a mirror 10 meters in diameter instead of a mirror that is only 5 meters, as is the case with the Palomar Telescope. Building such a huge mirror presented a major problem. To solve this problem Dr. Jerry Nelson, a professor at the University of California at Santa Cruz, suggested making the large mirror out of 36 smaller mirrors. Once secured into place, the 36 2-meter mirrors make a solid reflective surface. Sensors at the edges of each individual mirror make constant adjustments to insure proper alignment.

Astronomers are using this "giant eye to the sky" to learn new information about our universe. Pictures of the impact of the Shoemaker-Levy 9 comet on Jupiter enabled scientists to learn a great deal about Jupiter's atmosphere and how a similar collision might affect Earth. This powerful telescope is also allowing astronomers to study some of the most distant objects in space. To study these faint objects, the telescope is turned to a relatively blank area of the sky and allowed to "look" for a long time to collect as much light as possible. Such surveys are turning up new galaxies and stars never seen before. Some astronomers count, catalog, and map these newly discovered objects; others study these objects in detail to learn about their origin, composition, and evolution.

The Keck telescope is an important tool to scientists, but it has not been totally free from problems. Many hours have been spent in making adjustments and learning how to compensate for changes caused by temperature and mechanical variations. In spite of these problems, astronomers have been enjoying the use of this giant telescope. As Dr. Cowie, of the Institute for Astronomy in Honolulu states, the Keck telescope "truly is a spectacular beast."

Questions:

1. Where is the 10-meter telescope located?
2. What did Dr. Nelson suggest to solve the impossible problem of making such a huge single mirror?
3. How do technicians ensure that each individual mirror stays properly aligned?
4. How are astronomers using the Keck Telescope?

17-3 RADIATION

VOCABULARY

electromagnetic spectrum
radiation

OBJECTIVES

• Identify the parts of the electromagnetic spectrum.
• Explain how astronomers study invisible energy present in space.

DID YOU KNOW?

The identifying fingerprint of an atom is carried on the light it emits.

RESEARCH IT

How did William Herschel contribute to the study of astronomy?

Optical telescopes have helped scientists increase their knowledge about stars and other objects in space. However, the visible light these instruments study is just one form of the energy produced in space. To learn about the other forms of this **radiation**, or energy that travels in waves, special instruments are required.

You have learned that a spectroscope can be used to separate the light of stars to form the visible spectrum. In a similar way, the other radiation produced by stars can also be separated. This spectrum of energy is called the **electromagnetic spectrum** (fig. 17-19). It begins with electric waves such as the 60-cycle power delivered to your home by the power company and includes radio waves, microwaves, infrared waves, visible light, ultraviolet light, and X-rays.

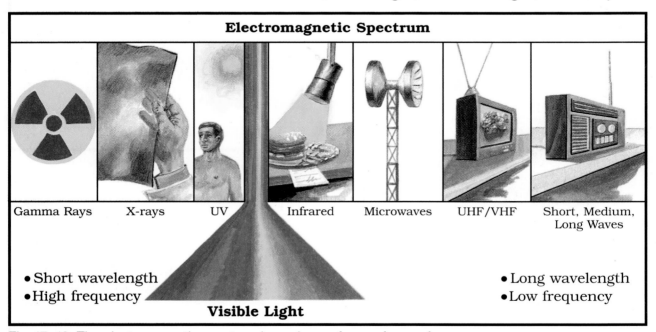

Electromagnetic Spectrum

| Gamma Rays | X-rays | UV | Infrared | Microwaves | UHF/VHF | Short, Medium, Long Waves |

• Short wavelength
• High frequency

• Long wavelength
• Low frequency

Visible Light

Fig. 17-19 The electromagnetic spectrum is made up of many forms of energy waves.

These energy waves are arranged according to their wavelength, radio waves being the longest and radiation being the shortest. The electromagnetic spectrum shows that light is only a small part of the total spectrum of energy in space. To study the other forms of radiant energy, other types of telescopes are used. These include ultraviolet telescopes, X-ray telescopes, infrared telescopes, and radio telescopes.

ULTRAVIOLET TELESCOPES

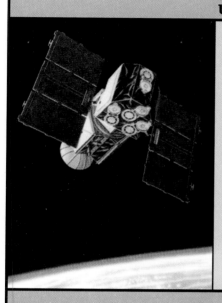

Ultraviolet energy is next to violet light in the spectrum. This invisible energy is emitted from the outer parts of many stars. Scientists study the ultraviolet energy emitted from a star to learn about the features of the star's surface, such as the temperature and types of gases present. Since most of the ultraviolet energy coming to Earth is blocked by the atmosphere, it is necessary to study ultraviolet energy from telescopes that are carried above the atmosphere by satellites. One such telescope is the International UV Explorer Observatory (IUO) that orbits 150 miles above Earth's surface. This telescope has collected thousands of images of objects in space.

X-RAY TELESCOPES

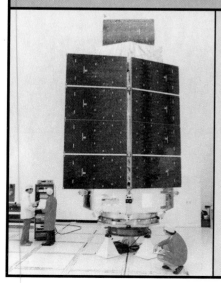

X-rays and other high-energy waves have shorter wavelengths and higher energy than ultraviolet waves and are located to the left of ultraviolet waves on the electromagnetic spectrum. In order to study high-energy waves, astronomers designed special telescopes called X-ray telescopes. These instruments collect high-energy waves by bouncing them along a curved surface, much the same way you skip a stone across a pond or lake. The data collected by these telescopes can be translated into images. In 1970 NASA launched a series of three X-ray telescopes, called High Energy Astronomy Observatories (HEAO). These telescopes have allowed astronomers to study high-energy X-rays that previously were unstudied and have helped them locate and study black holes.

INFRARED TELESCOPES

Because infrared energy has a longer wavelength than red light, it is located to the right of red light on the electromagnetic spectrum. Earth and many stars are not hot enough to emit visible light, but they do produce infrared energy. By using special telescopes, such as the Infrared Astronomical Satellite (IRAS), astronomers can study objects in space that emit infrared energy. Many of these objects are thought to be stars that are just beginning to form. By studying the infrared energy, astronomers are able to learn about the birth of stars.

RADIO TELESCOPES

Radio waves are next to the infrared waves on the spectrum. People use radio waves to broadcast radio and TV signals. In space, gas produces radio waves naturally. Scientists use radio telescopes to collect and study the radio waves from space. These waves have helped astronomers learn about quasars, pulsars, and neutron stars. Because radio waves interact less with other components of the universe, they can travel farther in space than any other form of energy. Thus, their study allows astronomers to learn about the most distant objects in the universe. One of the largest radio telescopes is the Very Large Array (VLA), located in New Mexico. This array of telescopes is made up of 27 mobile satellite dishes, each 25 m (82 ft) in diameter. The VLA is able to detect radio waves that have a source billions of light years from Earth.

REVIEW IT

1. Describe the electromagnetic spectrum.
2. What do astronomers learn by using each telescope?
   a. ultraviolet telescope
   b. infrared telescope
   c. X-ray telescope
   d. radio telescope

17–4 EXPLORING SPACE

- Describe the major projects in the U.S. space program.
- Explain the advantage of the space shuttle over earlier manned spacecraft.

"Flash Gordon" was a popular science fiction character created in Hollywood during the 1930s (fig. 17-20). Often the dashing adventurer would meet an evil villain who mistreated other beings or threatened life on Earth. During the course of the episode, Flash would invariably outsmart and outfight the villain and save the day.

Fig. 17–20 Before anyone traveled into space, the Flash Gordon adventures of the 1930s depicted how people imagined space and space travel would be.

While this series of adventures, with its amateur special effects and its inaccurate representation of space and space travel, seems ridiculous to us today, to the children living at that time, it was exciting.

Because no one had yet been in space, no one could prove

Fig. 17–21 The successful launch and return of the basketball-sized Russian satellite *Sputnik I* began the Space Age.

that things were different from how they looked when watching Flash Gordon and his escapades.

The Space Age began on October 4, 1957, when Russia launched a rocket that boosted the first satellite, "*Sputnik I*," into orbit high above Earth (fig. 17-21). The United States followed a few weeks later with its launch of the satellite "*Explorer I*," the first U.S. satellite in space. The launch of these two spacecraft began an intense race that resulted in the U.S. sending men to the moon. On July 20, 1969, Neil Armstrong became the first person to walk on the moon (fig. 17-22).

Fig. 17–22 The race to land a man on the moon ended when Neil Armstrong walked on the moon.

TRY THIS 17-4: "I Can't Get a Drink!"

Fig. A

Materials:
    chair   glass of water
    drinking straw

Procedure:
1. Place the glass of water on the floor and lie across the chair. Position yourself so your stomach is higher than your mouth as shown in figure A.
2. Now bend your head down toward the glass and get a drink.
   - Is it easy to get a drink this way?
3. Repeat step 2; only this time use a drinking straw.
   - Is it easy to get a drink this way?
   - Why is it difficult to get a drink when your stomach is higher than your mouth?
   - How do astronauts overcome the lack of gravity when getting a drink?

The United States space program has involved numerous components (fig. 17-23).

A SUMMARY OF THE U. S. SPACE PROGRAM	
Project	**Description and Purpose**
Pioneer (unmanned)	• Spacecraft designed to operate in deep space. • Measure and analyze magnetic fields, cosmic rays, and solar winds.
*Explorer (unmanned)	• Includes the first U. S. satellite. • Measure and analyze the magnetosphere, radiation belts, and the ionosphere; search for strong X-ray sources.
Orbiting Astronomical Observatory (unmanned)	• Large satellites equipped with 11 telescopes. • Map the entire electromagnetic spectrum and measure and analyze meteoroids.
Mariner (unmanned)	• A series of planetary probes. • Analyze Mars, Venus, and Mercury.
Viking (unmanned)	• Two planetary probes. • Land on Mars and study its surface and atmosphere.
*Voyager (unmanned)	• Two planetary probes. • Fly close to Jupiter, Saturn, Uranus, and Neptune and record data.
*Mercury (manned)	• First manned spacecraft. • Demonstrate that humans could survive conditions of space.
*Gemini (manned)	• A series of maneuverable (mə nōō′ vər ə bəl) spacecraft. • Develop skill in rendezvous with a target and docking.
*Apollo (manned)	• A series of maneuverable spacecraft. • Land a person on the moon.
Skylab (manned)	• The first U. S. space station. • Demonstrate that humans could live for extended periods in space. • Study medical and biological factors related to living in space.
*Space Shuttle (manned)	• A series of reusable spacecraft. • Carry out missions that have commercial, military, educational, and scientific value.
	*Major projects of the U.S. space program

Each of these missions had a specific purpose. Some, such as the Mercury and Gemini projects, were designed to test the practicality of manned space flight. Others, such as the Pioneer, Mariner, and Voyager projects, were designed to explore the solar system and learn about the features of the planets (fig. 17-24). The Apollo mission had the goal of landing a person on the moon.

The advantage of the space shuttle program is that it continues to launch and return shuttle craft, allowing many branches of science the opportunity for firsthand observation in space (fig. 17-25). These shuttle missions have

Fig. 17—24 Voyager and similar space probes provided scientists with important information about the planets and the solar system.

Fig. 17—25 The space shuttle program continues to launch and return shuttle craft.

launched satellites in orbit, repaired broken satellites, performed a host of experiments, and carried sophisticated telescopes and other instruments that enhance our ability to study the universe (fig 17-26).

Although the information gathered and the data sent back to Earth by the spacecraft have expanded our understanding of the universe, new questions arise. These new questions stimulate further space research.

Fig. 17–26 The space shuttle allows satellites to be launched into orbit high above Earth's surface.

REVIEW IT

1. What was the purpose of each of the following missions?
    a. Mercury   c. Skylab
    b. Apollo   d. Pioneer
2. What advantage does the space shuttle have over other spacecraft?

CHAPTER 17 WRAP-UP

THINKING SKILLS: Comparing and Contrasting

One of the ways scientists learn about the things they study is by looking at their similarities (comparing) and differences (contrasting). They compare and contrast the way things are made, how they work, and their function. Using the skills of comparing and contrasting enables scientists to understand things better.

In this activity you will compare and contrast the two types of optical telescopes. Look at the diagrams below and answer the questions.

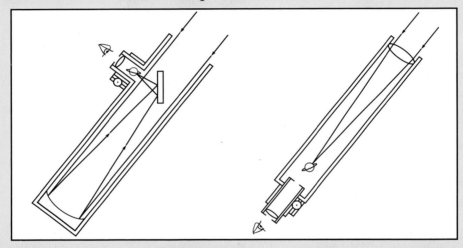

1. For each part write L if it corresponds to a reflecting telescope and R if it corresponds to a refracting telescope. If it corresponds to both, write L/R on the blank.

   a ____ eyepiece   f ____ convex lens

   b ____ concave mirror   g ____ body tube

   c ____ collects light   h____ magnifies light

   d ____ the light is bent toward a focal point as it passes through a lens

   e ____ the light is bent toward a focal point as it is reflected off a concave mirror

2. Which will collect more light, a four-inch reflecting telescope or a four-inch refracting telescope?
3. A pair of binoculars is most like which type of telescope?
4. Which type of telescope would you most likely stand behind to look through?
5. Which type of telescope would be affected the most by vibration?
6. Why are two mirrors necessary in a reflecting telescope?

QUESTIONS AND PROBLEMS

1. Why is it necessary to separate the light collected from objects in space?
2. How is a spectroscope different from a telescope?
3. Why did people living long ago rely on superstition and myth to explain what they saw in space?
4. How was Galileo able to verify the ideas of Copernicus?
5. How is the space shuttle different from other spacecraft?
6. Why don't astronomers spend much time looking through optical telescopes?
7. What is an optical telescope?
8. Why is a reflecting telescope called "reflecting"?
9. Who developed the first reflecting telescope?
10. Why was it necessary for the Gemini missions to precede the Apollo missions?
11. What type of telescope is used to learn about the birth of stars?
12. Which series of satellites have provided the most information about the planets beyond Mars?
13. Why is it necessary for ultraviolet telescopes to be above Earth's atmosphere?
14. How does the study of astronomy support the idea of God as the Creator?

RESEARCH

1. Develop a bulletin board that summarizes and illustrates the U.S. space program.
2. Make an illustrated time line of astronomy.
3. Use library resources to find out about the Hubble telescope and discoveries it has helped to make. Give an oral presentation of your findings.
4. Draw a large detailed diagram of a space shuttle. Label the important parts.
5. Construct a series of posters that illustrates and teaches about the different types of telescopes.

REVIEW

HIGHLIGHTS

1. The universe is composed of everything that exists. It includes everything that is visible and invisible, all the energy present, and all the empty space.
2. Early astronomers include Aristarchus, Aristotle, Copernicus, Galileo, and Newton.
3. Astronomy has helped us understand the rotations of the moon and planets and has led to a better understanding of gravity and other forces. It has helped us to design better bridges, buildings, cars, airplanes, and bicycles. It has improved our understanding of Earth's geology and weather.
4. The immensity and predictability of space, the workings of natural laws, the movement of the stars and planets, and the overall design of the universe provide strong evidence of an intelligent Creator.
5. Telescopes are special instruments designed to study the energy produced by objects in space. These instruments enable astronomers to see many objects in the universe more clearly.

6. Refracting telescopes use lenses to collect and refract the collected light. Reflecting telescopes use mirrors to collect and reflect the light.

7. A spectroscope separates light into very fine bands of light, called a spectrum. When analyzed, a star's spectrum provides important information about the composition of the star, its temperature, and the processes that are taking place on its surface.

8. The electromagnetic spectrum is made up of radio, infrared, visible light, ultraviolet light, X-rays, and radiation.

9. Studying ultraviolet energy helps astronomers learn about surface features of stars, such as temperature and the gases present on the star. The study of X-rays has helped scientists learn about high-energy cosmic rays that previously were unstudied and has helped them locate and study black holes. Infrared energy is emitted from newly formed stars and provides astronomers with information about the life of stars. Radio waves are used to study the most distant objects in space. Astronomers have learned about quasars, pulsars, and neutron stars by studying radio waves.

10. Major projects of the U.S. space program are summarized in figure 17-23.

11. The space shuttle's greatest advantage is that it is a reusable spacecraft. This allows many branches of science the opportunity for firsthand observation in space.

VOCABULARY LIST

astronomy	radiation	spectrum
electromagnetic spectrum	reflecting telescope	telescope
observatory	refracting telescope	universe
optical telescope	spectroscope	

PRACTICE

Multiple Choice. Choose the best answer.

1. Which is not part of the universe?
   a. matter inside Earth
   b. things we can't see
   c. matter outside Earth
   d. none of these

2. Which feature of the universe provides evidence of a Creator?
   a. its size
   b. its predictability
   c. its shape
   d. all of these

3. What makes up light from the sun?
   a. atoms from space
   b. many colors
   c. gas and moisture
   d. electrical energy

4. What does a reflecting telescope use to gather light?
   a. a battery
   b. a lens
   c. a mirror
   d. an antenna

5. Who developed the first refracting telescope?
   a. Copernicus
   b. Galileo
   c. Hubble
   d. none of these

6. What information about a star is not provided by spectroscope?
   a. its size
   b. its temperature
   c. its composition
   d. its internal processes
7. What telescope is used to learn about the most distant objects in space?
   a. a refracting telescope
   b. a reflecting telescope
   c. a radio telescope
   d. an infrared telescope
8. Which has a wavelength longer than yellow light?
   a. radio waves
   b. X-rays
   c. green light
   d. blue light
9. The first satellite in space was
   a. *Apollo*
   b. *Sputnik*
   c. *Voyager I*
   d. *Explorer I*
10. What U.S. space project was the first to put an American astronaut in space?
   a. the space shuttle
   b. Viking
   c. Gemini
   d. Mercury

Matching. Match each word with its definition or description.
1. study of the universe
2. uses a mirror to gather light
3. instrument designed to study energy
4. separates light into colors
5. used to study visible light
6. made up of everything that exists
7. uses a lens to gather light
8. arrangement of radiant energy
9. fine bands of light
10. energy that travels in waves

a. astronomy
b. electromagnetic spectrum
c. optical telescope
d. radiation
e. reflecting telescope
f. refracting telescope
g. spectroscope
h. spectrum
i. telescope
j. universe

CHAPTER 18

THE SOLAR SYSTEM

INTRODUCTION

In the summer of 1994, a spectacular event occurred that caught not only the interest of astronomers and other scientists, but also the attention of the public. Pieces of a comet (Levy-Shoemaker 9) that had broken up in space came hurtling toward Jupiter at more than 200,000 km/hr (130,000 mi/hr). Everyone watched to see what would happen when these massive chunks hit the planet. Many theories were proposed, but none proved to be entirely accurate.

Detailed pictures, like the one on page 408, provided scientists with valuable information. They discovered, for example, that one of the first pieces of comet to slam into the planet made a crater 6440 km (4000 mi) wide and 40 km (25 mi) deep. These scientists estimated that the explosion created by this impact was equivalent to 6 million megatons of TNT, 100,000 times more powerful than the largest nuclear explosion on Earth.

Although the photos taken of the comet fragments' impact with Jupiter answered some questions, they left others unanswered—and raised more questions.

Jupiter and the comet that collided with it are both part of our solar system. In this chapter you will explore the makeup of our solar system and how objects in the solar system interact.

SECTION TITLES

The dark spot in this photo of Jupiter is the G impact site, one of the larger features caused by the impact of a piece of the Levy-Shoemaker comet.

18-1 OUR PART OF THE SKY

ellipse
focus
period of revolution
solar system

OBJECTIVES

- Identify the parts of the solar system.
- Describe the position of the planets in the solar system.
- Describe Kepler's laws of planetary motion.
- Explain how Newton proved Kepler's laws to be true.

About how old would you be if you lived on Mercury? On Jupiter? On Saturn? On Uranus? On Pluto?

Although there are many stars that can be seen without the aid of a telescope, only one star, the sun, is part of our solar system. The major bodies in our **solar system** are the sun, the nine known planets and their satellites, or moons. The sun, of course, is seen in the daytime sky. Some of our planets are always visible in the night sky.

As we study the positions of stars, we see that while the constellations are visible in different places in the sky at different times of the year, the positions of the stars within a constellation do not change. Other objects, however, seem to wander across the sky. Some travel slowly; others grow a tail as they move across the sky; and still others streak across the sky and disappear (fig 18-1). These moving objects in the night sky are the planets, asteroids, comets, and meteors. All are part of our solar system.

Fig. 18-1 The trail of a meteor can be seen in this time-lapse photograph of the night sky.

Although there are vast spaces between the objects in our solar system, they are closer to each other than they are to other objects in space. These nine known planets orbit the sun in an orderly pattern. Study figure 18-2 to learn the order of these planets. Closest to the sun is Mercury. Next comes Venus, then Earth, and Mars. These are known as the inner planets. They are solid and are smaller than the other planets of the solar system.

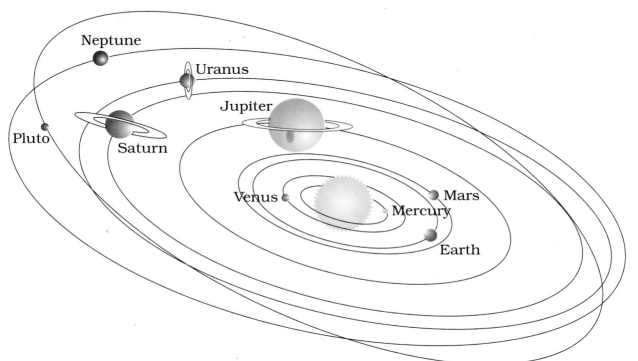

Fig. 18–2 Mercury, Venus, Earth, Mars, Jupiter, Saturn, Neptune, Uranus, and Pluto are the nine planets that make up the solar system.

Between Mars and Jupiter a belt of asteroids orbits the sun. Beyond the asteroid belt are the outer planets. These planets—Jupiter, Saturn, Neptune, Uranus, and Pluto—are very different from the solid inner planets. Except for Pluto, these planets are gaseous and much larger than the inner planets.

In the early 1600s, Johannes Kepler, a German astronomer, made a careful, detailed study of the position of the planets (fig. 18-3). Kepler proposed three laws to describe these positions. These laws are summarized in figure 18-4.

Fig. 18–3 Johannes Kepler made careful observations of the movements of the planets.

Fig. 18—4

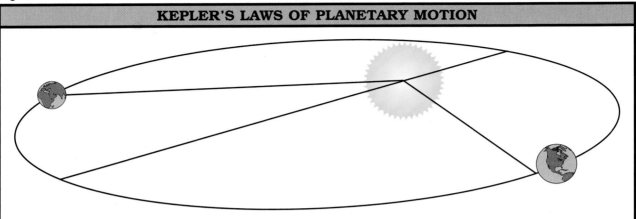

KEPLER'S LAWS OF PLANETARY MOTION

Kepler's First Law

- Describes the orbit of the planets around the sun as an ellipse. An **ellipse** is an oval that has two points called **foci** (fō′ sī). Kepler found that the sun is located at one of the foci in the elliptical orbit of the planet.

Kepler's Second Law

- Describes the speed of a planet as it orbits the sun. Kepler found that the closer a planet is to the sun, the faster the planet revolves around the sun.

Kepler's Third Law

- Describes the relationship between a planet's **period of revolution**, the time it takes the planet to orbit the sun, and the diameter of the planet's orbit. Kepler found that the longer the period of revolution, the greater the diameter of the planet's orbit.

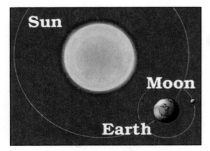

Fig. 18—5 The gravitational attraction between the planets and the sun keeps them in their orbits.

While Kepler's laws fit his observations, he did not know why his laws were true. In the mid-1600s an English scientist, Sir Isaac Newton, developed his laws of motion. These laws helped to explain why Kepler's laws were true. Newton's law of gravity was perhaps his most important contribution to our understanding of the movement of bodies in the solar system. Newton's law of gravity explained that objects exert a force on other objects. The larger the objects are and the closer they are to each other, the greater this gravitational force. This gravitational pull of matter on matter is what keeps the planets and other objects in the solar system in their respective orbits (fig. 18-5).

TRY THIS 18-1: Planet Orbits

Materials:

cardboard - 30 x 30 cm
plain paper
push pins - 2

thread (heavy) - 30 cm
transparent tape

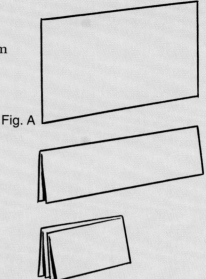

Fig. A

Procedure:

1. Find the center of the sheet of paper by folding as shown in figure A.
2. Tape the paper to the cardboard.
3. Stick a push pin into the center of the paper.
4. Securely tie the ends of the thread together. Place the loop around the push pin. Put a pencil inside the loop and carefully pull the loop tight with the pin at one end of the loop and the pencil at the other.
5. Draw a pattern on the paper by moving the pencil that is inside the loop around the push pin.
   - What kind of figure did you draw?
6. Stick the second push pin into the paper along the folded line about 2 cm away from the first pin. Place the loop around both pins. Repeat step 5, this time keeping the pencil and both push pins inside the loop.
   - What kind of figure did you draw?
7. Move the second push pin 5 cm away from the first, along the folded line, and repeat step 6.
   - What kind of figure did you draw?
   - How does this figure compare to the one you drew in step 6?
8. Move the second push pin 10 cm away from the first along the folded line and repeat step 6.
   - What kind of figure did you draw?
   - How does this figure compare to the other figures you drew?
   - Based on this experience, is a planet always the same distance from the sun? Why?

REVIEW IT

1. What makes up our solar system?
2. List the planets in order, starting with Mercury.
3. What are Kepler's laws of planetary motion?
4. How did Newton help to verify Kepler's laws?

18-2 THE INNER PLANETS

inner planets

OBJECTIVES

- Identify the characteristics of the inner planets.
- Describe features of Mercury, Venus, Earth, and Mars.
- Contrast Earth with the other inner planets.

DID YOU KNOW?

Where would you see the sun rise if you lived on the south pole of Uranus?

Mercury, Venus, Earth, and Mars are called the **inner planets**. They lie between the sun and the asteroid belt. All four of the inner planets seem to be made of a dense metal core surrounded by a rocky mantle. They differ from the larger planets in that they contain only small amounts of hydrogen and helium, and they have a liquid mantle instead of a gaseous one. Study figure 18-6 as you learn about the features of the inner planets.

Fig. 18–6

MERCURY
• Closest planet to the sun. • Fastest-moving planet. • One year = 88 Earth days. One day = 176 Earth days. • Temperatures range from 400° C on the lighted side to -180° C on the dark side. • Lacks an atmosphere; numerous craters dot its surface. • No moon.

VENUS
• Earth's "twin planet." • The brightest object in the sky except for the sun and moon. • One year = 225 Earth days. One day = 243 Earth days. • Has a reverse rotation. • Has dense atmosphere of sulfuric acid and carbon dioxide. • Covered by dense bands of clouds. • Winds on the surface reach 730 mph. • No moon.

Fig. 18-6 Continued

EARTH	
	• Often called the "blue planet." • The only known planet that supports life. • One year = 365 days. One day = 24 hours. • Has an atmosphere of nitrogen, oxygen, and carbon dioxide. • Atmosphere protects from harmful radiation but allows necessary heat and light to reach surface. • Axis tilt gives seasons. • One moon.
MARS	
	• Often called the "red planet." • Red color due to iron oxides that make up the crust. • One year = 687 Earth days. One day = about 24 Earth hours. • Has an atmosphere of carbon dioxide. • Has two large polar ice caps. • Shows channels that may have been cut by water. • Has large volcanoes; Olympus Mons is 27 km high. • Axis tilt gives seasons. • Two moons.

While Earth shares common characteristics with the other inner planets, it is different in an important way. As far as we know, life in our solar system only exists on Earth. The features of Earth and the conditions that allow life to exist here provide strong evidence of an intelligent Creator.

DID YOU KNOW?
Olympus Mons, the largest mountain in the solar system, is an inactive volcano on Mars. This huge geological feature is more than 27 km (17 mi) high and more than 595 km (370 mi) wide at the base. A volcano this big on Earth would collapse under its own weight.

Fig. 18-7 Earth is just the right distance from the sun. If it were closer (A), temperatures would soar. If it were farther away (B), temperatures would plumet. In either case life could not exist.

Earth is the proper distance from the sun to support life (fig. 18-7). If it were twice as far from the sun, it would receive only one-fourth of the heat it receives now. Living things would be frozen. If Earth were twice as close to the sun, it would receive four times as much heat and would become a burning desert.

Fig. 18–8 Earth's atmosphere is designed to provide the right conditions for living things to survive and grow.

Earth has the right type of atmosphere to sustain life (fig. 18-8). Our atmosphere contains a balance between nitrogen, oxygen, and carbon dioxide. Any change in this balance spells doom for living organisms. The atmosphere protects Earth's surface from being bombarded by dangerous radiation. Finally, the atmosphere traps heat and moisture and prevents their escape into outer space.

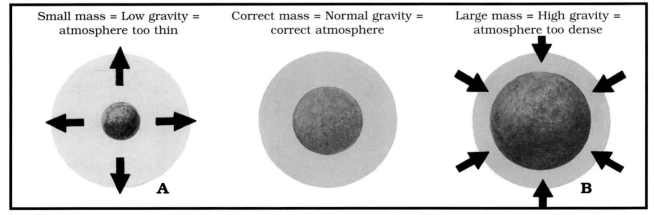

Fig. 18–9 Earth's mass is just right. If it were smaller (A), the atmosphere would escape into space, and life would suffocate. If it were larger (B), the atmospheric pressure would crush out life.

416

Earth is just the right size (fig. 18-9). If it were smaller, Earth's gravity could not hold our atmosphere or water. If Earth were twice as large, the atmosphere would be pulled closer to the surface, and pressures would crush most living creatures.

If Earth did not have a large moon revolving around it, there would be no tides in the sea (fig. 18-10). This could cause the oceans to grow stagnant, unable to produce the food and oxygen needed by life on Earth.

Fig. 18–10 Earth's tides keep the waters of the ocean from becoming stagnant.

These features of our planet demonstrate that the conditions present on Earth did not result randomly by chance but were planned and ordained by an intelligent Creator, one who still controls and sustains His creation.

REVIEW IT

1. What are the characteristics of the inner planets?
2. How are the inner planets different from the outer planets?
3. Identify the planet that has each of the following characteristics:
   a. has a reverse rotation
   b. has no atmosphere
   c. has a protective atmosphere
   d. has a crust made up of iron oxide
4. How is Earth different from the other inner planets?

18–3 THE MOON

eclipse
full moon
lunar eclipse
maria
new moon

OBJECTIVES

- Describe the topography of the moon.
- Describe the moon's phases.
- Explain how a lunar eclipse occurs.

The moon is our closest neighbor. At night it is the most visible thing in the sky (fig. 18-11). For centuries it has been the subject of myths and superstitions. It has also been the most studied object in the sky.

Fig. 18–11 At 402 250 km (250,000 mi) away, the moon is Earth's nearest neighbor.

Fig. 18–12 The dark and light patches on the moon identify high and low regions.

Look at the moon in figure 18-12. What do you see? You should see a pattern of light and dark patches. The light patches represent highland areas. The dark regions represent **maria** (mä′ rē ə), areas thought at one time to be seas. But the moon does not have any water. Instead, these dark areas are places where molten material flowed out of the interior of the moon and covered large areas of the surface, hardening into basalt.

418

Fig. 18—13 Craters cover the moon's surface.

Craters dot the entire surface of the moon, especially the back side, which never faces Earth (fig. 18-13). Why does the moon show so many craters? Remember that the moon does not have any atmosphere. An atmosphere like Earth's creates friction that burns up most of the meteors that enter it. But the moon has no atmosphere to burn up the meteors, so they crash to the surface. Also, since there is no water or air movement, there is nothing to erode the craters that form.

The moon revolves around Earth every 29.5 days. Because its speed of rotation matches its period of revolution, the same side of the moon always faces Earth (fig. 18-14).

Fig. 18—14 The same side of the moon is always facing Earth.

Our view of the moon changes because its position changes as it moves around Earth. As it moves around Earth, it moves through several phases. Study figure 18-15 to learn about these phases.

Fig. 18—15

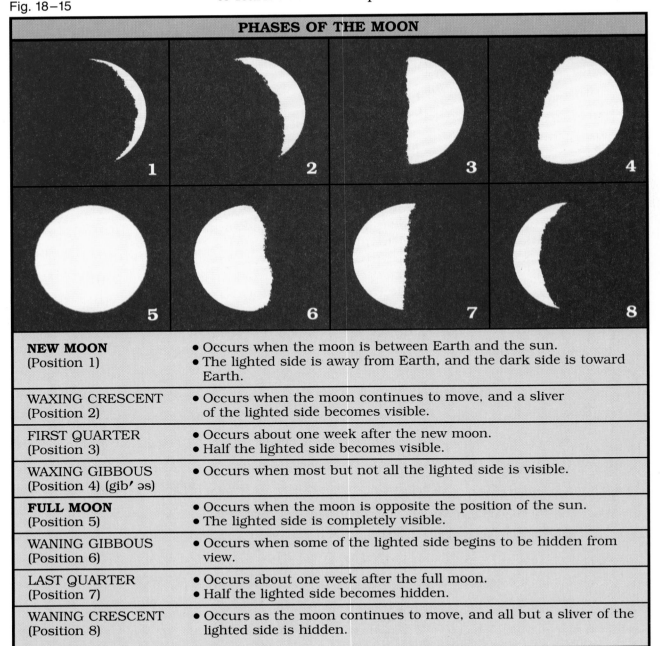

PHASES OF THE MOON	
NEW MOON (Position 1)	• Occurs when the moon is between Earth and the sun. • The lighted side is away from Earth, and the dark side is toward Earth.
WAXING CRESCENT (Position 2)	• Occurs when the moon continues to move, and a sliver of the lighted side becomes visible.
FIRST QUARTER (Position 3)	• Occurs about one week after the new moon. • Half the lighted side becomes visible.
WAXING GIBBOUS (Position 4) (gib′ əs)	• Occurs when most but not all the lighted side is visible.
FULL MOON (Position 5)	• Occurs when the moon is opposite the position of the sun. • The lighted side is completely visible.
WANING GIBBOUS (Position 6)	• Occurs when some of the lighted side begins to be hidden from view.
LAST QUARTER (Position 7)	• Occurs about one week after the full moon. • Half the lighted side becomes hidden.
WANING CRESCENT (Position 8)	• Occurs as the moon continues to move, and all but a sliver of the lighted side is hidden.

TRY THIS 18-3: The Diameter of the Moon

Materials:

doorstop molding - 2 m	safety razor blade
index card (3 x 5)	transparent tape
meterstick	

Procedure:

1. Cut a square in the middle of the index card exactly 1 cm on each side.

2. Fold the card as shown in figure A and tape it to the end of the molding.

3. Aim the card and molding at the moon and sight along the molding until the diameter of the moon just fills the 1 cm square hole. Mark the place on the molding next to your eye.

Fig. A

4. Measure the distance from the mark to the card in centimeters (cm). This is distance X.

   • What is this distance (cm)?

5. It is 386 000 km to the moon. By setting up the proportion below, it is possible to calculate the diameter of the moon.

$$\frac{1 \text{ cm}}{X \text{ cm}} = \frac{Y \text{ (diameter of the moon in km)}}{386\ 000 \text{ km}}$$

   • What is the diameter of the moon?

Because the sun shines on both Earth and the moon, each produces a shadow in space. However, since the plane of the moon's orbit is tipped in relation to Earth's orbit, the shadows usually fall above or below Earth or the moon. Sometimes, however, if the sun, moon, and Earth form a straight line, the shadow of the moon may strike Earth, or the shadow of Earth may hit the moon. When one object passes through the shadow of another object, an **eclipse** occurs. Two kinds of eclipses occur: lunar eclipses and solar eclipses (solar eclipses are discussed in chapter 19).

During a **lunar eclipse** Earth blocks the sunlight that normally shines on the full moon, causing the moon to be darkened. When this occurs, anyone on the dark side of Earth can see this eclipse. Figure 18-16 shows the position of the sun, Earth, and moon during a lunar eclipse.

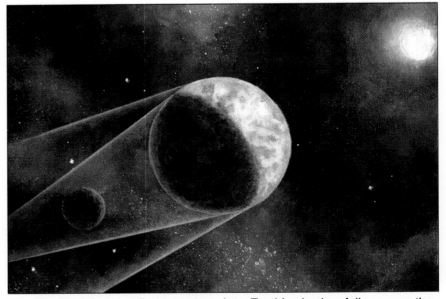

Fig. 18–16 A lunar eclipse occurs when Earth's shadow falls across the moon's surface.

REVIEW IT

1. What is the difference between the dark and light areas of the moon?
2. What phase of the moon follows each phase listed below:
   a. a waning gibbous moon?
   b. a full moon?
   c. a first-quarter moon?
   d. a last-quarter moon?
3. Draw a simple diagram that shows the position of Earth, the sun, and the moon during a lunar eclipse.

18–4 THE OUTER PLANETS

- Identify the characteristics of the outer planets.
- Describe features of Jupiter, Saturn, Neptune, Uranus, and Pluto.

outer planets

The planets Jupiter, Saturn, Uranus (yoor′ ə nəs), Neptune and Pluto make up the **outer planets** of our solar system. With the exception of Pluto, the outer planets are made mostly of light elements, hydrogen and helium, and are thus called "gas giants."

Study figure 18-17 as you learn about the outer planets.

For each planet find its date of discovery and the person who discovered it.

Fig. 18–17

JUPITER

- The largest of all the planets.
- One year = 12 Earth years. One day = 10 Earth hours.
- Has an atmosphere of ammonia, sulfur compounds, and water.
- Gives off more energy than it receives from the sun.
- Red spot visible on the surface is a storm threes times the diameter of Earth.
- 16 moons.

SATURN

- Often called the "ringed planet."
- The second-largest planet.
- Has an atmosphere of hydrogen and helium.
- Gives off more energy than it receives.
- One year = 29 Earth years. One day = 10+ Earth hours.
- Characterized by many complex rings.
- 20 moons.

Fig. 18—17 Continued

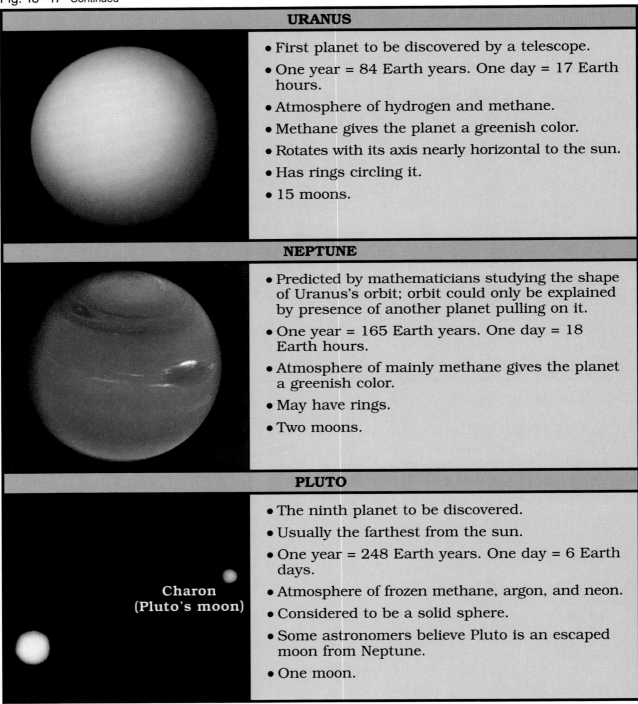

URANUS

- First planet to be discovered by a telescope.
- One year = 84 Earth years. One day = 17 Earth hours.
- Atmosphere of hydrogen and methane.
- Methane gives the planet a greenish color.
- Rotates with its axis nearly horizontal to the sun.
- Has rings circling it.
- 15 moons.

NEPTUNE

- Predicted by mathematicians studying the shape of Uranus's orbit; orbit could only be explained by presence of another planet pulling on it.
- One year = 165 Earth years. One day = 18 Earth hours.
- Atmosphere of mainly methane gives the planet a greenish color.
- May have rings.
- Two moons.

PLUTO

Charon (Pluto's moon)

- The ninth planet to be discovered.
- Usually the farthest from the sun.
- One year = 248 Earth years. One day = 6 Earth days.
- Atmosphere of frozen methane, argon, and neon.
- Considered to be a solid sphere.
- Some astronomers believe Pluto is an escaped moon from Neptune.
- One moon.

Clyde Tombaugh

When Clyde was 12 years old, his Uncle Leon lent him a small telescope. Clyde enjoyed observing the stars. When he moved with his family to Kansas, his interest in astronomy continued. In 1928, at age 22, Clyde sent drawings he had made of the planetary surfaces to Lowell Observatory in Flagstaff, Arizona. A few weeks later, after examining his drawings and being amazed at their accuracy, the astronomers offered 22-year-old Clyde Tombaugh a job. Clyde's job at the observatory was to begin a systematic study of the night sky, looking for Planet X, a ninth planet that some believed existed beyond the orbit of Neptune.

To search for this new planet, Tombaugh used a techique called "blinking." This tecnhique involves comparing photos of the sky taken on different nights. To do this, an astronomer looks through a device called a blink compara-tor. A light blinks on and off, alternating between two photographic plates of the same part of the sky but taken at different times. Each plate is viewed momentarily, but the blinking proceeds so rapidly that the image appears continuous, even though it is not. An out-of-place speck in the sky will appear to jump up and down or side to side, while all the relatively fixed stars appear to stand still.

After two years of painstakingly studying hundreds of photographic plates, Clyde Tombaugh hit pay dirt. On the night of February 18, 1930, he discovered the missing Planet X. This planet was renamed Pluto, the ninth planet of our solar system. During his years of observing the night sky, Tombaugh also discovered one globular star cluster, one super cluster of galaxies, five open galactic star clusters, one comet, and more than 775 asteroids.

REVIEW IT

1. What are the characteristics of the outer planets?
2. Identify the planet fitting each characteristic or description.
   a. may be an escaped moon from Neptune
   b. rotates horizontally on its axis
   c. has a large red spot
   d. is often called the "ringed planet"
   e. was predicted by mathematicians

18–5 ASTEROIDS, METEOROIDS, AND COMETS

asteroid
asteroid belt
coma
comet
meteor
meteorite
meteoroid
nucleus
tail

DID YOU KNOW?

The weight of Earth is increased by about 25 tons every day. This extra material is made mostly of space dust, micrometeors that are too small to see.

OBJECTIVES

- Define the terms **asteroids**, **meteoroids**, and **comets**.
- Distinguish between a meteor and a meteorite.
- Describe how the sun affects a comet.

Johann couldn't understand it. According to his calculations there should be a planet between Mars and Jupiter. He had been studying this for weeks and was convinced that his idea was correct. In 1772, Johann Bode decided to publish his theory with a formula that predicted the distances between the planets. Other astronomers read Bode's ideas and agreed with him, but no one could find the missing planet. Then in 1801, Guiseppi Piazzi (pē ät′ tsē) found something there. He named it Ceres.

Ceres turned out to be much too small and oddly shaped for a planet. In 1802, another small object was found in the region between Mars and Jupiter. By the late 1800s more than 300 rocky objects had been discovered orbiting the sun between Mars and Jupiter. These objects range in size from 3 to 96 km (2 to 60 mi) in diameter and are called **asteroids** (as′ tər oid) (fig. 18-18). Some scientists believe these chunks of space debris to be the remnants of planets or moons that collided and broke apart. There are so many asteroids in this region that it is known as the **asteroid belt** (fig. 18-19).

Fig. 18–18 Ida is one of the many asteroids in the asteroid belt that astronomers have named.

Fig. 18–19 The asteroid belt includes hundreds of large chunks of space debris.

Astronomers wondered how the asteroids came to occupy this space. Some suppose that the asteroids represent pieces of a planet that once existed but was torn apart long ago. Others believe that the asteroids are material that never came together to form a planet in the first place.

Many pieces of rock, from the size of a grain of sand to tens of meters across, are found moving randomly about between the planets and asteroids. These pieces of space debris are called **meteoroids**. Those with diameters of less than a meter are from the tails of comets moving through the solar system. Larger meteoroids may come from collisions of asteroids.

If you have ever been outside on a dark night, you may have seen a bright flash streak across the sky (fig. 18-20). These "shooting stars" are produced by meteoroids that have been pulled into the atmosphere by Earth's gravity. When these objects enter Earth's atmosphere, or the atmosphere of any other planet, they are called **meteors**. Each year several meteor showers occur (fig. 18-21). These events happen because Earth passes through the debris left behind by the comet. This debris becomes the meteors we see.

Fig. 18–20 Meteors, sometimes called "shooting stars," are pieces of meteoroids that enter Earth's atmosphere.

METEOR SHOWERS			
Name	Date of Maximum	Approximate Limits	Number/Hour at Maximum
Quadrantids	January 4	January 1–6	110
Lyrids	April 22	April 19–24	12
Eta Aquarids	May 5	May 1–8	20
Delta Aquarids	July 27, 28	July 15–August 15	35
Perseids	August 12	July 25–August 18	68
Orionids	October 21	October 16–26	30
Taurids	November 8	October 20–November 30	12
Leonids	November 17	November 15–19	10
Geminids	December 14	December 7–15	58

Fig. 18–21 Meteor showers occur on a regular schedule.

Most meteors that enter our atmosphere are completely burned up by the heat of friction. Some of the larger meteors, however, may not burn up completely and may actually strike Earth's surface. Meteors that strike Earth are called **meteorites**. Most meteorites are fist-sized or smaller, but some are quite large (fig. 18-22). When large meteorites

Fig. 18–22 The Hoba West Meteorite is nearly 1 m (3 ft) thick, 3 m (10 ft) long, and weighs about 60 tons. It was found in Namibia on the African continent.

Fig. 18–23 One of the largest meteorite craters found is the Barrington Crater near Winslow, Arizona.

428

crash into the surface, tremendous craters are created (fig. 18-23). Scientists have identified more than 100 major craters on Earth's surface that were caused in this way. The largest crater on Earth lies beneath the icecap of Antarctica (fig. 18-24). Geologists estimate that this crater is 240 km (150 mi) in diameter and more than 790 m (2600 ft) deep. They believe that it was caused by a huge meteorite weighing more than 14 trillion tons (14,000,000,000,000) striking Earth at 20 km/sec (45,000 mph).

Orbiting through space are numerous balls of ice, dust, and gas (fig 18-25). These objects are called **comets**.

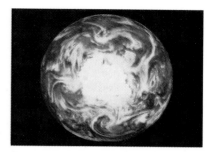

Fig. 18−24 A large meteorite crater lies beneath the icecap of Antarctica.

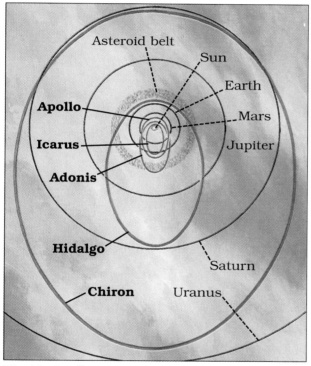

Fig. 18−25 Comets are chunks of frozen dust, gas, and debris that travel through the solar system.

Fig. 18−26 About every 77 years Halley's comet passes close enough to be seen from Earth.

Sometimes the gravity of a star causes a comet to fall toward the star. When this happens in our solar system, the orbit of the comet cuts through the orbits of the planets and for a while is part of our solar system (fig. 18-26). In addition to these comets, there are periodic comets. Periodic comets are those that have been captured by the sun's gravity, trapping them in large elliptical orbits that become part of our solar

The "falling of the stars" that preceded the events of the William Miller's Great Disappointment was one of many such events that have taken place throughout Earth's history.

system. Figure 18-27 shows a diagram of a comet. As you can see, it consists of three main parts: a nucleus, a coma (kō′ mə), and a tail. The **nucleus** of the comet is the solid chunk of ice and dust at the center. Usually the nucleus is only a few kilometers wide. The **coma** (kō′ mə) is the cloud of vapor that forms around the nucleus as energy from the sun evaporates some of the ice. In some comets, the coma reaches 1 million km in diameter. Together with the nucleus, it makes up the comet's head.

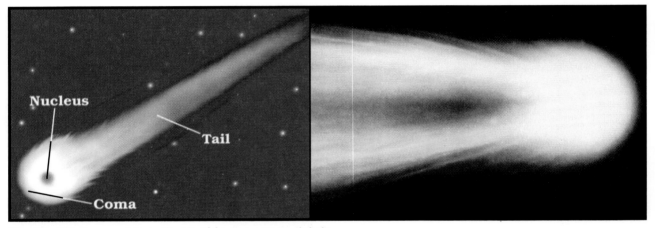

Fig. 18−27 A comet is a chunk of frozen space debris.

The most noticeable part of a comet is the tail. The **tail** of a comet forms as water vapor, dust, and gas are released from the comet's outer layer. The solar wind, which streams out from the sun, pushes the material from the tail outward away from the sun. The tails of comets contain very little matter but can extend hundreds of millions of kilometers out into space.

REVIEW IT

1. What is the difference between an asteroid and a meteoroid?
2. What is a comet?
3. What is the difference between a meteor and a meteorite?
4. What happens to a comet as it nears the sun?

CLASS ACTIVITY 18-5: Making Dents

Question: How do meteorites form craters on the surface of planets?

Materials:
aluminum baking dish (9" x 12")	metric ruler
gum ball	paprika
lead split shot	sifted flour
marble	tweezers
meterstick	washer

Procedure:
1. Cover the bottom of the baking dish with about 4 cm of flour.
2. Gently shake the pan back and forth to make an even layer. Sprinkle a thin layer of paprika over the surface of the flour.
3. Hold the lead split shot 10 cm above the surface of the flour and drop it into the pan. Record the diameter (mm) and depth (mm) of the crater formed.
4. Use the tweezers to carefully remove the split shot so as to not damage the crater.
5. Repeat steps 3 and 4, dropping the split shot from 20 cm and 40 cm.
6. Repeat steps 3 to 5 for the other three objects.

Data:

Object/Height	Crater	
	Diameter	Depth
Split shot 10 cm		
Split shot 20 cm		
Split shot 40 cm		
Gum ball 10 cm		
Gum ball 20 cm		
Gum ball 40 cm		
Marble 10 cm		
Marble 20 cm		
Marble 40 cm		
Washer 10 cm		
Washer 20 cm		
Washer 40 cm		

Questions:
1. What formed the smallest crater? What formed the largest?
2. How does increasing the height of the drop affect the crater?
3. What factors affect the size of the crater?
4. Would you expect to find many or few craters on Venus? Why?

Conclusion: Write 3–5 sentences about what you learned from this activity.

CHAPTER 18 WRAP-UP

THINKING SKILLS: Making Models

In this activity you are going to make a scale model of the solar system on a sheet of butcher paper.

Materials:

butcher paper - 30 m
drawing compass
index cards (3" x 5") - 10

meterstick
metric ruler

Procedure:

1. Draw the sun on the butcher paper so that its left edge extends about 5 cm in from the left margin of the paper (fig. A).
2. Measure out from the edge of the sun 1 cm and make a mark. Draw a 3.1 cm diameter circle so the edge nearest the sun hits this mark. The circle you have drawn represents Mercury.
3. Measure 18 cm from the edge of the circle farthest from the sun and draw a circle 7 cm in diameter.
3. Use the chart below to find the distance from the sun for each planet and each planet's diameter. Repeat step 3 for each of the other 7 planets. Remember to always measure the distance from the previous circle.
4. When you have drawn each planet on the butcher paper, add art work and color to make the planets look realistic. Use the index cards as an information label for each planet.

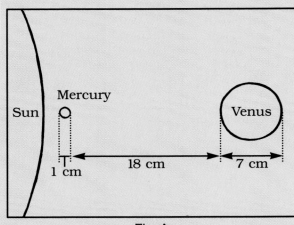

Fig. A

Planet	Diameter	Distance
Mercury	3.1 cm	1 cm
Venus	7.0 cm	18 cm
Earth	7.9 cm	25 cm
Mars	4.2 cm	38 cm
Jupiter	86.8 cm	130 cm
Saturn	71.5 cm	240 cm
Uranus	32.0 cm	480 cm
Neptune	31.0 cm	750 cm
Pluto	6.0 cm	1000 cm

QUESTIONS AND PROBLEMS

1. What caused the maria on the moon's surface?
2. Explain why the years of the outer planets are so long.
3. How do some believe the asteroid belt formed?
4. Why do both Uranus and Neptune look greenish?
5. Why does Mercury have so many craters on its surface?
6. About how many days would you expect between the beginning of a waxing crescent and a waning crescent?
7. Why do some comets return regularly, while others are visible only once?
8. Why don't we ever see the back of the moon from Earth?
9. How is Venus different from the other inner planets?
10. Why are the orbits of the planets elliptical instead of circular?
11. How are meteorites and meteors similar? How are they different?

RESEARCH

1. Some believe that a comet colliding with Earth destroyed the dinosaurs. Use library resources and find arguments for and against this theory. Write a report on your findings.
2. Construct a mobile of the solar system. Make the sun as the center. Be sure to include all components of our solar system.
3. Make a series of posters that can be used to teach K-2 students about the solar system. Use the materials you produce to teach a class to younger students. Report on your experience.
4. Use library resources and find out what probes have been used to explore the outer planets. Describe the findings. Present an oral report on your findings.
5. Use library resources to find out information on Johannes Kepler. Write a biographical report on his life and work.

REVIEW

HIGHLIGHTS

1. The solar system includes the planets and their satellites (moons), comets, asteroids, and meteoroids.
2. The relative positions of the planets are illustrated in figure 18-2.
3. Kepler formulated three laws relating to the position and orbits of the planets. These laws are summarized in figure 18-4.
4. Newton's law of gravity helped to validate Kepler's ideas because gravity explained why Kepler's laws were true.
5. The inner planets—Mercury, Venus, Earth, and Mars—have dense metal cores surrounded by a rocky mantle. They contain only small amounts of hydrogen and helium.
6. The features of the inner planets are summarized in figure 18-6.

7. Earth is different from the other planets in that it is the only one with life. Its size, distance from the sun, atmosphere, available water, and other features all provide evidence of the Creator's design for life on Earth.

8. The moon's topography includes both highland areas and many craters and maria, which are dark regions created by molten material from the core flowing out over the moon's surface.

9. The moon's phases are illustrated and described in figure 18-15.

10. A lunar eclipse occurs when Earth passes between the sun and the moon, casting a shadow on the moon.

11. The outer planets, except for Pluto, are often called the "gas giants." These planets—Jupiter, Saturn, Uranus, and Neptune—are made mostly of the light elements, hydrogen and helium.

12. The features of the outer planets are summarized in figure 18-17.

13. Asteroids are rocky objects of various sizes orbiting the sun. Most asteroids occur in the asteroid belt between the inner and outer planets. Meteorites are pieces of rock and debris found moving randomly about between the planets and asteroids. Comets are chunks of ice, dust, and gas pulled in by gravity.

14. A meteor is a meteoroid that enters Earth's atmosphere; a meteorite is a meteoroid that strikes Earth's surface.

15. As a comet approaches the sun, it begins to melt. The solar wind then blows the melted material away, forming the comet's tail.

VOCABULARY LIST

asteroid	full moon	new moon
asteroid belt	inner planet	nucleus
coma	lunar eclipse	outer planet
comet	maria	period of revolution
eclipse	meteor	solar system
ellipse	meteorite	tail
focus	meteoroid	

PRACTICE

Multiple Choice. Choose the best answer.

1. According to Kepler, which is true?
    a. planets have a circular orbit
    b. planets near the sun orbit faster than those farther away
    c. a planet's size determines its period of revolution
    d. all of these

2. Which planet is next to Saturn?
    a. Mars
    b. Neptune
    c. Pluto
    d. Uranus

3. Which is *not* an inner planet?
   a. Mercury
   b. Saturn
   c. Venus
   d. Earth
4. Which planet has a day that is longer than its year?
   a. Pluto
   b. Mercury
   c. Jupiter
   d. none of these
5. How is the moon different from Earth?
   a. it has craters
   b. it lacks an atmosphere
   c. it doesn't rotate on its axis
   d. all of these
6. Which phase would follow a waxing gibbous moon?
   a. a first quarter
   b. a new moon
   c. a waxing crescent
   d. a full moon
7. Which is a feature of Uranus?
   a. it gives off more energy than it receives
   b. its axis is tilted horizontally
   c. it has 13 moons
   d. all of these
8. Which planet many have been a moon of Neptune?
   a. Pluto
   b. Mercury
   c. Uranus
   d. Saturn
9. Which would probably be the largest?
   a. a comet
   b. a meteor
   c. a meteoroid
   d. an asteroid
10. Why don't more meteors crash into Earth?
   a. the magnetic field repels them
   b. Earth is too close to the sun
   c. the atmosphere burns them up
   d. all of these

Matching. Match each word with its definition or description.
   1. the time it takes a planet to orbit the sun
   2. made up of the sun and planets
   3. the cloud of vapor around a comet
   4. occurs when the sun and moon are on opposite sides of Earth
   5. debris that enters Earth's atmosphere
   6. a frozen ball of dust and gas
   7. dark regions on the moon
   8. occurs when the sun is behind the moon
   9. an oval orbit
   10. a small to large piece of debris that moves randomly through the solar system

   a. coma
   b. comet
   c. ellipse
   d. full moon
   e. maria
   f. meteor
   g. meteoroid
   h. new moon
   i. period of revolution
   j. solar system

CHAPTER 19

STARS AND GALAXIES

INTRODUCTION

As long as people have looked up into the night sky, they have wondered about the stars. The Bible mentions stars in many places. In Job 38:31, God asks Job, "Canst thou bind the sweet influences of Pleiades, or loose the bands of Orion?" Pleiades (plē′ ə dēz) is a group of seven stars that can be easily seen on dark nights during winter. Scientists have discovered that although the seven stars are easily visible, there are actually more than 200 stars in the cluster. The Pleiades is in the Milky Way Galaxy about 6.6 quadrillion km (4.2 quadrillion mi) from Earth and covers an area nearly 285 trillion km (180 trillion mi) in diameter. Each of the seven stars in this constellation is more than 800 times the size of our own sun.

What are stars? Are there different types of stars? What processes take place in them? You will explore these and other questions as you study this chapter.

SECTION TITLES

Pleiades is a group of seven stars that can be easily seen on dark nights during winter.

19–1 WHAT ARE STARS?

H-R diagram
magnitude
main sequence
nuclear fusion
red giant
star
supergiant
white dwarf

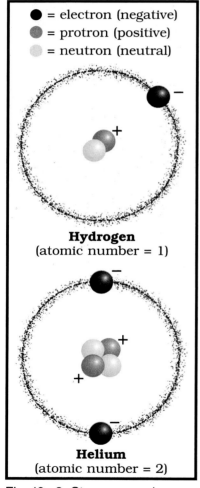

= electron (negative)
= protron (positive)
= neutron (neutral)

Hydrogen
(atomic number = 1)

Helium
(atomic number = 2)

Fig. 19–3 Stars are made
mainly of hydrogen and helium.

438

OBJECTIVES

- Define the term **star**.
- Explain how stars produce energy.
- Explain how stars are classified.
- Distinguish among the various types of stars.

The star in our solar system is the sun. A **star** is a glowing ball of hot gas that makes its own energy (fig. 19-1). Stars shine because processes taking place deep within them produce large amounts of energy. This energy, called radiation, moves outward to the surface of the star and is released into space. Some of this energy we see as visible light (fig. 19-2).

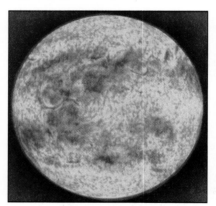

Fig. 19–1 Like our own sun, a star is a glowing ball of gas.

Fig. 19–2 Visible light from the sun allow us to see things.

All stars contain two main elements, hydrogen and helium (fig 19-3). These elements react to produce the energy of stars by a process called **nuclear fusion**. In this process two or more atoms combine to form a single larger atom.

Look at figure 19-4 to see how this process occurs. A star's core, which contains hydrogen, is very hot. For example, at the core of our sun, temperatures reach about 15 000 000° C. At these extreme temperatures atoms of hydrogen move at incredibly high speeds. Sometimes, when moving at such speeds, the nuclei of the hydrogen atoms, which contain only one proton in the nucleus, collide to form a single,

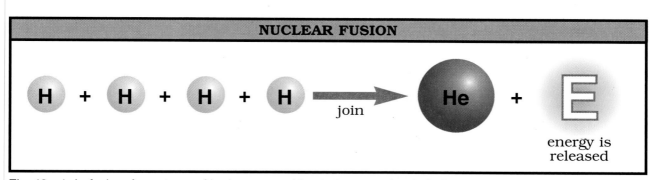

Fig. 19–4 In fusion, four atoms of hydrogen combine to form one larger helium atom, with a release of energy.

larger helium atom. The helium nucleus formed in this way includes two protons and two neutrons. Nuclear fusion, which takes place in the star's core, releases tremendous amounts of energy. This energy moves upward to the star's surface, where it is released into space as radiation.

The helium formed by fusion contains slightly less mass than the two original hydrogen atoms. This difference in mass appears as energy. Albert Einstein showed that a small amount of mass can change into a lot of energy (fig. 19-5). The fusion that takes place in stars changes small amounts of mass into large amounts of energy. This energy makes the stars hot and makes them shine.

Remember the last time you looked at the stars? What differences did you see? One of the major differences between stars is their **magnitude**, or brightness (fig. 19-6). Some stars are so bright they can be seen even when the sky is

Fig. 19–5 Albert Einstein showed that a small amount of mass can be converted to a large amount of energy.

DID YOU KNOW?

One gram of hydrogen that undergoes fusion to become helium releases more than 600 billion joules of energy.

Fig. 19–6 The brightness of a star is described as its magnitude.

439

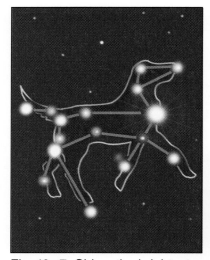

Fig. 19–7 Sirius, the brightest star in the night sky, is part of the constellation Canis Major.

lighted by the full moon or city lights. Others are so dim they can be seen only on a dark, clear night when viewed through a telescope. The magnitude of a star depends on its total energy output and its distance from Earth. Scientists use numbers to describe the magnitude of stars. The larger the number, the fainter the star. The smaller the number, the brighter the star. The brightest star in the sky is Sirius (sir′ ē əs), the "dog star" of Canis Major (fig. 19-7).

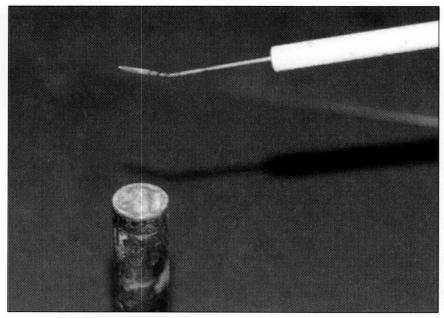

Fig. 19–8 When a metal rod is heated, it first turns red, then yellow, then blue-white.

Another way stars differ from each other is in their color. Although most stars appear white, some appear bluish or reddish. The color of a star depends on its surface temperature. When an iron rod is heated, it first turns red (fig. 19-8). Then, as it continues to be heated, it turns orange, yellow, white, and finally blue-white. In a similar way the coolest stars appear red, while the hottest stars appear blue-white. The surface temperature of stars ranges from 2400°C to more than 60 000° C. The sun is a yellow star and has a surface temperature of about 5500° C (fig. 19-9). A red star, such as Betelgeuse (bet′ 'l jōōz) in Orion has a temperature of 2100° C (3800° F), while the super hot white star Vega has a surface temperature of over 50 000° C (90,000° F) degrees.

Fig. 19–9 The sun is a yellow middle-sized star.

In the early 1900s astronomers discovered a relationship between stars' magnitude and their temperatures. They plotted the temperatures and magnitude on a diagram called the **H-R diagram** (fig. 19-10). On this diagram the temperature of a star increases from right to left. The magnitude increas-

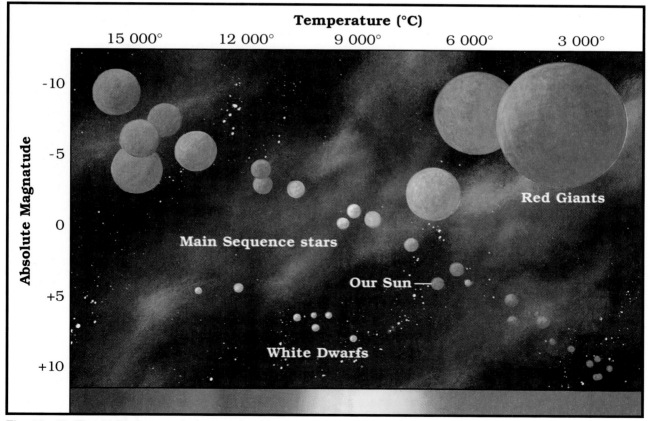

Fig. 19–10 The H-R diagram helps to classify stars.

es from top to bottom. When the stars were plotted on the diagram, a pattern was formed. Most stars formed a band from upper left to lower right. This band of stars is called the **main sequence**. Stars in the lower left region, below the main sequence, are called **white dwarfs.** These small stars are whitish, instead of being yellow or red as the stars lying above them on the chart. Those stars found in the upper right region, above the main sequence, have a distinctive reddish color and a large size. They are called the **red giants.** Stars larger than red giants are called the **super-giants**. Figure 19-11 summarizes the types of stars.

TYPES OF STARS
Red Giants • These stars lie in the upper right region of the H-R diagram. • They are brighter than other stars. • They are usually reddish. • The largest and brightest of the giants are the supergiants.
Main Sequence • These stars form a diagonal band from upper left to lower right on the H-R diagram. • They are small or medium in mass. • They are similar in chemical composition to the sun. • They shine at a steady rate.
White Dwarf • These stars lie in the lower left region of the H-R diagram. • They are smaller and fainter than other stars. • They are the densest of all stars.

Fig. 19—11

REVIEW IT

1. What is a star?
2. What is fusion?
3. What is an H-R diagram?
4. Describe each of the following:
   a. main-sequence stars
   b. white dwarf
   c. red giant

CLASS ACTIVITY 19-1: Graphing Stars

Question: How does the H-R diagram help classify stars?

Materials:

colored pencils   Special Master R493

Procedure:

1. Plot the 20 sample stars listed on the Special Master. Make a dot of the proper color for each star listed.

Data:

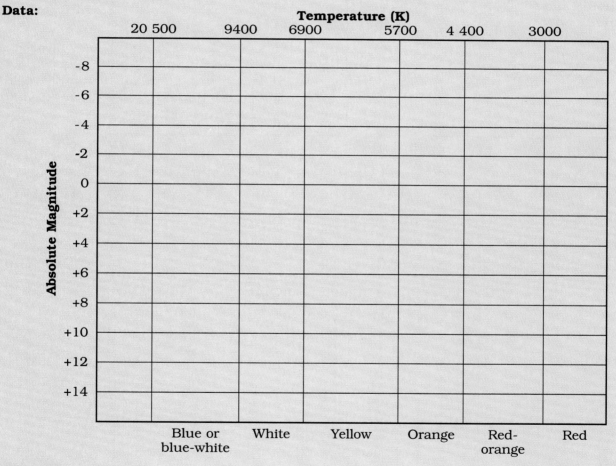

Questions:

1. How does color relate to the star's position on the diagram?
2. What is the name of the region formed by most of the stars on the diagram?
3. What type of stars are most of the stars you plotted on the diagram?

Conslusion: Write 3–5 sentences about what you learned from this activity.

19–2 OUR STAR, THE SUN

VOCABULARY
chromosphere
core
corona
photosphere
prominence
solar eclipse
solar flare
solar wind
sunspot

OBJECTIVES

- Describe the structure of the sun.
- Identify features of the sun.
- Describe the position of the sun, Earth, and moon during a solar eclipse.

Our star, the sun, is 1 392 000 km (865,000 mi) in diameter, contains more than 99 percent of the total mass of the solar system, and has a surface temperature of 5500° C. It is classed as an average-sized, middle-aged star. Study figure 19-12 to learn about the sun's structure.

Fig. 19–12

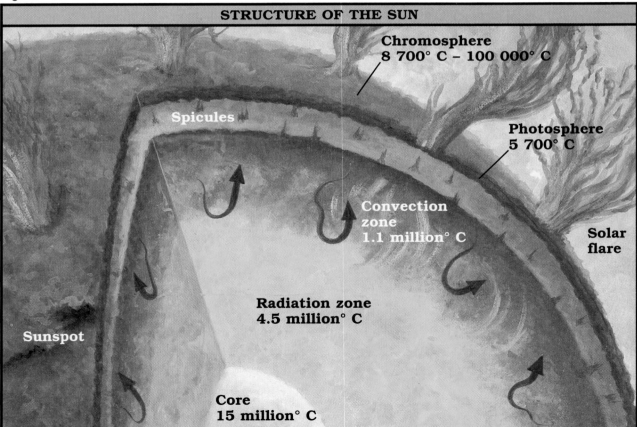

STRUCTURE OF THE SUN

Chromosphere
8 700° C – 100 000° C

Photosphere
5 700° C

Spicules

Convection zone
1.1 million° C

Solar flare

Radiation zone
4.5 million° C

Sunspot

Core
15 million° C

Fig. 19–12 Continued

Core	• The central part of the sun. • The area in which nuclear fusion occurs. • Temperatures reach 15 million° C.
Photosphere (fōt′ ō sfir)	• The surface of the sun. • Produces the visible light we see.
Chromosphere (krō′ mō sfir)	• A layer of hot gas beyond the photosphere. • Forms a bright red halo extending beyond the photosphere. • Red color is due to presence of hydrogen gas.
Prominences (präm′ ə nəns)	• Flames of gas that shoot out from the chromosphere. • Extend hundreds of thousands of kilometers from the surface.
Corona (kə rō′ nə)	• Thin transparent zone beyond the chromosphere. • Made up of hot gas and plasma.

Radiation from the sun is so intense that it should never be looked at directly. To safely observe the sun, it is best to use a telescope to project the sun's image onto a shaded screen (fig. 19-13). The solar observatory at Kitt Peak, Arizona, has a telescope with a light shaft more than 150 m (492 ft) long (fig. 19-14). Most of this unusual telescope is underground, where the temperature is uniform, and air currents are minimal.

Fig. 19–13 Rather than look directly at the sun, astronomers project its image onto a large screen.

Fig. 19–14 The solar observatory at Kitt Peak, Arizona, is a place where scientists study the sun and its processes.

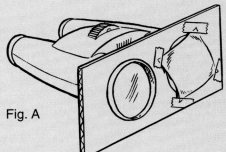
Sunspots are relatively cool, dark places on the sun's surface (fig. 19-15). These features first appear as small dark regions on the photosphere that may be only 1500 km

DID YOU KNOW?
Solar flares are one of the major hazards that face astronauts. A major solar-flare eruption can send lethal doses of radiation toward an unshielded spacecraft.

Fig. 19–15 Sunspots are relatively cool regions on the sun's surface.

(930 mi) in diameter. However, within a few days after their first appearance, they may expand to many thousands of kilometers in diameter. One of the largest sunspots ever identified grew to more than 100,000 km (62,140 mi) in diameter! These strange features may last for less than a day or as long as several months. Scientists have discovered that sunspots seem to occur in an 11-year cycle. A sunspot cycle occurred in 1991, and the next one should occur in 2002.

Solar flares occur as sudden bright spots near sunspot groups (fig. 19-16). These features produce a stream of protons and electrons that move at speeds of 800 km/sec. Many of these particles reach Earth, where they disturb radio and TV reception as they interact with Earth's magnetic field. The interaction deflects these charged particles toward the poles. There they excite gases in the upper atmosphere and cause them to radiate light in bright, wavy patterns that follow Earth's magnetic field (fig. 19-17). These events are most visible at the North and South poles. The displays that occur in the Northern Hemisphere are called the aurora borealis (ô rôr′ ə bôr ē al′ is), or northern lights. The similar displays that occur simultaneously in the Southern Hemisphere are called aurora australis (ô rôr′ ə ô strā′ lis), or southern lights.

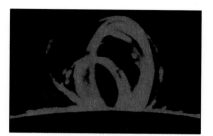

Fig. 19–16 Solar flares often reach great distances into space.

Fig. 19–17 Energy produced by solar flares interacts with the magnetosphere when it reaches Earth and causes the northern lights.

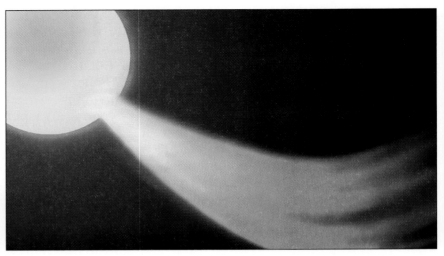

Fig. 19–18 The solar wind produces a steady stream of energy particles that move outward from the sun's surface.

Fig. 19–19 This picture of the sun's corona was taken during a total solar eclipse.

In addition to sunspots and solar flares, the sun also produces solar wind (fig. 19-18). The **solar wind** is a steady stream of particles from the sun's outer atmosphere that extends beyond the planet Pluto. Although these particles are called "wind," they are really a flow of energy, not air. This flow of energy is especially strong after solar-flare activity.

The picture in figure 19-19 shows the sun's corona and was taken during a total solar eclipse. A total **solar eclipse** occurs when the moon completely hides the sun (fig. 19-20). During such an eclipse, the part of Earth where the shadow of the moon falls becomes very dark. The total eclipse is seen

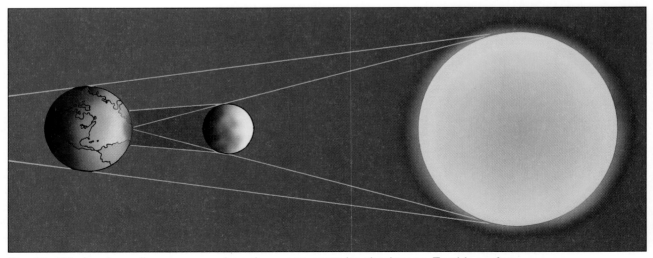

Fig. 19–20 A solar eclipse occurs when the moon casts its shadow on Earth's surface.

448

Materials:

finish nail (small)
index cards (4 x 6) - 2
masking tape

meterstick
safety razor blade

Procedure:

1. Slit each card to allow the meterstick to slide through.
2. Tape the cards to the meterstick 90 cm apart.
3. Using the nail, punch a hole in one card about half way down.
4. Aim the meterstick using the card with the hole facing the sun. Position the meterstick so the sun shines through the hole in the first card onto the second card.
5. Mark the edges of the sun's image on the second card. Measure the diameter of the sun's image.
6. Calculate the diameter of the sun by placing the measure of the sun's diameter (cm) into the formula below.

$$\text{Diameter of the sun (km)} = \frac{150,000,000 \text{ km}}{90 \text{ cm}} \times \text{measure (cm)}$$

- What is the diameter of the sun?
- How does your answer compare to that of other classmates?

only where the shadow of the moon falls. A total eclipse can last from a fraction of a second to about seven minutes. Before and after a total eclipse, the moon blocks only part of the sun, creating a partial eclipse which may last as long as several hours. Areas outside of this shadow do not experience the total eclipse but may see a partial eclipse.

REVIEW IT

1. What are the layers that make the sun?
2. What is a sunspot?
3. What is the difference between a prominence and a solar flare?
4. Draw a simple diagram that shows the arrangement of the Earth, sun, and moon during a solar eclipse.

19-3 CONSTELLATIONS

VOCABULARY
asterism
circumpolar constellation
constellation

OBJECTIVES

- Explain what a constellation is.
- Describe circumpolar constellations.
- Identify several common stars and constellations.

RESEARCH IT
Research three constellations
and report on the myths
surrounding each.

When you look at the night sky, you can see thousands of stars. If you look closely and use your imagination, you will find that the stars appear to form recognizable patterns (fig. 19-21). In ancient times people imagined that these patterns of stars represented people, animals, or objects, and they associated the figures with myths and legends. A group of stars named for a particular pattern or figure is called a **constellation**.

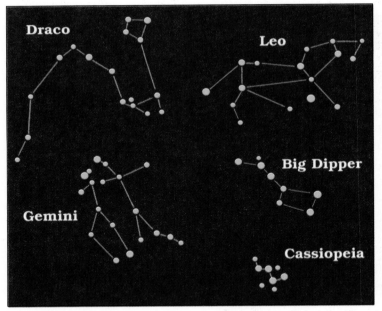

Fig. 19–21 Some stars form recognizeable patterns in the night sky.

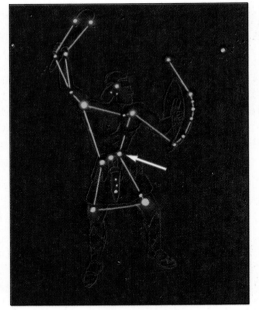

Fig. 19–22 Three stars make up Orion's belt.

The ancient Greeks identified 48 constellations. One commonly known constellation is Orion. By drawing lines to connect the stars of Orion, the figure of a hunter is formed. You probably recognize the three stars that form the hunter's belt (fig. 19-22).

Today astronomers identify 88 different constellations. While the stars of a constellation appear to form a recognizable pattern, they are not necessarily related to each other in any other way. For example, they may appear to be near each other or on the same plane in the sky, but they are not (fig. 19-23). They are simply located in the same direction from Earth.

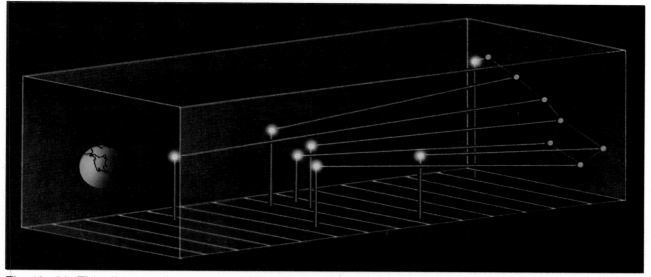

Fig. 19–23 This diagram shows that the stars that make up a constellation are not near each other but appear to be because of our perspective as we view them from Earth.

Some star groups, such as the Big Dipper and Little Dipper, do not make up constellations but are only part of a constellation. Such groups of stars are called **asterisms** (fig. 19-24).

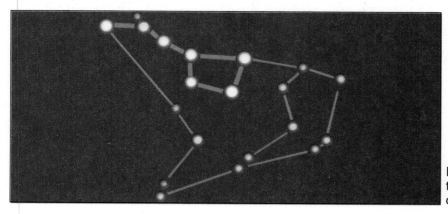

Fig. 19–24 The asterism called the Big Dipper is part of a larger constellation called Ursa Major.

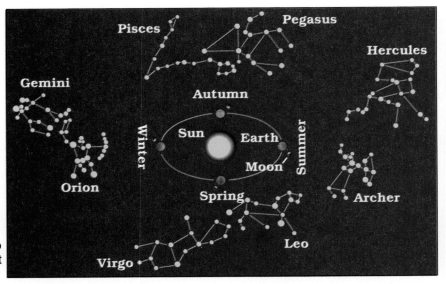

Fig. 19-25 As Earth moves in its orbit around the sun, different constellations and stars come into view and become part of the night sky we see.

Constellations are often classified according to whether they appear in the Northern or Southern Hemisphere. Most stars and constellations appear to move east to west in the sky, following the sun's movement. This apparent movement is not due to the movement of the stars but is a result of Earth's orbit around the sun. Earth's movement also results in various stars and constellations being visible at different times of the year (fig. 19-25).

Some constellations are visible throughout the year and appear to rotate around the North or South poles (fig. 19-26). These constellations, called **circumpolar constellations**,

Fig. 19-26 Circumpolar constellations appear to rotate around the North and South poles.

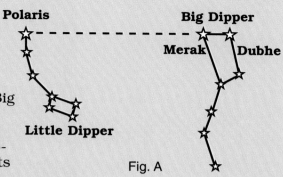
include Ursa Major (the Great Bear), which includes the Big Dipper; Ursa Minor (the Little Bear), which includes the Little Dipper); Draco (the Dragon); and Cassiopeia (kas ē ō pē′ ə) (the queen) in the Northern Hemisphere. In the Southern Hemisphere, circumpolar constellations include the Southern Cross and Centaurus (sen tô′ rəs).

Some stars and constellations are only visible from the Northern Hemisphere; others are visible only from the Southern Hemisphere.

REVIEW IT

1. What is a constellation?
2. What is a circumpolar constellation?
3. Give the name of each constellation pictured below.

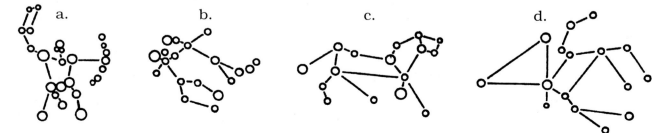

a. b. c. d.

453

19-4 A UNIVERSE OF GALAXIES

VOCABULARY

absolute magnitude
apparent magnitude
light-year
parallax

OBJECTIVES

- Define the term **light-year**.
- Explain how distances in space are determined.
- Distinguish between apparent and absolute magnitude.

Some night when you are camping, look up into the sky. You will notice a thick band of stars that is part of the Milky Way Galaxy. Our planet and solar system are located in this Galaxy. When you look at this feature in the night sky, you are looking at the edge of the Milky Way Galaxy, one of the largest structures in the universe (fig. 19-27). It is hard to imagine the size of our Milky Way Galaxy. It is even harder to imagine the size of the universe.

DID YOU KNOW?

Until the twentieth century, estimates of the size of the universe were grossly inaccurate. For example, the Greek philosopher Heraclitus estimated the diameter of the sun to be about one foot.

Fig. 19—27 The Milky Way Galaxy stretches across the night sky.

To understand the size of the universe a little better, it is helpful to look at it as a series of pictures that move farther and farther into space. To do this we will use the speed of light. As far as we know, nothing in the universe travels faster than light. If you point a flashlight at the moon and turn it on, the light from the flashlight will reach the moon in about 1.3 seconds.

The length of time it takes for light to travel from one place to another is a convenient way to compare distances in the universe. A light second is the distance light travels in one second, about 300 000 km (186,000 mi). At this speed it takes a light beam about 0.1 second to go around Earth's equator. For light to travel the 150 000 000 km (93,000,000 mi) from the sun to Earth takes about eight minutes. Because of the tremendous distances in space, astronomers use the light-year as the unit for measuring of distance. A **light-year** is the distance light travels in one year, about 9.5 trillion kilometers (6 trillion miles).

The closest star to our sun is Proxima Centauri. It is about 4.5 light-years away. The light we see tonight from this star left its surface more than four years ago. If something happened that caused this star to stop shining, we would not be aware of it for four years. Other stars are hundreds, thousands, even millions of light-years from Earth (fig. 19-28). Since the light we see from these objects left the stars millions of years ago, we are, in a sense, looking back in time.

A question many people ask is, "How do astronomers determine distances to stars and galaxies?" For nearby objects, the distance is determined by observing the object's location in the sky in relation to more distant objects (fig. 19-29). Astronomers first mark the location of a star or other object. Then they wait for a few months while Earth moves in its orbit around the sun. They observe and mark the object's location a second time. When the first location is compared with the second, a shift in position is observed.

DID YOU KNOW?
When you see the sun setting in the evening, it has already been set for eight minutes.

Fig. 19–28 Quasars, such as this one, are some of the most distant objects in space.

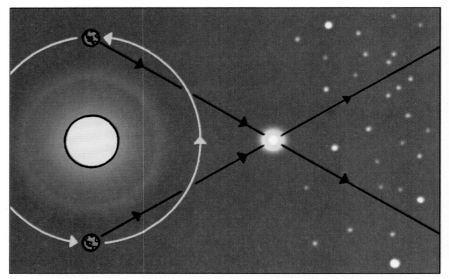

Fig. 19-29 The distance of a nearby star is determined by comparing its apparent shift in position as observed from different places as Earth moves in its orbit.

This shift, called a **parallax** (par′ ə laks), is measured and used to calculate the object's distance from Earth. The closer the star is to Earth, the greater its parallax. Stars that are at great distances from Earth have parallaxes that are too small to measure (fig. 19-30).

Fig. 19-30 The farther away an object is, the smaller its parallax.

456

Fig. 19–31 A star's magnitude is a measure of its brightness.

To measure the distances to distant stars, astronomers use another method. This method involves comparing the magnitude, or brightness, of the stars (fig. 19-31). For example, suppose you have two friends who have flashlights with the same brightness. On a dark night one friend stands 30 m away, and the other stands 100 m away. The flashlight that is nearest to you will "seem" brighter than the one farther away, even though both flashlights have the same brightness (fig. 19-32). The apparent brightness of a star (in this case the flashlight) is called its **apparent magnitude**. The actual brightness of the star (flashlight) is called its **absolute magnitude**.

If we know that two stars have the same absolute magnitude, but one appears brighter, we know that the brighter star is closer to Earth. However, it is necessary to determine the absolute magnitude of a star before this comparison can be made. To do this, scientists use a spectroscope to determine a star's spectrum.

Fig. 19–32 The flashlight that is nearest looks the brightest; the flashlight farthest away looks the faintest.

Many characteristics of an individual star are revealed in its spectrum. When two stars have identical spectra (plural for *spectrum*), not only will their chemical compositions, atmospheric pressures, and surface temperatures be identical, but also their absolute magnitudes. Knowing the absolute magnitude of a star allows astronomers to compare it to the star's apparent magnitude and calculate its distance from Earth. The farther away a star is, the greater the difference between these two magnitudes.

Imagine now that we are going to make ten jumps out from Earth. At each jump we will stop to see what the universe looks like.

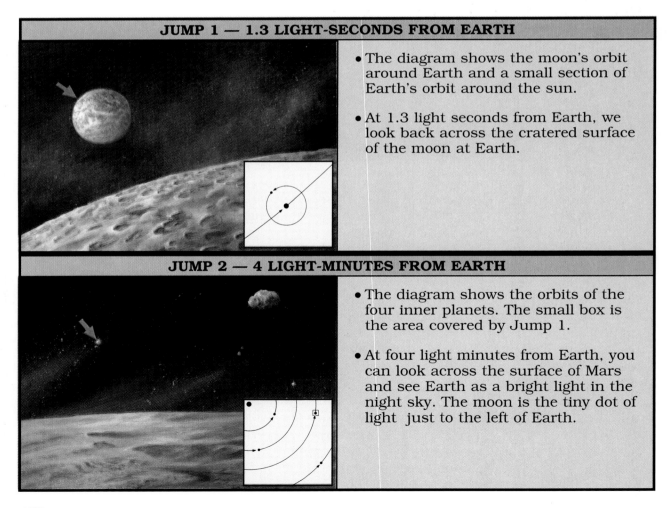

JUMP 1 — 1.3 LIGHT-SECONDS FROM EARTH

- The diagram shows the moon's orbit around Earth and a small section of Earth's orbit around the sun.

- At 1.3 light seconds from Earth, we look back across the cratered surface of the moon at Earth.

JUMP 2 — 4 LIGHT-MINUTES FROM EARTH

- The diagram shows the orbits of the four inner planets. The small box is the area covered by Jump 1.

- At four light minutes from Earth, you can look across the surface of Mars and see Earth as a bright light in the night sky. The moon is the tiny dot of light just to the left of Earth.

JUMP 3 — 4 LIGHT-HOURS FROM EARTH

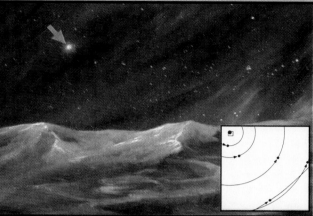

- The diagram shows the orbits of the outer planets. The small box is the area covered by Jump 2.

- At this distance out we look back toward Earth from the surface of Pluto.

- Earth and most of the other planets cannot be seen because they are too far away. At this distance, the sun appears as a very bright star.

JUMP 4 — 2 LIGHT-MONTHS FROM EARTH

- The diagram shows an orbit of a comet that passes through our solar system. The small box represents the area covered by Jump 3.

JUMP 5 — 4.3 LIGHT-YEARS FROM EARTH

- The diagram shows some of our closest star neighbors. The small box shows Jump 4.

- Proxima Centauri is our nearest star. From here our sun appears as a bright star in the Milky Way Galaxy.

JUMP 6 — 10,000 LIGHT-YEARS FROM EARTH

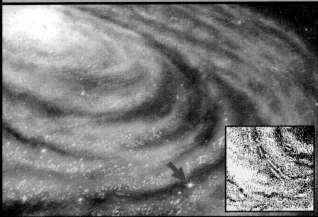

- The diagram shows where we are in the Milky Way Galaxy. The small box shows Jump 5.

- From here you can see the the area of the galaxy where our sun, one of over 100 billion stars in the galaxy, is located. Place your thumb near the bottom edge of the picture. Your thumb covers all the stars you can see in the sky on a dark night.

JUMP 7 — 170,00 LIGHT-YEARS FROM EARTH

- The diagram shows the Milky Way Galaxy and the two nearest galaxies. The small box shows Jump 6.

- The picture shows an imaginary view of the Milky Way Galaxy from a planet in the Large Magellanic Cloud, the small galaxy nearest to the Milky Way.

JUMP 8 — 2,500,000 LIGHT-YEARS FROM EARTH

- The diagram shows our galaxy and another in the Local Group. The box shows the area represented by Jump 7.

- The picture presents an imaginary view of the Milky Way and its two companion galaxies floating in deep space as seen from the Triangulum Galaxy.

JUMP 9 — 10,000,000 LIGHT-YEARS FROM EARTH

- The diagram shows the Milky Way and the Andromeda (an dräm′ ə də) Galaxy, the nearest large spiral galaxy. The box depicts Jump 8.

- At 10 million light-years from Earth the three largest galaxies of the Local Group can be seen. The largest of these, the Andromeda Galaxy is 2.3 million light-years from the Milky Way.

JUMP 10 — 300,000,000 LIGHT-YEARS FROM EARTH

- In the diagram, the small box shows the area covered by Jump 9.

- At 300 million light-years from Earth, the Milky Way Galaxy is just a small dot in an immense array of millions of galaxies that make up only a small part of the universe.

It is difficult to imagine the extent of our universe and to comprehend the distances that separate objects in space. Yet the universe is governed by the Creator. He established the laws that control the movement of galaxies and stars and the processes that take place.

REVIEW IT

1. What is a light-year?
2. How do astronomers determine the distances between objects in space?
3. What is the difference between a star's apparent magnitude and its absolute magnitude?

19-5 TYPES OF GALAXIES

galaxy
Local Group
Milky Way Galaxy

OBJECTIVES
- Define the term **galaxy**.
- Compare and contrast the main types of galaxies.
- Describe the galaxy that includes our solar system.
- Identify Earth's position in the galaxy.

Sombrero Galaxy

Large Magellanic Cloud

Spiral Galaxy of Cephas

Fig. 19–33 Edwin Hubble was the first astronomer to identify galaxies.

Figure 19-33 shows several galaxies. Before the 1920s astronomers believed these objects to be clouds of dust and gas between stars. In 1924 Edwin Hubble, an American astronomer, used the 250-cm telescope at the Mount Wilson Observatory, in southern California, to observe and study these "clouds of dust". He found that these objects, thought to be clouds of dust and gas, were actually galaxies (fig. 19-34). A **galaxy** is a group of millions, or perhaps billions, of stars held together by their mutual gravity.

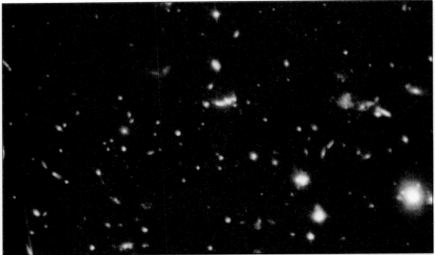

Fig. 19–34 Galaxies were once thought to be clouds of dust and gas.

Using his extensive observations of galaxies, Hubble established a system of classifying galaxies according to their shape. Based on this system, Hubble identified four basic types of galaxies: spiral, elliptic, peculiar, and irregular. Study figure 19-35 to learn about the types of galaxies.

Fig. 19-35

CHARACTERISTICS OF SPIRAL GALAXIES

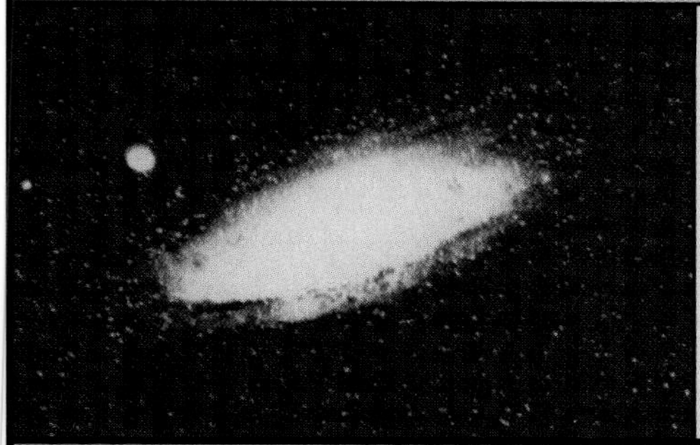

- Spiral galaxies look like pinwheels; arms appear to unwind from the center.
- They are the brightest galaxies.
- They are the least common type of galaxy.
- The Milky Way Galaxy and Andromeda Galaxy are spiral galaxies.

CHARACTERISTICS OF ELLIPTIC GALAXIES

- Elliptic galaxies have an oval, or elliptical, shape.
- They are the largest type of galaxy.
- They are the most common type of galaxy.
- They cannot be seen with the unaided eye.
- The M87 Galaxy in the constellation Virgo is an elliptic galaxy.

CHARACTERISTICS OF PECULIAR GALAXIES

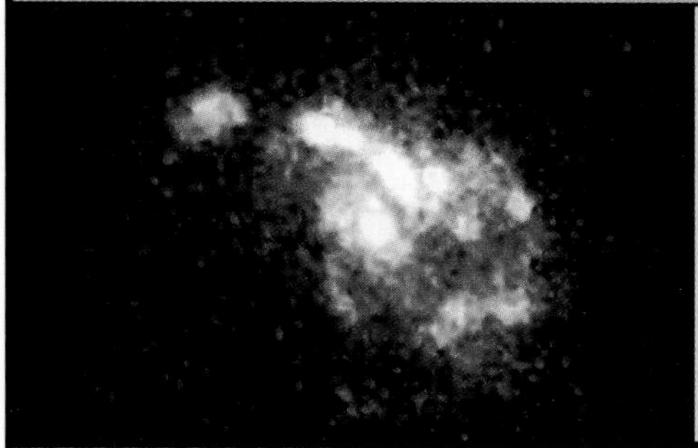

- Peculiar galaxies may be spiral or elliptic but have unusual features.
- They may have dark bands of dust wrapped around them.
- They possibly form when neighboring galaxies interact.
- The Centaurus A Galaxy in the constellation Centaurus is a peculiar galaxy.

CHARACTERISTICS OF IRREGULAR GALAXIES

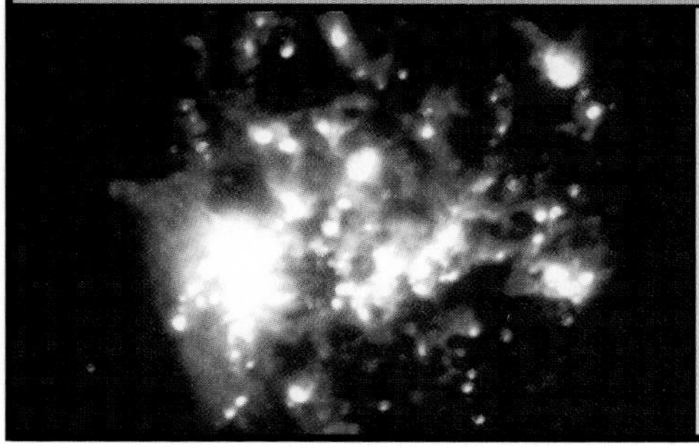

- Irregular galaxies have no regular shape.
- They were first discovered by Magellan and his crew during their voyage around the world.
- The Large and Small Magellanic Clouds are the two galaxies nearest to the Milky Way Galaxy.

The ancient Greeks called the broad band of light that stretches across the night sky the Milky Way. To the Greeks, who had vivid imaginations, this band of stars looked like drops of milk splashed across the sky. Much of the light that comes from the Milky Way comes from billions of stars that appear close together. The remaining light comes from clouds of interstellar dust and gas. The band of stars you see at night is only part of the **Milky Way Galaxy**, the galaxy to which Earth, the sun, and the rest of our solar system belong. Because we are part of this galaxy, we can never see all of it from Earth. The Milky Way Galaxy is one of a cluster of galaxies, called the **Local Group**. The two galaxies nearest to the Milky Way Galaxy are the Large and Small Magellanic Clouds (fig. 19-36).

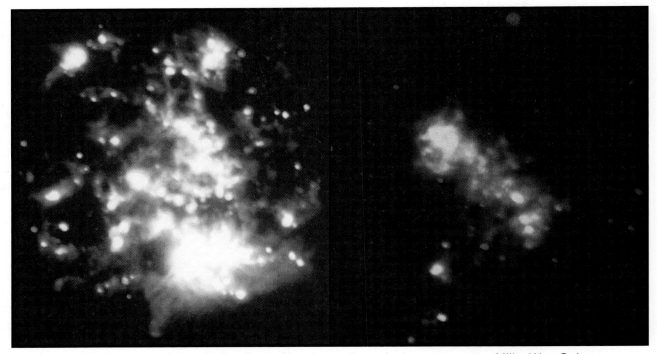

Fig. 19–36 The Large and Small Magellanic Clouds are the galaxies nearest our Milky Way Galaxy.

Almost everything you see when you look at the night sky is part of the Milky Way Galaxy. This galaxy is a spiral galaxy made up of about 100 billion stars. It is so large that it would take 100,000 years traveling at the speed of light just to cross it from edge to edge, and 10,000 years to pass from top to bottom at the center of the galaxy.

Location of our solar system

Fig. 19–37 The Milky Way, our galaxy, is s spiral galaxy.

Figure 19-37 shows a top view and a side view of the Milky Way Galaxy. If you look at the top view, you can see that our sun is located near the edge of the galaxy on one of the arms that spirals out from the center. To understand why we see the Milky Way as a band of light, look at the side view of the galaxy. At night when you look up at the sky, you are looking at our galaxy on edge; it appears as a dense band of stars—the Milky Way.

REVIEW IT

1. What is a galaxy?
2. Describe the four types of galaxies.
3. What is the Local Group?
4. How big is our galaxy?
5. Where in the Milky Way Galaxy is Earth located?

CHAPTER 19 WRAP-UP

THINKING SKILLS: Reading Maps

Below are two star maps. Study each map and answer the questions.

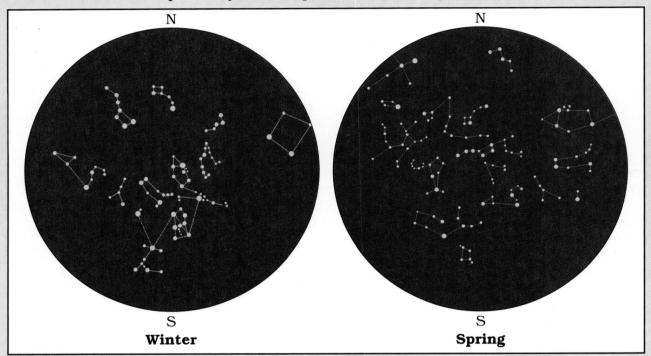

Winter   **Spring**

1. During the winter, in what part of the sky would you look to find the following?
   - a. Cassiopeia
   - b. Regulus
   - c. Sirius
   - d. Pleiades
2. During the spring, in what part of the sky would you look to find the following?
   - a. Spica
   - b. Vega
   - c. Procyon
   - d. Cassiopeia
3. If you were facing south during the spring, what star would you see almost directly overhead and a little to the southwest?
4. During what time of the year would you find Vega near the horizon in the north-east?
5. To what constellation does each star belong?
   - a. Sirius
   - b. Arcturus
   - c. Polaris
   - d. Capella
   - e. Betelgeuse
   - f. Pollux

QUESTIONS AND PROBLEMS

1. How do astronomers determine the absolute magnitude of stars?
2. What makes stars different colors?
3. What is the difference between a constellation and an asterism?
4. List these in order of brightness from least to greatest: red giant, white dwarf, main sequence, supergiant
5. What casts a shadow on Earth during a solar eclipse?
6. What is the Local Group?
7. How are sunspots different from other features of the sun?
8. Elliptic galaxies are the largest and most common galaxies. Why can none be seen without the use of a telescope?
9. Why is it wrong to assume that the brightest star in the night sky is the closest one to Earth?
10. Proxima Centauri is 4.5 light-years from Earth. How far is that in kilometers?
11. How do elliptic galaxies differ from spiral galaxies?

RESEARCH

1. Use salt dough or similar material to make a scale model of the sun. Show both internal and external features. Be sure to color and label your model.
2. Make a bulletin board display of the Milky Way Galaxy. Show Earth's position and the location of several familiar stars.
3. Make a bulletin board display of common constellations.
4. Use library resources to find out the names of the astronomers who developed the H-R diagram. Present a brief oral biography on each of the astronomers involved.
5. Obtain a star chart and observe the locations of several well-know constellations. Observe the constellations at different times and record how they change positions. Write a report of your findings, including diagrams, if possible.

REVIEW

HIGHLIGHTS

1. A star is a glowing ball of hot gas that produces its own energy.
2. Stars produce energy by the process of nuclear fusion. During fusion two nuclei of hydrogen combine to form one nucleus of helium with a release of energy.
3. Stars are classified by their temperature and their magnitude. The H-R diagram organizes the stars based on these characteristics. The H-R diagram is shown in figure 19-10.
4. The major types of stars are the Main Sequence, white dwarf, and red giants. They are illustrated and discussed in figure 19-11.
5. The sun includes the core, photosphere, chromosphere, prominence, and corona. All are described in figure 19-12.
6. Features of the sun include sunspots, solar flares, and the solar winds.
7. During a total solar eclipse, the moon passes between the sun and Earth.

8. A constellation is a group of stars named for a particular pattern.
9. Circumpolar constellations are constellations that appear to circle the poles.
10. Common stars and constellations are identified in figure 19-21 and OH 19-3A, B.
11. A light-year is the distance light travel in one year. Since the speed of light is about 300 000 km/sec, this distance is equal to about 9.5 trillion km.
12. Astronomers determine the distance for nearby objects in space by measuring the size of their parallax. They determine the distance of more distant objects by analyzing their magnitude.
13. The actual brightness of an object is called its absolute magnitude. These magnitudes have been determined by analyzing information obtained from observation with optical and other telescopes. The apparent brightness of an object is called its apparent magnitude.
14. A galaxy is a group of millions of stars held together by their mutual gravity.
15. There are four basic types of galaxies: spiral galaxies, elliptic galaxies, peculiar galaxies, and irregular galaxies. The characteristics of each of these are identified in figure 19-35.
16. The Milky Way Galaxy is one of a cluster of galaxies, called the Local Group. Nearest to us are the Large and Small Magellanic Clouds.
17. Our sun is located near the edge of the Milky Way Galaxy on one of the arms that spirals out from the center (see figure 19-37).

VOCABULARY LIST

absolute magnitude	H-R diagram	prominence
apparent magnitude	light-year	red giant
asterism	Local Group	solar eclipse
chromosphere	magnitude	solar flare
circumpolar constellation	main sequence	solar wind
constellation	Milky Way Galaxy	star
core	nuclear fusion	sunspot
corona	parallax	supergiant
galaxy	photosphere	white dwarf

PRACTICE
Multiple Choice. Choose the best answer.
1. How hot does it have to be in order for fusion to occur?
    a. hundreds of degrees
    b. thousands of degrees
    c. millions of degrees
    d. billions of degrees
2. What characteristics of stars does the H-R diagram show?
    a. composition and distance
    b. temperature and magnitude
    c. size and magnitude
    d. temperature and composition
3. What part of the sun produces the visible light?
    a. solar wind
    b. solar flare
    c. photosphere
    d. chromosphere

4. What feature of the sun causes the auroras observed on Earth?
   a. the corona
   b. solar flares
   c. solar wind
   d. sunspots
5. Which best describes a constellation?
   a. a group of stars named for a pattern they form
   b. a group of stars that are close together
   c. a group of stars that form a galaxy
   d. none of these
6. Which is a circumpolar constellation?
   a. Draco
   b. Ursa Major
   c. the Southern Cross
   d. all of these
7. What is used to determine distance from Earth to the most distant stars?
   a. magnitude
   b. size
   c. color
   d. composition
8. Which would show the greatest parallax?
   a. a star that is nearby
   b. a star that is far way
   c. a star with a large magnitude
   d. a star with a small magnitude
9. Which is an example of an irregular galaxy?
   a. the Andromeda Galaxy
   b. the Centarus A Galaxy
   c. the Small Magellanic Cloud
   d. none of these
10. The brightest galaxies are
   a. peculiar galaxies
   b. elliptic galaxies
   c. irregular galaxies
   d. spiral galaxies

Matching. Match each word with its definition or description.
1. transparent zone
2. a diagonal band on the H-R diagram
3. in the lower left of the H-R diagram
4. how bright a star seems
5. the apparent shift in position of a star
6. the area where nuclear fusion takes place
7. produces energy
8. a group of stars in a constellation
9. a bright spot near sunspots
10. layer of hot gas beyond the photosphere

a. asterism
b. apparent magnitude
c. chromosphere
d. core
e. corona
f. main sequence
g. nuclear fusion
h. parallax
i. solar flare
j. white dwarf

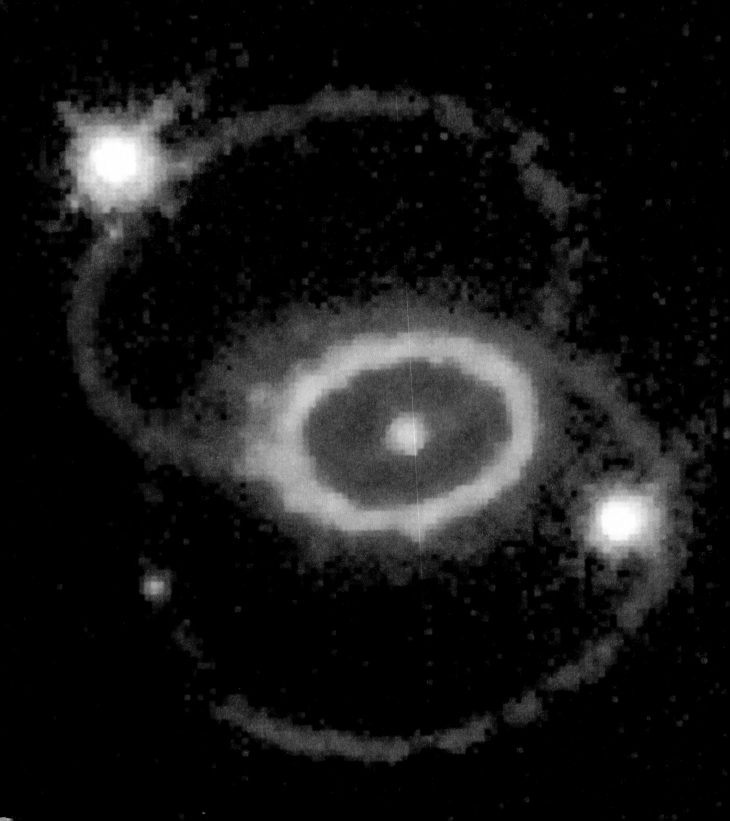

CHAPTER 20

QUESTIONS ABOUT ORIGINS

INTRODUCTION

The unusual object pictured on page 470 is Supernova 1987A. It is part of the Large Megellanic Cloud, one of the galaxies closest to our Milky Way. Before this supernova occurred, only a faint star like the thousands of others were visible in this place. Astronomers believe that supernovas represent the final stages in the life of supergiant stars. They believe the cloudlike nebulas in this photo are where stars are born.

Do stars really go through a life cycle? How does the idea of stars forming and dying fit with the Genesis account of Creation? You will have an opportunity to explore these and related questions as you study this chapter.

SECTION TITLES

Supernova 1987A was recently discovered by astronomers studying the Large Magellanic Cloud.

20–1 HOW DID THE UNIVERSE BEGIN?

VOCABULARY
big-bang theory
dark matter
experimental science
historical science

OBJECTIVES

- Distinguish between historical science and experimental science.
- Describe the big-bang theory.
- Identify the evidence that supports the big-bang theory
- Identify the evidence that contradicts the big-bang theory.

The question in the title of this section is one that is asked by many people. Questions such as this are part of historical science. **Experimental science**, the science with which you are most familiar, deals with events in which the beginning conditions are known (fig. 20-1). Such experiments can be repeated to allow us to observe the event as many times as we wish.

Fig. 20–1 Experimental science works with an event in which the beginning conditions are known.

Historical science studies events in which beginning conditions are unknown. This science tries to explain past events by examining their results. Obviously, we cannot repeat an event if we do not know what the beginning conditions were. We may also be limited in our study of historical science because the scale of the event is too large for us to control. For example, no one can experiment with a worldwide flood or the impact of an asteroid with Earth.

Neither does anyone know what the exact conditions were that led to the arrival of humans in the New World. These are questions of history, and we may never be certain of the answers.

Fig. 20—2 The Bible tells us that God created the stars, but we don't know exactly how He accomplished this.

Another historical question is the origin of the universe. The Bible tells us that God made the universe, the stars, and Earth by speaking, but it doesn't explain exactly how He did it (fig 20-2). There is no way for us to answer such a question with an experiment. But scientists would like to find an answer, if possible. Can humans learn enough to be certain about how God created the universe? No. But we may gain new knowledge by studying the universe, and we may learn to appreciate God's power and wisdom (fig. 20-3).

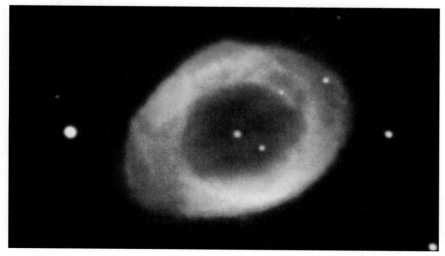

Fig. 20-3 Looking at and studying the universe helps us to better appreciate God's power and wisdom.

Some people feel that if we were to understand how something happened, it would mean that God didn't do it. It is true that some people have used their knowledge of nature as an excuse to deny God's power. However, this is not logical. Just because scientists speculate how something might have happened does not mean that it happened without God. Also, just because scientists have ideas how events might have happened does not mean that the event actually happened in that manner.

There are several theories that try to explain the origin of the universe; some are more common than others. For example, the pulsating-universe theory states that the universe is slowly going through a cycle of expansions and contractions, similar to an accordian expanding and contracting (fig. 20-4). Another theory, the most common, is the big-bang theory. Although it is the most common, it is not necessarily correct.

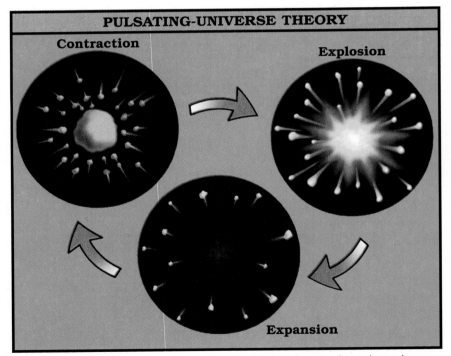

PULSATING-UNIVERSE THEORY

Contraction

Explosion

Expansion

Fig. 20-4 According to the pulsating-universe theory, there have been a series of expansions and contractions of our universe.

Keep these ideas in mind as we study a scientific theory of how the universe might have been created. Several lines of evidence have been offered to support this theory. These include background radiation in space, the abundance of light elements (hydrogen and helium), and the red shift. These evidences have led to the theory of the beginning of the universe mentioned above, known as the big-bang theory. Many scientists believe that this theory explains most of the observations they have made concerning the universe.

Fig. 20–5 Many scientists believe that the universe may have begun as a huge explosion millions of times greater than the largest nuclear explosion on Earth.

The **big-bang theory** suggests that the universe began as a large explosion (fig. 20-5). It states that at one time all the matter of the universe was contained in a small core of unimaginable density. A massive explosion occurred that caused the mass of this dense core to expand outward at incredible speed (fig 20-6). The matter, dust and gas, moved rapidly away from where the core once was. As it moved outward, it began to slow, allowing the gravity of larger pieces of matter to clump together. From these clumps, galaxies, stars, and solar systems formed.

Fig. 20–6 The big bang is theorized to have caused matter to spread out, cool, clump together, and form the structures of the universe.

Some people believe that God created the universe using a process similar to the big bang.

There are some scientific problems with this theory. Like most theories scientists propose, the big-bang theory may be incomplete, or perhaps incorrect. We simply do not know how God created the universe. However, you should at least know what the theory is so you can recognize its meaning.

Although the big-bang theory explains many observations of the universe, some things contradict it. For example, according to the theory, the universe should contain more matter than scientists have been able to find. The "missing" matter has been called **dark matter**, because no one can see it. It is possible that someone will discover this missing matter, but so far no one has.

TRY THIS 20-1: Find Me!

Materials:
Bible concordance

Procedure:
1. Form a group with one or two of your classmates.
2. Make a chart like the one shown below.
3. Use a concordance and list Bible references to suns, stars, galaxies, constellations, or anything to do with the universe.
4. Compare your list with those of other groups.

Sun	Stars	Galaxies	Constellations	Other

Another problem with this theory is that some stars appear to be older than the universe itself. Of course this is not possible. No matter what theory is being considered, it seems that the more we learn about nature, the more we realize there is still so much to learn.

REVIEW IT

1. What is the difference between historical and experimental science?
2. What does the big-bang theory state?
3. What evidence supports the big-bang theory?
4. What evidence contradicts the big-bang theory?

—

20-2 LIFE CYCLE OF STARS

VOCABULARY

black hole
equilibrium
nebula
neutron star
nova
pulsar
supernova

OBJECTIVES

- Describe the relationship between a nebula and new stars.
- Describe the life cycle of stars.
- Distinguish between a nova and a supernova.
- Explain what a black hole is.

At this time many astronomers theorize that stars go through a series of changes that can be compared to a "life cycle." Study figure 20-7 as you read about the life cycle of stars.

Fig. 20—7

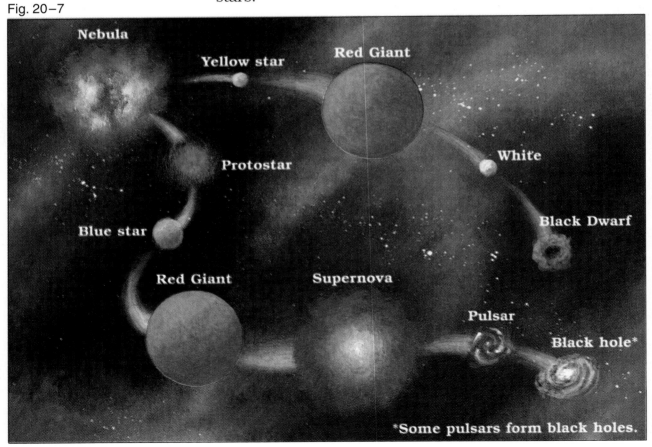

*Some pulsars form black holes.

478

The space between stars is filled with gas and dust. This dust is too cold to emit any energy. When matter accumulates, its temperature increases, and nuclear reactions begin to occur. As this happens the matter, now a gaseous cloud, begins to emit energy and is called a **nebula**.

Fig. 20–8 The bright areas in the Horsehead Nebula of Orion are places where many astronomers believe new stars are forming.

Scientists believe that stars form when the force of gravity causes a nebula to contract. Sometimes these clouds become so dense they can be seen as dark areas against the background of a brighter nebula (fig. 20-8). As gravity pulls the cloud together into a spherical shape, its density and pressure increase, causing an increase in temperature. When the central temperature rises to about 10 million° C, nuclear fusion begins. The radiation produced by nuclear fusion tends to drive matter away from the star's central part, or core. At the same time gravity is still pulling matter toward the center. When a state of **equilibrium** (ē kwi lib′ rē əm), or balance, is reached between these two opposing forces, a star has been "born" (fig. 20-9).

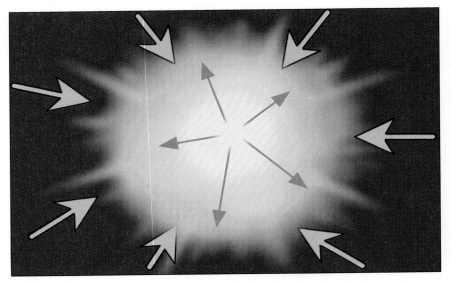

Once a star begins to shine, it starts to use the fuel that makes its core. Scientists believe that as stars use this fuel, they pass through a life cycle. This life cycle causes changes to take place as the star ages.

When the fuel in the core of a small star is used up, no more radiation pushes outward to prevent the overlying matter from collapsing on the core. This collapse causes the temperature of the core to rise. At the higher temperature, nuclear fusion, involving the matter left over as "ashes" from the previous phase, may again start up. This causes the star to expand and form a red giant. What happens next depends on the original mass of the star.

Small stars that have used up all the central nuclear fuel suffer a final collapse that turns them into white dwarfs that slowly die away.

Red giants, formed from medium-size and large-size stars, suffer a more violent final core collapse. This event, called a **nova**, occurs when a massive explosion of the core causes the outer layers to expand explosively. Novas cause the stars to become larger and brighter for a short while; then they collapse to become white dwarfs that slowly fade away.

In the most massive stars, the supergiants, a similar condition occurs. These **supernovas** are much greater than a nova. Supernovas are the most violent explosions that have been observed in the universe and cause these massive dying stars to become many times brighter than before.

In 1054, Chinese astronomers recorded a supernova. They were able to observe this amazing feature for two years. The remnants of this supernova make up the faint Crab Nebula visible today in the Taurus constellation (fig. 20-10).

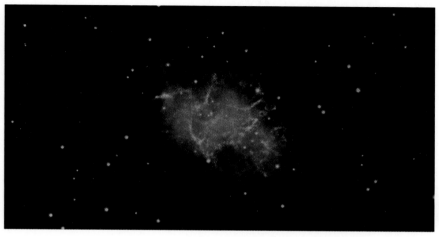

Fig. 20–10 The Crab Nebula is the remains of a supernova that occurred in A.D. 1054.

When a supernova occurs, part of its mass collapses and becomes a dense star called a **neutron star**. The collapsing matter is forced into such a small space that one spoonful of this neutron star would have a mass of 100 000 000 metric tons. While neutron stars are not visible with optical telescopes, they can be detected by X-ray telescopes.

Some neutron stars are formed when supernovas spin. These spinning neutron stars are called **pulsars** (fig. 20-11).

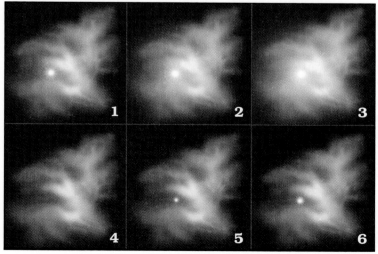

Fig. 20–11 Pulsars are spinning neutron stars.

Fig. 20–12 Radio telescopes let astronomers observe and study pulsars.

Pulsars emit radio waves as they spin. Astronomers can use radio telescopes to study these whirling stars (fig. 20-12).

Astronomers believe that the last stage in the life cycle of very large stars is a black hole. A **black hole** is a star in which matter is so condensed that its gravity field prevents anything, including light, from escaping. Astronomers estimate that there may be as many as 100,000 black holes in the Milky Way Galaxy alone. By using X-ray telescopes, they can observe the matter of other objects, usually nearby stars, being "pulled" into the black hole by its intense gravity (fig. 20-13).

Fig. 20–13 Astronomers find black holes by observing the matter of another object being "pulled" into a black hole by its intense gravity.

Current ideas on the life cycle of stars are based on observations made over a relatively short time. In the future, astronomers may find that current theories need revision. In the end we must realize that only the Creator knows for sure about the life cycle of the stars.

REVIEW IT

1. What is the relationship between a nebula and a star?
2. Describe the life cycle of a middle-sized star.
3. What is the difference between a nova and a supernova?
4. What is a black hole?

20–3 AN EXPANDING UNIVERSE

- Explain the Doppler effect.
- Define the term **red shift**.
- Explain the importance of the red shift to astronomers.

At one time or another you have probably heard the siren of an emergency vehicle as it sped past you (fig. 20-14). As the ambulance, fire truck, or police car passed, you may have heard the sound of the siren change. As the truck

Fig. 20–14 You can hear an emergency vehicle's siren change pitch as it approaches you and then passes by.

moved toward and passed you, the sound was higher; as it moved away the sound was lower. Waves that are close together have a higher pitch, while waves that are farther apart have a lower pitch. Figure 20-15 shows that as the siren approaches you, sound waves are pushed together, giving them a higher pitch. As the siren passes, the waves are stretched out, producing a lower pitch. This compression and expansion of sound waves created by moving objects is called the **Doppler effect**.

483

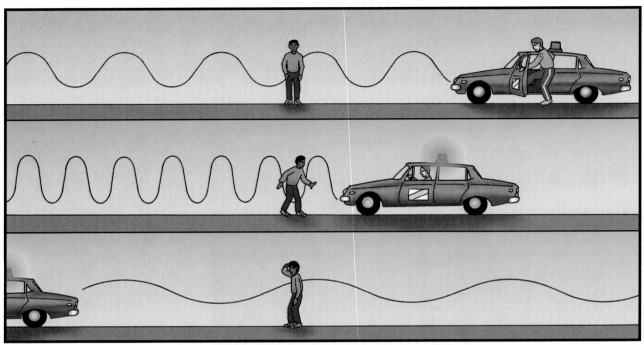

Fig. 20—15 The change in the pitch of a siren is explained by the Doppler effect.

Light waves behave in a similar way. As light waves move toward or away from you, they change color. As an object emmitting light moves toward you, the light waves are pushed together, and the color becomes bluer. When the object moves away, the light waves are stretched out, and the color becomes redder (fig. 20-16). The reddening of receding objects is called the **red shift**.

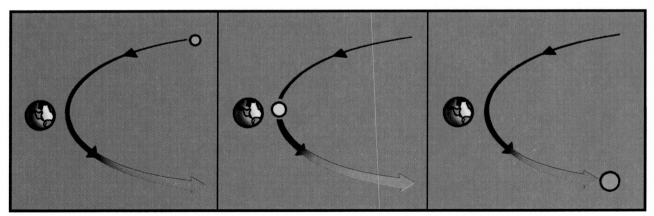

Fig. 20—16 The red shift is caused by light waves that stretch out as they move away.

In 1929, Edwin Hubble discovered that distant galaxies show a red shift. The most logical explanation for this observation is that these galaxies are moving away from us. The larger the red shift of a galaxy, the faster it is moving away. This discovery has led astronomers to believe that the universe is expanding (fig. 20-17).

Fig. 20–17 The discovery of the red shift has led many astronomers to believe that the universe is expanding.

Since many scientists believe galaxies themselves do not expand, stars within our galaxy are not expected to show red shifts. Scientists were, therefore, surprised to find in the early 1960s that certain starlike objects within our galaxy showed red shifts as large or larger than those of the faintest galaxies. Because these objects emit radio waves, they are called quasi-stellar radio sources, or **quasars** (kwā′ zär). Since quasars have the largest red shifts known, astronomers believe that they are the farthest objects from us. Some quasars have been measured to be more than 14 billion light-years away from Earth. This suggests to some scientists that these quasars are at least 14 billion years old.

The theory of the expanding universe has interesting implications for the early history of the universe. Some Creation scientists believe that Genesis 1:1 can agree with the time frame of the big-bang theory. They believe the universe did have a beginning and that God created the universe billions of years ago.

Fig. 20–18 The Creator made Earth as a home for humans.

Genesis 1:2 indicates that Earth may have been a shapeless and formless uninhabited planet until God decided to make it the home for humans beings (fig 20-18). The rest of Genesis 1 tells us what happened when God executed His plan in seven 24-hour days, first by creating an environment that could support human life and, second, by creating our first parents. It is important to remember that the Bible tells Who created the universe and what took place on Earth during Creation week, but it does not tell us when Creation occurred or exactly how it happened.

While the theory of the expanding universe may be widely accepted, we should not forget that it is based on a specific interpretation of the red shift. This interpretation, based on the Doppler effect, need not be the correct one; we just don't know. Since ideas regarding the expanding universe may change as more evidence is discovered, it is good to keep an open mind.

Our study of the universe shows us how great God must be in order to have planned and created it (fig. 20-19). Surely we can say with the psalmist, "The heavens are telling the glory of God" (Psalm 19:1).

REVIEW IT

1. What is the Doppler effect?
2. What is the "red shift?"
3. Why is the "red shift" important to astronomers?

Fig. 20–19 Studying the universe points us to the Creator.

CLASS ACTIVITY 20-3: An Expanding Universe

Question: How is the universe expanding?

Materials:
    balloon (white)   metric tape measure
    marker pens (red and black)

Procedure:
1. Have your partner blow up the balloon just enough to make it taut; hold it closed. Measure the balloon's diameter. Record.
2. Draw red dots about 2 cm apart all over the balloon to represent galaxies.
3. Circle one dot near the middle with the black marker.
4. Choose another 6 dots, some close and some far way from the circled dot. Number the dots 1 to 6.
5. Measure the distance from the center dot to each of the numbered dots and record.
6. Have your partner inflate the balloon so its diameter is now doubled.
7. Repeat step 5.
8. Subtract the "Original Distance" from the "Distance after Expansion" to calculate "Change in Distance" and record.
9. Divide the "Change in Distance" by the "Distance after Expansion" to calculate the "Factor by which Distance Changed" and record.

Data:

Dot	Original Distance	Expansion Distance	Change in Distance	Factor By Which Distance Changed
1				
2				
3				
4				
5				
6				

Questions:
1. Did all the dots have the same change in distance? Explain.
2. What relationship is there between the factor by which the distance changed and the original distance of the galaxy?
3. If the circled dot represents the Milky Way, what can be said about the other dots (galaxies) with regards to their position from the Milky Way?

Conclusion: Write 3–5 sentences about what you learned from this activity.

CHAPTER 20 WRAP-UP

THINKING SKILLS: Researching a Topic

Although much of the work of a scientist involves experimentation and observation, sometimes it is necessary for her to find out what has been written about a particular topic. To do this she may use indexes, the *Reader's Guide to Periodical Literature*, or computer searches. Once she finds what has been written, the scientist must examine the written material and decide what information is important to her research.

In this chapter we have discussed the question "How did the universe begin?" An equally important question is "What does the Bible say about this?" Use a concordance or a similar tool to make a list of the Bible texts that refer to God's creating and sustaining of the universe. When you have completed your list, pick out the 10 most important texts and list them below.

1. _____   6. _____

2. _____   7. _____

3. _____   8. _____

4. _____   9. _____

5. _____   10. _____

Questions:
1. Which of the 10 texts talk about God's creating the universe?
2. Which of the 10 texts talk about God's sustaining the universe?
3. Which of the 10 texts tell when God created the universe?
4. Which of the 10 texts tell how God created the universe?
5. Which is more important to know as a Christian, when God created the universe or that He created the universe?

QUESTIONS AND PROBLEMS

1. If a blue star is moving away from Earth, what color will it most likely appear?
2. Does knowing how the universe came into existence indicate that God is not involved? Explain.
3. What feature of a star determines its destiny when it dies?
4. If the theory of the big bang does not explain all the observations that scientists have made about the universe, which theory does? Explain.
5. If the big-bang theory is accurate, where might the matter that was in the dense core come from?
6. Which is most likely to be proven, experimental science or historical science? Why?
7. Why is the dust in the universe considered "cold" matter?
8. Why are quasars considered to be the most distant objects?
9. How hot does a star have to be for nuclear fusion to begin?
10. How many black holes may be in the Milky Way Galaxy?
11. How is "dark matter" different from other forms of matter?
12. Suppose two police cars are racing to the scene of a crime, Car 23D is coming from the north at 80 mph, Car 54 is coming from the south at 90 mph. The siren of which car will produce the highest pitch? Why?
13. What causes the increase in temperature of a forming star?

RESEARCH

1. Use library resources to find out about current research on black holes. Prepare an oral report on your findings.
2. Use library resources to find information about the life and work of Edwin Hubble. Prepare an illustrated written report on your findings.
3. Make a series of posters that depict the life cycle of stars.
4. Prepare a bulletin board display entitled "Evidence of Order and Design in the universe." Collect a number of pictures from magazines or develop your own art work that shows examples of this evidence.
5. Use salt dough or similar material to make a model that shows how a star is formed.

REVIEW

HIGHLIGHTS

1. Experimental science studies events in which the beginning conditions are known. It involves events that can be repeated to allow for further study. Historical science studies events in which beginning conditions are unknown. This science tries to explain past events by examining their results.
2. The big-bang theory states that at one time all the matter of the universe was contained in a small, dense core. A massive explosion occurred, causing the matter to expand outward. The matter, dust and gas, moved away from where the core was and began to slow. This slowing allowed gravity of larger pieces of matter to cause

them to clump together. Stars and galaxies formed from these clumps of matter.

3. Evidence that supports the big-bang theory includes the life cycle of stars and the red shift of stars and galaxies.

4. Evidence that contradicts the big-bang theory includes the absence of enough matter in the universe and that some stars appear to be older than the universe itself.

5. Stars form when gravity pulls together dust and gas of a nebula.

6. Gravity causes the matter of a star to come together. Fusion occurs when the temperature and pressure gets high enough. Fusion causes the gases to expand against the gravity. When gravity matches the force pushing out, a star is born. Once the fuel is used up, the star collapses. Depending on the size, several things can happen. Figure 20-7 summarizes the life cycle of stars.

7. A nova occurs when a red giant expands rapidly and then collapses. A supernova occurs when a supergiant expands rapidly and explodes instead of collapsing.

8. A black hole is the last stage of very large stars. In these stars, matter is so condensed that its gravity field prevents anything, including light, from escaping.

9. The compression and subsequent expansion of sound waves created by objects is called the Doppler effect.

10. The red shift occurs when an object is moving away from Earth. The light waves are spread apart, and its light shifts toward the red end of the spectrum.

11. The discovery of the red shift suggests that the universe is expanding.

VOCABULARY LIST

big-bang theory	experimental science	pulsar
black hole	historical science	quasar
dark matter	nebula	red shift
Doppler effect	neutron star	supernova
equilibrium	nova	

PRACTICE

Multiple Choice. Choose the best answer.

1. Which science would deal with events that can be repeated?
   a. repetitive science
   b. experimental science
   c. psychological science
   d. historical science

2. Which of these events is not included in the big-bang theory?
   a. an intense solar wind that caused the galaxy to explode
   b. large pieces of matter clumping together
   c. an explosion of a dense core of matter
   d. movement of matter away from the original core

3. The matter that the universe should contain but that can't be found is
   a. antimatter
   b. magnetic matter
   c. nuclear matter
   d. none of these

4. Where does fusion take place?
   a. in the center of a star
   b. in the center of a planet
   c. in the center of the galaxy
   d. in the center of the universe
5. The word that describes the balanced forces that cause a forming star to begin to glow is
   a. magnetic
   b. theoretical
   c. equilibrium
   d. intensity
6. Which might develop into a supernova?
   a. a supergiant
   b. a white dwarf
   c. a red giant
   d. a neutron star
7. What is the only thing that can escape a black hole?
   a. water
   b. gravity
   c. light
   d. none of these
8. Which produces a higher pitch?
   a. compressed light waves
   b. expanded light waves
   c. compressed sound waves
   d. expanded sound waves
9. Who was the first astronomer to observe and identify the red shift?
   a. Aristotle
   b. Galileo
   c. Copernicus
   d. Hubble
10. Which objects in space are moving the fastest away from Earth?
    a. galaxies
    b. stars
    c. quasars
    d. none of these

Matching. Match each word with its definition or description.
1. forms when a supernova collapses
2. invisible matter
3. the most distant objects in space
4. the explosion of a supergiant
5. areas of extreme gravity
6. suggests an object is moving away from Earth
7. the explosion of medium-sized stars
8. a gaseous cloud that emits energy
9. a spinning neutron star
10. suggests that the universe began with a mighty explosion

a. big-bang theory
b. black hole
c. dark matter
d. nebula
e. neutron star
f. nova
g. pulsar
h. quasar
i. red shift
j. supernova

CAREERS

Astronomer

Description of Work
Astronomers are scientists who expand our basic knowledge about the universe. They observe and interpret celestial occurrences and relate research to basic scientific knowledge, such as navigation. They use the laws of physics and mathematics in their study of matter and energy throughout the universe.

Personal Qualifications
Astronomers must be patient and careful workers who can focus for months or even years on the details of a research problem. They must also be able to communicate their findings to others. They must also be good at science and mathematics.

Requirements
A high-school diploma and four to six years of college. An advanced degree is recommended.

Career Information
American Astronomical
   Society
2000 Florida Avenue, NW
Washington, DC 20009

Physicist

Description of Work
Physicists attempt to discover basic principles involved in the structure and behavior of matter, the making and using of energy, and the interaction of matter and energy. Physicists design and perform experiments that can help to describe the forces in nature. Most physicists work in research and development.

Personal Qualifications
Physicists must be patient, careful workers. They must enjoy working with difficult questions and experimenting to come up with a solution. They must have a good knowledge of mathematics and science.

Requirements
A high-school diploma and four to six years of college. An advanced degree is also required.

Career Information
American Instute of Physics
335 East 45th Street
New York, NY 10017

Aerospace Technician

Description of Work
Aerospace technicians assist scientists and engineers in the design, development, testing, and production of aircraft and spacecraft. They work on rockets, missiles, helicopters, airplanes, and space vehicles.

Personal Qualifications
Aerospace technicians must be able to work with others. They should also be good at science and mathematics and be able to concentrate on the details of their work. Technicians also need to be responsible people who can work well with their hands.

Requirements
A high-school diploma and two years of college.

Career Information
American Society for
   Engineering Education
11 Dupont Circle, NW
Washington, DC 20036

Commercial Pilot

Description of Work
Commercial pilots fly airplanes to transport passengers, mail, or freight. They determine weather and flight conditions, check flight plans, and have them approved by the Federal Aviation Agency (FAA). They fly the airplane and make radio reports to ground control stations about altitude, speed, weather conditions, and other flight details.

Personal Qualifications
Commercial pilots must give special attention to details. They must be very alert at all times. Pilots must also have perfect vision and hearing. They must have excellent coordination and be able to respond effectively in emergencies.

Requirements
A high-school diploma and a license by the Federal Aviation Agency (FAA). Some college may be recommended.

Career Information
International Airline Pilots
  Association
1625 Massachusetts Avenue,
  NW
Washington, DC 20036

Airplane Navigator

Description of Work
Navigators locate position and direct the course of airplane on international flights, using navigational aids, such as charts, maps, sextants, and slide rules. They establish the position of the airplane by the use of navigation instruments and charts and celestial observation. They direct deviation from the set course required by weather conditions. Navigators also keep a log of the flight.

Personal Qualifications
Airplane navigators must be very responsible and careful. They must be very attentive and meticulous in their work. They must be able to deal effectively with changing situations. Navigators must be able to communicate with others.

Requirements
A high-school diploma and a license from the Federal Aviation Agency (FAA).

Career Information
International Airline Pilots
  Association
1625 Massachusetts Avenue,
  NW
Washington, DC 20036

Astronaut

Description of Work
Astronauts attempt to extend our knowledge of both outer space and physical and mental adaptation to that environment. They conduct experiments and gather information while in actual spaceflight and on the moon. They also conduct experiments with the spacecraft itself to develop new concepts in design, engineering, and navigation outside Earth's atmosphere.

Personal Qualifications
Astronauts must have a desire to learn about outer space and to participate in the exploration of it. They must have a deep curiosity, with extremely fine and quick reactions, and an ability to think quickly and logically.

Requirements
A high-school diploma and four to six years of college.

Career Information
NASA
Office of Educational Programs
  and Services
400 Maryland Avenue
Washington, DC 20025

ACKNOWLEDGMENTS

Special acknowledgment and appreciation are give to the following individuals who participated in the preparation of *Explore God's World.*

Dick Duerksen for collecting and producing photographic images.
Bonnie Casey for her technical assistance in preparing the materials for publication.
All the teachers and students who participated in field testing the components of this series.

Science/Health Steering Committee

Marion Hartlein, Associate Director, Office of Education, North American Division of Seventh-day Adventists
Marilyn J. Bauer, Science Curriculum Development, Hinsdale, Illinois
Jerry Beem, Superintendent of Education, Oklahoma Conference
Henry Farr, Associate Superintendent of Education, Georgia-Cumberland Conference
Delano A. Gilliam, Associate Superintendent of Education, Florida Conference
Donald F. Hodder, Principal, St. John's, Newfoundland, Canada
Joyce W. Hopp, Professor of Health Promotion and Education, School of Public Health, Loma Linda University
James C. Mason, Principal/science teacher, Sandpoint, Idaho
Alyce J. Pudewell, Associate Director for Elementary Curriculum and Instruction, Pacific Union Conference
Gary E. Randolph, Associate Director of Education, Lake Union Conference
James Stephan, Superintendent of Education, Pennsylvania Conference

Technical Readers

Paul Buckheim, Ph.D., Loma Linda University
Kenneth Burke, Ph.D., Loma Linda University
Mart de Groot, Ph.D., Armagh Observatory, Armagh, Northern Ireland
Sue Dixon, Ph.D., Walla Walla College
Jim Gibson, Ph.D., Geoscience Research Institute
Joyce Hopp, Ph.D., M.P.H., Loma Linda University
Patricia Johnston, Dr.P.H., Loma Linda University
Edwin Karlow, Ph.D., La Sierra University
John Lewis, Ph.D., Loma Linda University
Robert Ludeman, Ph.D., Andrews University
Gilbert Muth, Ph.D., Pacific Union College
Michelle Naden, Ph.D., Loma Linda University
Myra Rodriquez, Ed.S., Associate Superintendent of Education and School of Psychology, Florida Conference
David Steen, Ph.D., Andrews University
Roger Tatum, Ph.D., Loma Linda University

Pacific Press Development

Paul Hey, project coordinator
Ira Lee, initial design
Michelle C. Petz, art direction and layout
Mike Seymore, electronic publishing design assistant
Bonnie Tyson-Flyn, in-house editor
Mark Winchester, art direction and layout

Credits for illustrations used in *Explore God's World:*

GLOSSARY

Abdomen–One of the three body parts of an insect. The abdomen contains the digestive, respiratory, and reproductive structures.

Abortion–Artificial termination of a pregnancy.

Absolute magnitude–The actual brightness of a star.

Acceleration (ak sel ər ā′ shən)–A change in speed.

Active transport–The transport of materials that requires energy.

Adenine–One of nucleotide bases that make up nucleic acid. Adenine combines with thymine to form one of the base pairs of the DNA molecule.

Adolescence (ad′l es′ ′ns)–A time when people change from children to adults. It includes puberty.

Aerobic (er ō′ bik) bacteria–Bacteria that require oxygen to live.

AIDS–A disease caused by HIV in which the immune system cannot protect the body against invasion by pathogens.

Algae (al′ jē)–Protists that contain chlorophyll and can photosynthesize. They may be unicellular or form colonies.

Algin–A gummy substance produced by brown algae. It is used in making cosmetics, ice cream, and tires.

Allele (ə lēl′)–One part of a gene pair.

Anaerobic bacteria–Bacteria that do not require oxygen to live.

Annelida (an′ ə lid ə)–A phylum of worms characterized by a cylindrical body divided into segments. It includes earthworms and leeches.

Antenna–An elongated, movable structure that functions as a sense organ in arthropods.

Antibody–A protein substance produced by B-lymphocytes. Antibodies attach to the surfaces of pathogens, making it difficult for them to attach to healthy cells.

Apparent magnitude–The apparent brightness of a star.

Arachnid (ə rak′ nid)–A class of arthropods characterized by a body divided into two parts and four pairs of legs. Arachnids include spiders, scorpions, mites, and ticks

Arthropod (är′ thrō päd)–The largest phylum of animals. Arthropods include all animals that have an exoskeleton, segmented body, jointed legs, and antennae. Arthropods include crustaceans, arachnids, millipedes, centipedes, and insects

Asterism–A star group that is part of a larger constellation.

Asteroid (as′ tər oid)–A rocky object of varying size that orbits the sun between Mars and Jupiter.

Asteroid belt–The region in which asteroids are found.

Astronomy–The study of the universe.

Atomic force–The force that holds the protons in the nucleus together.

ATP–The form in which the energy from respiration is stored in the cell.

B-lymphocyte–A lymphocyte produced in

the bone marrow. It is programmed to make antibodies against foreign substances.

Bacteria (bak tir′ ē ə)–A prokaryotic organism that reproduces by fission. It lacks chlorophyll and is often equipped with a protective capsule.

Balance–An instrument used to determine the mass of objects. A triple-beam balance uses riders on a balance arm to record the mass of an object. An electronic balance has no riders and records the mass electronically and displays digitally.

Balanced force–Equal forces that act in opposing directions, resulting in no change in motion.

Base–A special protein that pairs with a similar protein to form the DNA molecule.

Big bang theory–The theory that suggests that the universe began as a result of an enormous explosion about 4 billion years ago.

Bilateral symmetry–A type of body symmetry characterized as having two matching sides: right and left.

Bivalve–A class of mollusk having two hinged shells. Also called pelecypods, bivalves lack the head region of other classes of mollusks.

Black hole–A corpse of a supernova in which matter is so condensed that its gravity field prevents anything, including light, from escaping.

Book lung–In spiders, small air-filled sacs that look similar to pages in a book. Book lungs are involved in respiration.

Botanist–A plant scientist.

Botulism (bäch′ ə liz əm)–Food poisoning that results from toxins produced by bacteria present in food.

Budding–A form of asexual reproduction that occurs in sac fungi. New organisms form from "buds" that form on parent cells.

Capsid–A protein coat that surrounds the nucleic acid core of a virus.

Carrageen (kar′ ə gēn)–A substance produced by certain red algae that is used as thickener and stabilizer in some foods and cosmetics.

Carrier–An organism that carries a recessive trait but does not exhibit the trait.

Cell division–A process that forms new cells. Meiosis and mitosis are two forms of cell division.

Cell respiration–A process of the cell in which energy is produced by the breakdown of sugar.

Cell theory–The theory that all living things are made of cells, that cells are the basic units of life, and that cells come only from other living cells.

Cell transportation–The process by which materials are moved in and out of the cell.

Center of gravity–A point of an object's mass in which the balance is located exactly at the center of mass.

Cephalothorax (sef ə lō thor′ aks)–The fused head and thorax of crustaceans.

Chancre (shaŋ′ kər)–A painless sore that forms on the genitals or mouth in a number of diseases, especially the STD syphilis.

Chromosome–A long ribbon of genetic material inside the nucleus that directs cell activities.

Chromosphere (krō mō sfir)–On the sun, a layer of hot gas that lies outside the photosphere.

Cilia–Short hairlike structures used for movement in some protists.

Circumpolar constellation–A constellation that is visible throughout the year and appears to rotate around the North or South Pole.

Cnidaria (ni der′ ē ə)–A phylum of animals that have no skeleton. Cnidaria have hollow saclike bodies and tentacles with stinging cells.

Collar cell–A type of cell that forms the inner layer of a sponge.

Coma (kō mə)–The cloud of vapor that forms around the nucleus of a comet as energy from the sun begins to melt the frozen matter.

Comet–A chunk of frozen dust and gas that passes through our solar system. Some comets appear at regular intervals.

Communicable (kə myo͞o′ ni kə bəl) disease–A disease that can be spread from one person to another.

Compound eye–An eye made up of hundreds of simple eyes, or facets. Animals that have compound eyes see objects as mosaics.

Compound machine–A machine made of two or more simple machines.

Conclusion–The part of an experiment that states the results from analyzing the data. The conclusion is an explanation of what was learned from the experiment.

Constellation–A group of recognizable stars named for a particular figure or shape.

Core–The central part of the sun, or other star, in which nuclear fusion occurs.

Corona (kə rō′ nə)–On the sun, the thin transparent zone beyond the chromosphere.

Crustacean (krus tā′ shən)–A class of arthropods that have a body divided into two parts and have five pairs of legs. Crustaceans include crabs, shrimp, crayfish, and barnacles.

Cryotherapy (krī′ ō ther ə pē)–A medical procedure used to remove warts. Cryotherapy involves freezing the wart with liquid nitrogen.

Current electricity–Electricity that results from a continuous flow of electrons.

Cyanobacteria (sī ə nō bak tir′ ē ə)–A prokaryotic organism that contains chlorophyll and is able to photosynthesize.

Cyst–A thick-walled structure formed by Amoeba to survive harsh conditions.

Cytosine–One of four bases that make up the rungs of the DNA double helix. Cytosine always connects with guanine to form a nucleotide pair.

Dark matter–Missing matter that should be present in the universe if the big bang theory is true.

Data–Information collected by performing an experiment.

Date rape–Rape that occurs during a date.

Density–A quality of an object or substance that describes the amount of matter (mass) per unit volume. It is determined by dividing the mass by the volume.

Diatom–Microscopic algae made of two glassy shells that fit together. They form the base of the marine food chain.

Diffusion–A type of passive transport that occurs when things move from greater concentration to lesser concentration.

Dinoflagellate (dī nō flaj′ ə lit)–A microscopic marine algae that has two flagella: one is used for propulsion; the other is used for steering. Dinoflagellates release toxins into the water.

Periodically concentrations of these organisms are so great they turn the water a rusty red, a condition referred to as the "red tide."

Direct contact–Transmission of disease that occurs when a pathogen from one person is carried to another person by physical contact or through the air.

Displacement–The straight-line distance between the starting point and finishing point.

Distance–The total distance an object travels.

DNA–Deoxyribonucleic acid controls all cell functions and holds all the genetic information of an organism. DNA is a double-helix molecule and looks much like a twisted ladder. The sides of the molecule are made up of alternating units of phosphate and ribose. The rungs are made up of nucleotide pairs.

Dominant–The form of a hereditary trait that always seems to be visible.

Dominant inheritance–A type of inheritance in which one allele is dominant and determines the trait.

Doppler effect–The change in the pitch of sound created by a moving object. It is caused when sound waves are pushed together as the object approaches and as the sound waves are subsequently stretched out as the object moves away.

Double helix–The arrangement of DNA that looks much like a long twisted ladder.

Dwarf–An average-sized star that appears on the main sequence of the H-R diagram.

Echinoderm (ē kī′ nō durm)–A phylum of animals characterized by radial symmetry, tube feet, and spines that extend from the outer covering.

Eclipse–A condition that occurs when one object passes through the shadow of another object.

Efficiency–The quality of a machine that compares the work output with the work input. Efficiency is a measure of the actual work a machine can do.

Effort arm–The part of a lever to which the effort force is applied.

Effort force–The force that must be applied to a machine to cause a change.

Elastic force–The force created when a stretched object returns to its original shape.

Electrical force–A force created by the movement of electrons.

Electromagnetic spectrum–The total radiant energy arranged by wavelength and frequency to form a spectrum.

Electron microscope–A microscope that uses a beam of electrons, rather than light and lenses, to "see" objects. Electron microscopes have much greater magnification abilities than do light microscopes.

Ellipse (e lips′)–The oval-shaped orbit followed by the planets in the solar system.

Elliptic galaxy–A galaxy that has an oval or elliptical shape.

Endoskeleton (en dō skel′ ə tən)–A skeleton formed inside the body of an animal.

Energy–The ability to do work.

Envelope–An additional layer of protein that surrounds the capsid in some viruses.

Epidemiologist (ep ə dē mē äl′ ə jest)–A scientist who traces the spread of a communicable disease in a population.

Equilibrium (ē kwi lib′ rē əm)–A state of balance that exists when opposing forces are balanced.

Estrogen (es' trə jən)–The primary female hormone. It is released from the ovaries and is responsible for the development of the secondary female characteristics.

Eukaryote (yo͞o kar' ē ōt) cell–A cell that has the chromosomes contained within a nucleus.

Exoskeleton (eks ō skel ə tən)–A skeleton formed on the outside of the body of an animal.

Experiment–A test, or trial, composed of a series of steps used to discover new information.

Experimental science–Science that deals with events in which conditions are known and can be studied.

Facet–One of many simple eyes that make a compound eye.

Fission–In biology, a form of asexual reproduction in bacteria.

Flagellum (flə jel' əm)–A long whiplike structure used for movement by some protists.

Focus (plural form: foci)–One of two points on an ellipse. Kepler found that the sun was located at one of these.

Foot–In mollusks, the muscular structure that extends from the body and is used for movement or attachment.

Force–Any push or a pull on an object.

Friction–The force created when two surfaces touch. Friction resists motion.

Fulcrum (ful' krem)–The point at which a lever rotates or pivots.

Full moon–The phase that occurs when the moon is opposite the position of the sun.

Fungi (fun' jī)–A kingdom of plantlike organisms that have cell walls but are unable to photosynthesize. Fungi must obtain their food from other organisms.

Galaxy–A cluster of millions or perhaps billions of stars held together by gravity.

Gay–A term used to refer to a homosexual male.

Gene–The packets of genetic information (DNA) that make up the chromosomes.

Gene therapy–An area of genetic engineering that involves replacing defective genes with healthy ones.

Genetic disease–An inherited disease caused by a chromosome mutation.

Genetic engineering–A process that involves transferring the genes from one organism to another organism.

Geneticist (jə net' ə sist)–A scientist who specializes in the study of heredity.

Genetics (jə net' iks)–The study of hereditary traits and how they are inherited.

Genotype–The set of alleles of a gene that an organism inherits.

Glucose–A simple sugar that produces energy as a product of cell respiration.

Gravity–The property of matter that produces a pulling force on another object.

Guanine–One of four bases that form the rungs of the DNA double helix. Guanine always connects with cytosine to form a nucleotide pair.

H-R diagram–A diagram that organizes stars according to their temperatures and brightness.

Head–In arthropods, the body the segment that contains the simple eye, sensory organs, and mouth. In mollusks, the part of the body that contains the mouth and sensory organs.

Heredity (hə red' i tē)–The transfer of traits or characteristics from one generation to the next.

Heterosexual orientation (het ər ō sek′ shoo əl)–A condition in which men and women are attracted to each other.

Heterozygous (het ər ō zī′ gəs)–A gene made of alleles of various forms.

Historical science–Science that deals with events in which the conditions are unknown and can't be studied or duplicated.

HIV–Human Immunodeficiency Virus, a lethal STD that attacks the cells of the immune system.

Homosexual orientation (hō mō sek′ shoo əl)–A condition in which members of the same sex are attracted to one another.

Homozygous (hō mō zī′ gəs)–A gene made of alleles of the same form.

Horizontal axis–The bottom of a line or bar graph.

Host cell–A cell invaded by a virus and taken over to produce copies of the virus.

Hyphae (hī′ fē)–The branching, threadlike structures that make up fungi.

Hypothesis (hī päth′ ə sis)–An educated guess as to the solution of a problem or the outcome of an experiment.

Immune system–The body system designed to protect the body from disease once pathogens have entered the body. It consists of macrophages, lymphocytes, and interferon.

Incest–Sexual abuse that occurs between family members.

Incomplete-dominance–A condition in which neither allele of a gene pair is dominant or recessive. This condition results in a blending of the traits.

Indirect contact–Transmission of disease that occurs when a pathogen from an infected person is transferred to an object and then to another person.

Inertia (in ur′ shə)–A property of matter, which causes an object at rest to remain at rest and an object in motion to remain in motion unless it is acted on by a force.

Infectious disease specialist–A person who treats people who have communicable diseases.

Inheritance–The acquisition of traits by offspring.

Inner planet–Any one of four planets that lie between the sun and the asteroid belt.

Insect–A class of arthropods that have three body parts, six legs, and usually one or two pairs of wings.

Interferon (in tər fir′ än)–A protein produced by special immune cells. Interferon inhibits a virus from entering the host cell, which prevents the duplication of the virus.

Invertebrate–An animal that lacks a backbone, or vertebrae.

Irregular galaxy–A galaxy that has no regular shape.

Joule (jool)–The SI unit for measuring energy.

Kinetic (ki net′ ik) energy–The energy of motion, which is present in all moving objects.

Larva (lär′ və)–One of the stages in insect metamorphosis; it develops from the egg.

Law of acceleration–Newton's second law of motion. This law that states that the acceleration of an object is determined by the object's mass and the size of the force acting on the object.

Law of action/reaction–Newton's third law of motion. This law states that for every action, there is an equal and opposite reaction.

Law of inertia–Newton's first law of motion. This law states that, unless acted on by an unbalanced force, moving objects keep moving, and resting objects remain at rest.

Law of the conservation of energy–The law that states that energy is neither created nor destroyed.

Law of the conservation of momentum–The law states that the momentum of an object cannot be lost. As an object loses momentum, the lost momentum is passed to another object.

Lesbian (lez' bē ən)–A term used to refer to a homosexual woman.

Light-year–The distance light travels in one year, about 9 460 billion km (5880 billion mi).

Local Group–The cluster of galaxies to which the Milky Way belongs.

Lubricant–A substance that reduces friction.

Lunar eclipse–An eclipse that occurs when Earth's shadow falls on the moon's surface.

Lymphocyte (lim' fō sīt)–A white blood cell designed to destroy an invading pathogen by engulfing it.

Macrophage (mak' rō fāj)–A specialized white blood cell designed to destroy an invading pathogen by engulfing it.

Magnetic force–The attractive force that occurs between two magnetic objects.

Magnetite–A naturally occurring, iron-bearing mineral that has magnetic properties.

Magnitude–The brightness of a star.

Main sequence–A band of medium-sized stars that extends from the lower-right corner to the upper-left corner of the H-R diagram.

Mantle–The fleshy tissue that covers and protects the internal organs of mollusks. The mantle also secretes the shell.

Maria (mä' rē ə)–Dark regions on the moon.

Mass–The amount of matter contained by an object.

Material–A list of the apparatus and supplies needed to perform an experiment.

Mechanical advantage–The increased effort force created by a machine.

Mechanical force–The force created by muscles or a simple machine.

Medusa (mə dōō' sə)–A cnidariana with a bell-shaped body designed for swimming.

Meiosis (mī ō' sis)–A type of cell division that produces daughter cells with only a half set of chromosomes.

Metamorphosis (met ə môr' fə sis)–A series of changes some animals pass through as they develop from a fertilized egg to an adult organism.

Meteor (mēt' ē ər)–A meteoroid that enters the atmosphere of a planet.

Meteorite (mēt' ē ər īt)–A meteor that strikes the surface of a planet.

Meteoroid (mēt' ē ər oid)–A piece of debris floating in space.

Microbiologist–A biologist who studies the structure, processes, and behavior of microscopic organisms.

Milky Way Galaxy–The galaxy to which Earth, the sun, and the rest of the solar system belong.

Mitosis–A type of cell division that produces daughter cells with a full set of chromosomes.

Mollusk (mäl' əsk)–A phylum of animals having a soft body made of a foot, head, and mantle. Mollusks include snails, slugs, clams, and octopus.

Molt–A process in which an arthropod crawls out of the old exoskeleton and emerges with a new, soft exoskeleton that has been growing underneath.

Momentum (mō men′ təm)–The strength of motion. Momentum is function of mass and velocity.

Monera (mə nir′ ə)–The kingdom that contains the smallest living things, bacteria and cyanobacteria. All monerans are prokaryotic.

Motion–The condition in which one object changes position compared to another object or point.

Mutation–A permanent change that occurs in DNA.

Mycelium (mī sē′ lē əm)–A structure formed when the hyphae of a fungus grow together and form a mass.

Nebula (neb′ yə lə)–A cloud of dust and gas. Scientists believe stars develop from nebulae.

Nematode (nem′ ə tōd)–A phylum of worms characterized by a cylindrical body that lacks any segmentation. Nematodes include the hookworm and trichina worm.

Neutron star–A dense star created as the matter of a supernova begins to cool.

New moon–The phase that occurs when the moon is between Earth and the sun.

Newton–The SI unit for measuring force.

Normal flora bacteria–Bacteria that live normally in the body with no negative effect.

Nova–A star that is produced when a red giant uses up its hydrogen fuel and begins to expand rapidly.

Nuclear fission–A process in which an atom is split, releasing energy.

Nuclear force–The force that holds the atomic nucleus together.

Nuclear fusion–A process that causes two or more nuclei of hydrogen to combine, forming a single larger nucleus of helium.

Nucleotide (noo′ klē ō tīd) base–The special molecules that join to form the "rungs" of the DNA ladder. These nucleotide bases are thymine, adenine, guanine, and cytosine.

Nucleus (noo′ klē əs)–In the cell, the area that contains all the chromosomes and DNA. It is often referred to as the "control tower" of the cell. In a comet, the central frozen core.

Nymph (nimf)–A stage in the process of incomplete metamorphosis. In insects, the nymph is a young insect that looks much like the adult but is smaller and lacks functional wings.

Observatory–A special building used to house large telescopes.

Opportunistic infection–An infection that attacks the body when the immune system has been weakened.

Optical telescope–A telescope that collects and magnifies light.

Organelle (ôr gə nel′)–One of many cell structures that carries out a specific function within the cell. Organelles function in a similar way to the way organs and systems function in the human body.

Osmosis–A type of passive transport that involves the movement of water across a semipermeable membrane.

Outer planet–Any one of five planets that lie outside the asteroid belt in our solar system.

Ovary–The female sex gland, which produces eggs and releases the female hormone, estrogen.

Parallax (par′ ə laks)–A shift in position that is measured to calculate an object's distance from Earth.

Passive transport–Transportation of materials that requires no energy.

Pasteurization–A process used to kill harmful bacteria. Pasteurization involves heating substances and then quickly cooling them.

Pathogen–Any disease-causing agent. Four common pathogens are viruses, bacteria, fungi, and protists.

Pathologist–A scientist who identifies and studies the effect of the pathogens in the human body.

Peculiar galaxy–A galaxy that may be spiral or elliptic, but that is characterized by unusual features.

Penicillin–An antibiotic obtained from sac fungi and used to destroy pathogenic bacteria.

Period of revolution–The time it takes a planet to orbit the sun.

Phenotype (fē′ nō tīp)–An organism's physical appearance created by one or more genes.

Photosphere (fōt′ ō sfir)–The layer of the sun's surface that produces visible light.

Pictograph–A graph that uses symbols to display quantitative data.

Pie graph–A round graph that has pie-shaped pieces. Pie graphs are used most often to display percentage data.

Pitch–The number of threads per unit of length on a screw or bolt.

Pituitary (pi tŌŌ′ ə ter ē) gland–A small, pea-sized, gland at the base of the brain that controls all other glands in the body. It releases growth hormone, signifying the beginning of puberty.

Platyhelminthes (plat i hel′ minth ēz)–A phylum of worms characterized by a flattened body having a distinct head and tail. Platyhelminthes includes Planaria and tapeworms.

Polyp (päl′ ip)–A body form of cnidarians shaped like a vase designed to be attached to something.

Pore–A small opening through which water, food, and oxygen enter the body cavity of a sponge.

Potential (pō ten′ shəl) energy–The energy of position.

Power–The rate at which work is done.

Procedure–A series of investigative steps used to gather data designed to test a hypothesis.

Prokaryote (prō kar′ ē ōt) cell–A cell that lacks a nucleus, causing the chromosome(s) to be distributed throughout the cell.

Prominence (präm′ ə nəns)–An eruption on the sun's surface that causes flames of gas to shoot out from the chromosphere.

Promiscuous (prō mis′ kyŌŌ əs)–Having sex with numerous partners.

Prostitution–Selling one's body for sexual activity.

Protista (prō tis′ tə)–The kingdom that includes eukaryotic, single-celled organisms that have nuclear membranes and cell organelles. Protista includes Amoeba, Paramecium, Euglena, and others.

Protozoan–-A single-celled protist that must get its food from other organisms.

Pseudopod (sŌŌ′ dō päd)–A fingerlike extension of cytoplasm present in some protists used for movement and for food gathering.

Puberty (pyŌŌ′ bər tē)–The change that

results in sexual maturity. Puberty occurs when hormones cause reproductive organs to produce sex cells.

Pulsar–A spinning neutron star.

Pupa (pyōō′ pə)–One of the stages in insect metamorphosis. The pupa is the stage in which a larva changes into an adult insect.

Quasar (kwā′ zär)–Quasi-stellar radio sources present in the universe. These objects give off radio waves and have the largest red shifts known. Quasars are the most distant object in space.

Question–The part of an experiment that identifies the experiment's purpose.

Radial symmetry–A type of symmetry in which an organism's body parts are arranged around a central axis.

Radiant energy–Energy that travels in waves.

Radiation–The energy released by a star.

Radula (raj′ oo lə)–In mollusks, a rasp-like tongue of some univalves used for scraping or drilling.

Rape–The act of using force to perform a sexual act.

Recessive–The form of a hereditary trait that is hidden by the dominant form of the trait.

Recessive inheritance–A type of inheritance in which one allele is hidden when passed to an offspring but is not exhibited in the presence of the dominant form of the trait.

Red giant–A relatively large star appearing in the upper-right region of the H-R diagram above the main sequence stars. Red giants are red or orange stars in the later stages of the life cycle.

Red shift–A shift to the red end of the spectrum caused by light waves that are moving away from the observer.

Reflecting telescope–A telescope in which light passes through an open tube to a large concave mirror. The light is then reflected to a flat mirror that reflects the light again through the magnifying lens of the eyepiece.

Refracting telescope–A telescope in which light is collected by a lens and is refracted toward a focal point. The refracted image is then magnified by a second lens in the eyepiece.

Regeneration–A form of asexual reproduction in some groups of animals that occurs when lost or damaged body parts are regrown.

Resistance arm–The part of a lever that performs the work.

Resistance force–The force that resists movement.

Retrovirus (re′ trō vī rəs)–A virus that reverses the flow of genetic information from DNA to RNA.

RNA–Also ribonucleic acid, RNA works as a messenger to carry the directions from the DNA in the nucleus out to the organelles in the cytoplasm.

Rolling friction–The friction created when the surface of a round object rolls over any other surface.

Salmonella (sal mə nel′ ə)–A type of food poisoning caused by eating food contaminated by toxic bacteria.

Saprophyte (sap′ rə fīt)–An organism that gets its nourishment from the remains of dead organisms.

Selective breeding–A process that involves the purposeful selection of parents with desirable characteristics in order to produce more desirable varieties of plants and animals.

Sex chromosome–The chromosome that

determines the sex of an organism.

Sexual abstinence (sek′ shoo əl ab′ stə nəns)–Making a choice to wait until marriage to have sexual intercourse.

Sexual abuse–A situation in which an adult forces a child or other adult to perform sexual acts.

Sexual feeling–The feeling of attraction between male and female. These feelings are common during adolescence.

Sexual harassment (sek′ shoo əl hə ras′ ment)–Unwanted teasing, badgering, or heckling because of gender.

Sexually transmitted disease–A disease spread through sexual contact with an infected person.

SI system–A system of measurement developed to standardize measurement, using standardized units and subunits expressed in powers of 10.

Simple eye–In insects the type of eye that has only one lens. The simple eye is primarily sensitive to changes in light and quick movement.

Simple machine–A device used to change the size or the direction of a force.

Sliding friction–The friction created when two surfaces slide past each other.

Solar eclipse–An eclipse that occurs when the moon's shadow falls on Earth's surface.

Solar flare–A bright spot on the sun's surface that suddenly appears near sunspot groups.

Solar system–The collection of the sun and the planets and other bodies that are in continuous orbit around it.

Solar wind–A stream of ions that moves outward from the sun into the solar system.

Spectroscope–An instrument used to separate light into very fine bands.

Spectrum–The distribution of component energy in order of wavelength.

Speed–The rate of motion.

Spicule (spik′ yool)–A rigid, spikelike structure that forms the support framework of sponges.

Spinneret (spin ə ret′)–A special structure on the abdomen of spiders that spins the silk into thin fibers used for building webs.

Spiracle (spir′ ə kəl)–In land-dwelling arthropods, an opening in the abdomen through which air can be taken into the body.

Spiral galaxy–A galaxy that looks like a pinwheel with arms that appear to unwind from the center.

Spirochetes (spī′ rō kēt)–Corkscrew-shaped bacteria.

Splice–The process of "gluing" together fragments of cut-up DNA.

Sponge–A phylum of animals characterized by numerous pores that allow water to pass in and out of the body.

Spongin–A flexible substance that forms a network of tissue between the cells and provides support for the bodies of some sponges.

Spore–A tiny reproductive cell present in Fungi.

Star–A glowing ball of hot gas that produces its own energy.

Static electricity–The form of electricity that involves a sudden flow of electricity due to the buildup or unequal distribution of electrons.

Static friction–Friction created when two nonmoving surfaces are in contact.

Stinging cell–A specialized harpoonlike cell present on the tentacles of most Cnidarians, used to capture and hold prey.

Sunspot–A relatively cool, dark place on the sun's surface.

Supergiant–The largest type of star. Supergiants appear in the upper-right corner of the H-R diagram.

Supernova–The explosion that occurs when heat of a collapsed supergiant rekindles the hydrogen ash and suddenly expands outward.

Surveillance (sər vā′ ləns)–The process used by pathologists and other scientists to trace the course of a disease.

Symmetry–Similarity of opposite parts. Two common types of symmetry in living things are radial and bilateral symmetry.

Synthesis (sin′ thə sis)–The process in the cell that produces new molecules and compounds.

T-helper cell–The master cell of the immune system, which activates the other immune cells.

T-lymphocyte–A lymphocyte produced in the bone marrow but programmed in the thymus gland to become either a T-helper cell or a T-suppressor cell.

T-suppressor cell–The immune cell that maintains a balance of T-helper cells and turn off the immune response after the infection has been suppressed.

Tail–The part of a comet that forms as the solar wind blows water vapor, dust, and gas away from the comet's outer surface.

Tare weight–The mass of the empty container before an object is placed in it to be weighed on the balance.

Telescope–An instrument designed to gather and magnify energy of objects in space so the energy can be studied.

Tentacle–The armlike extension of Cnidarians that is used to capture and bring food into the digestive cavity.

Testes–The male sex gland, which produces sperm and releases the male hormone, testosterone.

Testosterone (tes täs′ tər ōn)–The primary male hormone. It is released from the testes and is responsible for the development of the secondary male characteristics.

Theoretical mechanical advantage–The calculated mechanical advantage of a machine.

Thorax (thôr′ aks)–One of the three body parts of an insect. It connects the head to the abdomen and is the area to which the legs and wings are attached.

Thread–A spiraled inclined plane.

Thymine–One of four bases that make up the rungs of the DNA double helix. Thymine always connects with adenine to form a nucleotide pair.

Toxin–A poisonous substance produced by bacteria that causes harm to the host organism.

Transportation–The movement of materials in and out of the cell.

Tube foot–One of many special hollow structures present in echinoderms that are interconnected by a system of water-filled tubes. Tube feet aid movement and food gathering.

Unbalanced force–Unequal forces that work in opposite directions, resulting in the movement of objects.

Univalve–A class of mollusks that have a well-developed head region, complete with sensory tentacles, and usually have a single shell. Also called gastropods, univalves include snails and slugs.

Universe–All things that exist, including

Earth, the solar system, all galaxies, the space between objects, and all the energy that exists.

Vaccine–A substance containing inactive or weakened pathogens used to produce an immunity against specific diseases.

Velocity–The speed and direction of a moving object.

Venereal (və nir′ ē əl) disease–A term formerly used to refer to sexually transmitted disease.

Vertebrate–An animal having an endoskeleton including a backbone.

Vertical axis–The line that forms the side of a line or bar graph.

Virgin–A person who has never had sexual intercourse.

Virus–A noncellular structure that can replicate only within a living cell.

Volume–The amount of space occupied or contained by an object.

Watt–The SI unit for power.

Weight–A measure of the pull of gravity on an object.

White dwarf–A relatively small star appearing in the lower-left region of the H-R diagram below the main sequence stars. White dwarfs are white or bluish stars in the early stages of the life cycle.

Work–The process in which there is movement in the direction of the force. Work is calculated by multiplying the force acting on an object by the distance the object moves.

Work input–The amount of work put into the machine.

Work output–The amount of work produced by a machine.

Zoologist–A scientist who studies the classification, structure, process, and behavior of animals.

INDEX

Protein 49, 52, 53, 58, 59, 61, 107, 124
Prothorax 193
Protist 115, 124, 127, 129, 142, 256, 257
   characteristics 126
Protista 116, 124
Proton 311
Protozoan 127-129, 262
   characteristics of 127
Pseudopodia 128
Puberty 210, 211, 242
Public health organization 257
Public health worker 267
Pull of gravity *see* gravitational attraction
Pulley 337, 258, 350, 360, 362
Pulsar 398
Punnett square 77, 78
Pupa 194, 195
Pupil 391
Pus 279

* * * * * * * *

Q

Quasar 398
Question 21, 22

* * * * * * * *

R

Rabies 260, 275
Radiation 391, 396, 397
Radio 350
Radio signal 398
Radioactive element 85
Radula 164, 167
Rain forest 163, 180
Rape 219, 220
   date 220
Receptor 101, 108, 277
Recessive 72, 79, 80, 82
Recessive gene 75, 80
Recessive inheritance 80
Recessive trait 75, 80
Red light 398
Red tide 131

Refrigeration 123
Regenerate 170
Regeneration 148
Reproduce 41, 120
Reproduction 53
   asexual 128
Reproductive cell 56
Reproductive gland 210
Reproductive organ 263
Resistance 319, 351
Resistance arm 359
Respect 223
Respiration 53
Respiratory tract 275
Retrovirus 99, 276
Ribbon worm 141
Ribonucleic acid 52
Ribosome 45, 48, 49, 53, 61
Rider 25, 26
Ring 27
Ring stand 27
Ringworm 135
RNA 49, 52, 61, 99, 101, 108, 124, 276
Robotic arm 297
Rocky Mountain spotted fever 189
Rodent 260
Rope 360
Roundworm 143, 144, 153
   characteristics of 154
Rubber 20
Ruler 12
Runaway teenager 219
Russia 400

* * * * * * * *

S

Sac fungi 135
Sacramento, Calif. 337
Saliva 279
Salivary gland 103
Salmonella 123
Salt curing 123
Salt water 146
San Francisco 257
Sand 117
Sand dollar 169, 171
   characteristics of 172

Saprophyte 132, 134, 135
Satan 215, 216, 219, 222, 235, 285
Satellite 397, 403
Satellite dish 398
Saturn 401
Sauerkraut 124
Saw 337
Scale 12, 302
Scallop 161, 166
Schleiden, Matthias 37
Schwann, Theodor 37
SCID 90
Science 8, 35, 339, 389
Science fiction 399
Scientific equipment 27
Scientific instruments 391
Scientist 7, 11, 15, 24, 33, 34, 38, 39, 59, 88, 90, 109, 118, 120, 124, 127, 257, 273, 280, 307, 308, 342, 381, 391, 396-398
Scissors 368
Scorpion 188, 190
Scotland 37, 141
Screw 360
Sea anemone 149
Sea cucumber 171
Sea lily 171
   characteristics of 171
Sea star 170, 171
   characteristics of 171
Sea urchin 169, 171
   characteristics of 172
Seaweed 126, 129, 164
Segment 193
Segmented worm 143, 144, 153
   characteristics of 154
Selective breeding 87
Self-confidence 232
Semen 109, 279
Severe Combined Immunodeficiency Syndrome 89
Sewage 257
Sex 77, 213, 216
Sex gland 211
Sex hormone 82
Sex-influenced inheritance 79

Teenager 232, 240, 246, 262, 283
Teeth 117
Telescope 386, 391, 393, 401, 403
  optical 391, 392, 396
  radio 397, 398
  reflecting 392
  refracting 392
  ultraviolet 397
  X-ray 397
Telophase *see* cell division
Telophase I *see* cell division
Telophase II *see* cell division
Temperature 14, 121, 393, 397
Tentacle 149-152, 161, 164, 167, 172
Termite 115, 195, 196
Test tube 27
Test-tube holder 27
Test-tube rack 27
Testes 151, 210, 211
Testosterone 211
Tetanus 121
Thales 385
Theory 386, 389
Thermometer 14
Thorax 181, 193
Thread 360
Thrush 109
Thymine 60, 62
Thymus gland 107
Tick 188, 189
Tidepool 163
Time 14, 322, 323, 344
Tissue 39, 58, 146
Toad 88, 143
Toadstool 133, 135
Ton 8
Tongue 59, 79
Tongue rolling 80
Tool 24, 26
Tortoise 143
Toxin 123, 131, 256
Trait 70-72, 74, 77, 82, 87
Transfusion 280
Transportation *see* cell transportation
Trichina worm 154

Trichomoniasis 264
Triple-beam balance 25, 26
Trout 143
True bug 196
Trypanosoma 128
Tsetse fly 128
Tube feet 169-172
Tuberculosis 109, 260
Turtle 77
TV signal 398
Tympanum 193

* * * * * * * *

U

Unborn baby 219, 262, 267, 279, 283
United States 262, 280, 400
United States Postal Service 15
Univalve 167
Universe 298, 310, 311, 383, 385, 386, 388, 389, 393, 398, 403
Uranus 401
Urethra 263
U.S. Abalone 173
U.S. Centers for Disease Control and Prevention 257
U.S. Food and Drug Administration 91
U.S. space program 401

* * * * * * * *

V

Vaccine 104, 278
Vacuole 42, 45, 49, 53
Vacuum 350
Vagina 264
Vaginal fluid 109, 279
Vaginitis 263, 264
Values 240, 244
Velocity 322-324, 331, 339, 340
Venereal disease 262
Vent 117
Venus 392, 401
Vertebrate 143, 145

Verticle axis 16
Very Large Array (VLA) 398
Videotape 391
Viking 401
Violence 216, 220
  childhood 221
  protective steps 221
  sexual 220
  sexual, signs of 221
Virchow, Rudolf 37, 38
Virgin 233
Virus 97-102, 104, 117, 124, 256, 262, 276
Visible spectrum 396
Volume 11, 12, 14
  liquid 12
Voyager 401, 402

* * * * * * * *

W

Walking stick 193
Wasp 195, 196
Water 54
Water flea 180
Water wheel 337
Watson, James 63
Watt, James 347
Watt 9, 344
Wave 350, 396
  radio 396, 398
Wavelength 396-398
Wear 308
Weather 387
Wedge 360, 369
Weight 302, 304, 330, 339, 343, 363
Western Hemisphere 384
Wheel and axle 359, 370
White blood cell 107-109, 275, 277
Whooping cough 120
Width 12
Wife 214, 235
Wilkins, Maurice 63
Windmill 351
Wind resistance 365, 366
Wing 181, 193
Winter solstice 383
Wire 351